KEY

Diamond
Tourmaline
Ruby, Sapphire
Quartz crystal
Garnet

Azurite, Malachite, Chrysocolla, Turquoise
Emerald, Beryl
Agate
Jade
Amethyst

# Gem Hunter's Guide

# Gem Hunter's Guide

FOURTH REVISED EDITION

*The complete handbook for the amateur collector of gem minerals*

RUSSELL P. MACFALL

*Thomas Y. Crowell Company*

NEW YORK / ESTABLISHED 1834

This book owes much of its substance and usefulness to those who discovered the rich gem resources of this continent and have shared their discoveries. Many persons have given generously of information and criticism in the preparation of previous editions. Their kindness has not been forgotten.

Recognition should be given by name, however, to several others who have contributed to this edition. These include Russell Kemp of Chicago, Illinois, Marcus Daly Pruett of Butte, Montana, Walter Wright of the Prospectors Shop and Herbert Grand Girard, both of Santa Fe, New Mexico, Ken Kyte of Covington, Louisiana, Merton A. Young of Michigantown, Indiana, George E. Lambert of Wappingers Falls, New York, and D. L. Hathaway of Cosmopolis, Washington.

# Contents

# 1

## *It's fun to hunt for gems*

There's an old Indian legend about gem stones. It seems that the Thunder God grew jealous of the beauty of the rainbow. Maddened, he struck it with lightning. And fragments of vivid color fell to the ground.

Today less poetic accounts of the origin of gems are in fashion. Yet the fascination and lure of these mineral treasures continues as strong as ever.

Who has not thrilled to the sight of a jewel, sparkling with icy fire, radiating pure color? Through the ages the soft gleam of gold, the natural symmetry of crystals, the spectacular glitter of diamond have evoked admiring gasps of pleasure.

Until recent times, jewels were privileges of the rich. The mineral sources were tightly guarded secrets, as were the techniques of cutting and shaping the stones. But today, hunting for gems, collecting them, and fashioning them to display their hidden beauty is a hobby that anyone can enjoy. Gems are underfoot, to be had for the searching. Thousands of amateurs go out each year into the mountains and deserts of North America to collect a great variety of materials. Tens of thousands have learned to transform native stones into things of beauty and value.

Gem hunting offers many rewards—healthful and entertaining exercise for the whole family, the excitement of the search, and the thrill of discovery. No purchased stone can ever bring the pleasure that comes from opening a nodule or a pocket in rock and being the first to see a sparkling crystal fresh from nature's hand. And the gem hunter gains a direct, practical insight into geology and the earth sciences.

For variety of gem materials the United States is unrivaled. More than sixty kinds of gem minerals have been produced commercially from Alaska to the Mexican border and eastward to Maine and Florida. Still others are to be found in Canada and Mexico. What you cannot collect in person you can often obtain by exchanging your local materials with collectors in other parts of the country, or by buying from the many dealers who advertise in the mineral magazines or display their treasures at various regional and national conventions.

Perhaps among the stones you have skimmed over the water as you walked along a lake shore were some from which beautiful gems could be cut. Diamonds are still being found in gravel deposited by the glaciers that once covered the northern part of North America. As you can see from the directory of digging sites in this book, there are precious and semiprecious gems almost everywhere in the country, waiting to be found and shaped and polished.

For the purpose of this book, a gem material is considered to be any stone commonly used by hobbyists to make jewelry or ornaments such as book ends or table tops. Growth of interest in these uses has broadened the range of gem materials to include more species, such as granite and satin spar, and a wider choice of quality.

But just as it is not possible to work a problem in arithmetic without knowing how to add, so knowledge of the methods for locating and identifying gems is needed if you are to prospect successfully. The basic information is neither difficult to obtain nor to learn. The following chapters describe in simple language the distinguishing characteristics of gems, how to go about finding them, and sources of guidance information.

# 2

# How to identify gem minerals

Most gem stones are minerals. That is, they are naturally occurring chemical elements or compounds which were formed through inorganic processes. This means that they are not man-made, plant, or animal products; that they have a definite chemical composition; and, usually, that they exhibit a distinctive crystalline form. This definition distinguishes minerals from rocks, which are mixtures of minerals.

However, there are some exceptions. A few rocks, such as granite and unakite, are made into jewelry and ornaments. And pearl and amber are definitely gems, although they are not minerals—pearls are a product of animals and amber of ancient trees.

More than 1,500 distinct mineral species are known; only about 100 of these have been used as gems, and fewer than 30 ever appear in jewelry stores.

This is true because, to qualify as gem material, a mineral must be beautiful and rare enough to be desirable, and hard enough to stand up under wear. Gems may be beautiful because of their brilliance, as in diamonds; their color, as in emeralds; their pattern, as in moss agate; or their play of color, as in opals.

Fashion plays its part in creating a demand for certain stones. In ancient Greece, yellow stones were in high favor, while the Romans scorned yellow and preferred green gems to all others. In Renaissance times, green turquoise was greatly admired, but today blue turquoise is the only acceptable kind. Belief that opals were unlucky long made them unfashionable, and amethyst lost some of its high status when the abundant South American supply made it less costly. Promotion of diamonds as the symbol of an engagement of marriage has also helped create a steady market and a sentimental regard for that gem.

Rarity helps make stones precious, but too great rarity can be a disadvantage, because there is not a sufficient supply to make the stone known and create a demand for it. Demantoid garnet and euclase are examples of such rare but comparatively unwanted gems.

The facts related above will not help you tell a fortune in the rough from a pretty pebble. Gem hunters use a variety of methods for identifying stones, but the most useful clues are these:

1. Hardness.
2. Crystal structure—the innate shape of the mineral.
3. Cleavage—the pattern in which the crystal splits.
4. Fracture surface—the texture of a broken crystal.
5. Luster—the character of the surface gloss.
6. Diaphaneity—the degree of transparency.
7. Color.
8. Pattern of surface color or light refraction.
9. Specific gravity—the density, or comparative weight, of the mineral.

These characteristics for dozens of the more important gem stones are listed in detail in chapter 5.


## HARDNESS

Most gem stones are as hard as or harder than silica, the very common mineral which is everywhere present in dust. A softer stone would soon become dull and scratched from abrasion by dust. Hardness is so important that it has become one of the principal means used to identify gem minerals. Like all minerals, they are rated for hardness according to a comparative table known as Mohs' scale. (See Table A.) The steps on this scale are far from equal; the diamond,

**Table A. Mohs' Hardness Scale**

| | |
|---|---|
| 1. Talc | 6. Orthoclase |
| 2. Gypsum | 7. Quartz |
| 3. Calcite | 8. Topaz |
| 4. Fluorite | 9. Corundum |
| 5. Apatite | 10. Diamond |

for example, is rated on the scale as 10, but is actually 42.4 times · as hard as talc and more than twice as hard as corundum.

Sets of pencils tipped with these known minerals are used to test—by scratching—unidentified samples. But for simple field tests some rule of thumb methods are convenient. Minerals with a hardness of less than 2 on the Mohs' scale will mark paper. A fingernail will scratch gypsum, and a copper coin is just about as hard as calcite. A pocketknife blade will scratch apatite easily and feldspar with difficulty. Feldspar, in turn, will scratch glass. Test pencils must be used to try most of the hard gem minerals. In making hardness tests, it is necessary to make sure that what appears to be a scratch is not powder rubbed off the test piece. This can be done by wetting the specimen, rubbing the area, and examining it after the area dries.

## CRYSTAL STRUCTURE

Most transparent precious and semiprecious gems are crystals, which show a distinctive arrangement of their flat, smooth faces and of the angles at which the faces are placed with respect to one another. The quartz gems, for example, such as amethyst, form crystal prisms with six faces terminated by six triangular faces coming to a pointed apex. Sometimes crystals so nearly conform to the type or ideal for the mineral species that they can be identified by that characteristic alone. (See pages 8 and 9 for drawings of typical crystal forms.)

But, although crystals have been called the flowers of the mineral kingdom, they do not usually grow straight and free like blossoms in the sunshine. Instead, they are distorted by the conditions under which rocks are formed. They become twinned, or lopsided, because a few faces develop at the expense of others, or complex through variation from the simple form. Yet the angles between faces remain constant, and from these angles identification of the species is often possible.

Crystallography is too detailed a science to be discussed in a book on gem hunting, although a smattering of its principles is of value. Mineralogists have assigned all crystals to six systems, according to the position of imaginary lines known as axes which intersect to form a theoretical framework or skeleton for the crystal:

*The isometric system* is the most regular. It includes crystals having three axes equal in length and at right angles to one another. Cubic fluorite, octahedral diamond, and trisoctahedral garnet are typical examples of this system.

*The tetragonal system* is like the isometric system except that one axis (usually the vertical one) is longer or shorter than the other two, which are equal in length. All intersect at right angles. The crystals, such as zircon, commonly have a square cross-section.

*The hexagonal system* is like the tetragonal one except that there are three horizontal axes of equal length, intersecting one another at 60 degrees and intersected by a fourth vertical axis at right angles to the other three. Quartz and

# TYPICAL CRYSTAL FORMS

APATITE     AZURITE     BERYL     CHIASTOLITE

EMERALD     EPIDOTE     FELDSPAR

GARNET     IDOCRASE     IOLITE     KYANITE

RUBY     SAPPHIRE     SPHALERITE

TOPAZ CRYSTALS     TOURMALINE CRYSTALS
(Cross-section at right)

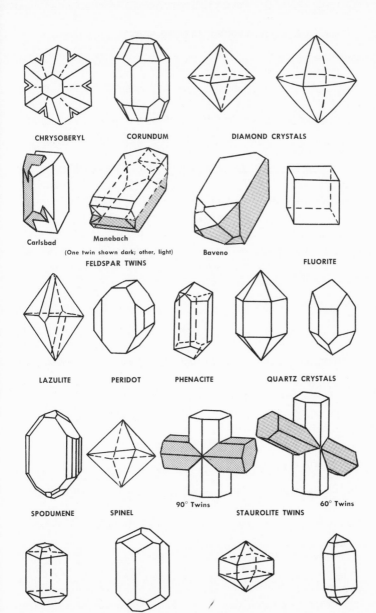

CHRYSOBERYL CORUNDUM DIAMOND CRYSTALS

Carlsbad Manebach
(One twin shown dark; other, light) Baveno FLUORITE
FELDSPAR TWINS

LAZULITE PERIDOT PHENACITE QUARTZ CRYSTALS

SPODUMENE SPINEL 90° Twins STAUROLITE TWINS 60° Twins

VESUVIANITE WILLEMITE ZIRCON CRYSTALS

apatite, with their six-faced pyramid terminations, and the flat-terminated prism of beryl belong here, as well as the many variations that calcite plays on the basic form.

*The orthorhombic system* again has three axes placed at right angles to one another, but all three are of unequal length. Into this domino-like system fall barite and topaz, often with considerable elaboration of secondary faces.

*The monoclinic* and *triclinic* systems are more difficult to visualize. The former is like the orthorhombic system except that only two of the axes meet at right angles. Such crystals, including those of spodumene and orthoclase feldspar, have a droopy appearance because of the tilted axis. In the triclinic system, the axes are all of unequal length and none is at right angles with the others. Rhodonite and some of the feldspars are classified here.

In many gem materials the crystal structure is so lost in the mass that it is not evident to the eye. Minerals of this sort, such as agate and jasper, are described as cryptocrystalline. For example, an agate nodule may contain a center of easily discernible quartz crystals surrounded by chalcedony that is crystalline only to the eye of the microscope.

A few gem materials—notably, opal and obsidian—are amorphous, lacking crystal structure altogether, like glass. They are a mineral jelly.

### CLEAVAGE

Cleavage is a property of parting along a smooth, flat surface, which is a plane of lesser molecular cohesion in the crystal. It is like splitting wood along the grain. Cleavage cracks across the prism or short direction of the crystal are characteristic of topaz and tourmaline, and the pearly cleavage of feldspar is unmistakable. Kunzite has two perfect cleavages that make cutting difficult, and easy cleavage of the diamond parallel to its octahedral faces is a property that is taken advantage of to shape the crystal for cutting.

## FRACTURE SURFACE

Many gem materials fracture with a smooth, curved surface shaped like the inside of a shell. Quartz is a notable example of this conchoidal fracture. Some fracture patterns are fibrous or splintery, like the end of a broken stick, or hackly or jagged, like broken cast iron. Jade breaks with a fibrous or hackly pattern because it is formed of crystal fibers matted together into a tough mass. Tenacity is a quality closely allied to fracture pattern; chalcedony and jasper, because of their cryptocrystalline makeup, are tougher than their crystal counterpart, quartz.

## LUSTER

Most gem stones have a high but nonmetallic luster. It may be vitreous or glassy, as in quartz or beryl, or the harder, glittering adamantine luster of diamond. Other types of luster less frequently encountered among gems are described as resinous, pearly, greasy, silky, waxy or dull.

## DIAPHANEITY

Another means of discriminating among gems is provided by optical characteristics, which create much of their beauty and distinction. Most precious stones are transparent and crystalline. Some, such as the diamond and zircon, are outstanding for brillance and fire. Brilliance depends on refractive index, the ability of a gem substance to bend light rays so that they are reflected from the back facets of a cut gem and out through the top of the stone. Fire is the product of the gem's ability to disperse or split white light into its constituent colors, so that the stone sparkles in prismatic splendor.

## COLOR

Color is the principal other quality that makes a stone precious. Emerald—for example, the grass-green variety of beryl—is almost priceless, but common opaque beryl is useful only as the ore of the metal beryllium and is valued in cents per pound. The color of a fine gem should be strong and pure, neither muddy, pale, nor too dark. In transparent stones evenness of color is desirable, although some gems such as sapphire and amethyst are often so parti-colored that they test the skill of the lapidary to exploit the best areas.

Color results from optical properties of a gem material that cause it to reflect or absorb certain wave lengths of the spectrum. Ruby of the best quality passes or reflects red wave lengths most readily, then the blue wave lengths. The result is red with a bluish cast, often described as pigeon-blood red. A material that passes or reflects all wave lengths is itself colorless; one that absorbs them all is black.

Color is the most conspicuous characteristic of any mineral, so it is tempting to use color as a means of identification. For some, such as azurite or malachite, the color is a primary characteristic and it becomes a reliable guide. But with most minerals, color can be misleading. A blue crystal may be diamond, aquamarine, topaz, tourmaline, cyanite, or apatite. Conversely, such a chameleon as tourmaline may be found in almost every color, or even with two or more colors in a single crystal.

## PATTERN

Among the translucent and opaque gem stones, pattern is both an important element of value and also of identification. The pattern may be some caprice with light such as creates the unique beauty of opal or labradorite, the starry splendor of star sapphire and garnet, or the dramatic cat's-eye effect in chrysoberyl or tigereye. Or it may be the more static but inexhaustibly various patterns of agate and jasper. So typical are their patterns that these materials are described according to whether they are orbicular (eyelike), fortification (with angular, banded structure), dendritic (mossy), poppy (red spotted), or show banded, tubelike, or plumelike designs.

## SPECIFIC GRAVITY

Specific gravity, which is the ratio of the weight of a substance to the weight of an equal volume of water, is one of the most useful tools for discriminating among minerals. The apparatus is not convenient for use in the field, but experience will teach the gem hunter that comparative weight, which is a rough way to judge specific gravity, is one of the almost instinctive tests by which he will judge a puzzling specimen. Obviously malachite, an ore of the heavy metal copper, or hematite, an ore of iron, will "heft" heavy, and massive topaz is noticeably heavier than quartz, although to the eye they appear identical.

In the laboratory, specific gravity is measured with a beam balance so arranged that the gem can first be weighed in air, then weighed again when suspended by a fine wire in a beaker of water. The weight in air divided by the difference between the two weights is the specific gravity. Specific gravity can also be determined by means of heavy liquids. Bromoform and methylene iodide are diluted to form a series of solutions of graded specific gravities in which the various gem minerals will just sink or float. A mineral that just barely sinks or just barely floats in a liquid has about the same specific gravity as that liquid. Some even heavier liquids are available. As gems lie in the range between opal (sp. gr. 2.1) and zircon (sp. gr. 4.7), quick and accurate determinations can be made with the heavy liquids. High cost and the poisonous nature of some of the heavy liquids are their only disadvantages.

In the laboratory, use is also made of many instruments —such as the refractometer, the dichroscope, the spectroscope, and the microscope—which not only are beyond the purse and skill of the average gem hunter, but also are useless for prospecting trips. Occasionally, he may find the Geiger counter, to determine radioactivity, and the ultraviolet lamp useful in his searches. Mainly, however, he will have to rely on simple tests and the sixth sense of experience.

## CHEMICAL CLASSIFICATIONS

Minerals are generally classified according to their crystal structure and their chemical nature. Some are elements, such as diamond (carbon); oxides, such as corundum (aluminum oxide); carbonates, such as malachite (copper carbonate); phosphates, such as apatite; or silicates. To the large and complex silicate family most gem minerals belong.

The silicates are compounds of one or more metals— such as calcium, iron, or magnesium—with silicon and oxygen. As a family they are hard and, when pure, transparent. The common chemical tests so useful with many minerals are of little value in distinguishing one silicate from another. The visual tests that have been described, readings of specific gravity, and such optical tests as measurements of refractive index are more useful.

Among the gem minerals that are not silicates, the largest single group is the carbonates. They can be identified by the fact that they fizz in hydrochloric acid. By this means rhodochrosite (manganese carbonate) can be distinguished from rhodonite (manganese silicate). Malachite and azurite are also carbonates.

Apatite, a phosphate, can be identified by the white precipitate formed when a few drops of sulphuric acid are added to a sample previously dissolved in hydrochloric acid. Turquoise is another phosphate. Powdered turquoise moistened with hydrochloric acid and held in a flame will color the flame blue.

Fluorite (calcium fluoride) when heated in a glass tube with potassium disulphate gives off hydrofluoric acid which etches the side of the tube, leaving it gray and pitted. To differentiate smithsonite from prehnite, heat the mineral in a closed glass tube. Smithsonite (zinc carbonate) becomes coated with a film that is yellow when hot and white when cold.

Hematite is easily recognized by its weight and by the red streak it makes on a slab of unglazed porcelain. Jet, a form of coal, is easily told from plastic imitations or from glass because it is lighter and burns to an ash. Amber, which is a fossil resin, can be recognized in the same way.

Nearly all the gem minerals have been synthesized in the laboratory, either commercially or experimentally. Even diamond is now manufactured. Opal, however, has resisted all efforts to manufacture it. It is still one of nature's monopolies. But the often complex identification of synthetic gem stones is a problem of the laboratory, not of the gem prospector.

# 3

# *Rock formations in which gems occur*

They say that gold is where you find it. But actually nature does not scatter her treasures blindly. Certain gems are usually associated with certain rock formations, so some acquaintance with geology makes gem hunting much easier and more fun.

Rocks are divided according to their origin into three major groups: igneous, sedimentary, and metamorphic. Gems are found in all three types, but by far the richest source is the igneous group.

## IGNEOUS ROCKS

This type of rock is formed by the cooling of molten material from deep within the earth. If the material remains beneath the surface, where it cools slowly, its constituent elements can grow into crystals large enough to be seen. Such crystals of quartz, feldspar, and hornblende are characteristic of granite.

As part of the buried melt crystallizes, other materials remain fluid. Where the rocks have been broken by earth movements, this fluid may be forced into cracks in the rocks to solidify as dikes. Such formations are very coarsely crystallized and consist largely of feldspar with quartz. In some instances hot solutions containing boron, fluorine, lithium, and beryllium compounds, among others, are trapped as liquid in the solidifying dike. They then form superb crystals of tourmaline, smoky quartz, beryl, topaz, spodumene, and apatite in cavities in the dike. Such pegmatite dikes in Maine, Connecticut, New Hampshire, North Carolina, South Dakota, and California are world-famous gem sources.

If the igneous material is ejected to the surface, as by a volcano, it cools so rapidly that its crystals are too small to be visible. Among the results are light-colored lavas such as rhyolite and felsite, which are identical with granite except in texture. As the viscous lava flows and cools, gas pockets form in it. In these cavities may be chalcedony or opal, derived from silica dissolved from the lava. Similarly, wood buried in volcanic ash or lava is petrified by replacement of the cells with silica, or a cast of chalcedony may form in the space left by decay or destruction of the wood. Agate and opal of gem quality formed in these ways are abundant in the great lava flows of Oregon, Washington, and northern Idaho.

Two other formations create conditions favorable to the crystallization of gem minerals. Cavities in granites that are permeable to hot solutions and vapors are likely sites for formation of beryl, topaz, and similar crystals. Likewise, rock fissures that are filled with quartz commonly contain metallic ores. With them, quartz crystals, rhodonite, and rhodochrosite may be associated.

Another type of igneous rock, porphyry, is often handsome enough to justify ornamental use. Porphyries are fine-grained rocks in which crystals have formed while the rest of the rock was still fluid, creating a spotted or lathlike pattern.

## SEDIMENTARY ROCKS

Sedimentary rocks are silent testimony to the fact that change is the first law of nature. Wind, water, heat, and cold break down the solid mountains into clay, sand, and gravel. These become consolidated into horizontal beds of shale, limestone, and sandstone. They are rich in fossils but comparatively barren of gem minerals except for quartz geodes and agates and jaspers eroded from older rocks. The Indiana and Iowa geodes and the Montana moss agates are produced from such beds by the action of weather.

## METAMORPHIC ROCKS

Any kind of rock that has been changed is called metamorphic. Heat, pressure, mineralizing solutions and vapors, or contact with other rocks may add or remove chemicals. Or the rock's own material may separate or combine in new ways. Or the physical state may alter. All this is metamorphosis, and the result is metamorphic rock.

Shale changes either to slate or to schist, which contains mica; sandstone alters to quartzite or gneiss, limestone to marble, and granite to gneiss. Metamorphic rocks are layered, like sedimentary rocks, but the layers are light and dark instead of being uniform as they are in sedimentary beds. They are hard like the igneous rocks and usually crystalline. Along with the gross changes occur others of more interest to the gem hunter: In the process of metamorphism, crystals of garnet, cyanite, idocrase, corundum, and jade may also be created, along with massive serpentine.

Weathering, a process to which all rocks are exposed, also creates and concentrates gem minerals. The action of air, water, and dissolved carbon dioxide changes the chemical character of minerals, especially ore minerals, lying close to the surface. Malachite and azurite, for example, are formed from copper sulphides by the action of carbon dioxide dissolved in ground water. Erosion removes broken pieces of rock, which are sorted by size and specific gravity by moving water. Gem minerals are usually heavier and more durable than the other rocks, and they become concentrated, like gold, in streams and on gravel bars. From such formations come the sapphires in the Missouri River near Helena, Montana, and the star garnets of Idaho.

## DISTRIBUTION IN AMERICA

All these formations are found in the United States, which offers a great diversity of collecting areas. Geologically, it falls into three major divisions: the mountains of the East, the mountains of the West, and the broad plains these mountains enclose. In the East, an ancient mountain system of folded and metamorphosed sediments and igneous rocks, the Appalachians, sweeps down from the province of Quebec to Alabama, affording a challenge to the collector, especially in Maine, New Hampshire, Connecticut, New Jersey, Virginia, and North Carolina.

In the West, the Rockies, the Sierra Nevada, and the coast ranges dominate a vast geological complex which includes the lava plains of the Northwest, the arid great basin, and the rugged and highly mineralized Southwest. Crystalline rocks of many kinds are exposed in the smaller mountains, canyons, and deserts that diversify the landscape.

The more level plains between the mountains are less dramatic, but they are by no means lacking in variety. At the foot of the Rockies, the high plains roll east to meet the Mississippi Valley. To the north lie the granite rocks of Canada and the lavas of the Lake Superior region, and to the south the Mississippi delta and vast coastal plain. In the Black Hills and the Ozarks, crystalline mountains break the monotony of the plains.

Debris eroded from the Rockies covers the high plains, and glacial sand, silt, and pebbles cloak the glaciated areas of the Mississippi Valley. It is idle to look for such gem minerals as agates in such regions except where water has brought them to the surface or concentrated them by stream action.

Geology is the fundamental clue to gem locations. Since hard-rock mining is too expensive for amateurs, the hobbyist will do most of his collecting where the forces of nature or man have exposed minerals. He will pick over stream beds, gravel pits, mine dumps, road cuts, and quarries. Some gems —agate, petrified wood, crystals—may also be dug from easily worked soil, disintegrated rock, and beds of volcanic ash.

Specific directions to promising sites are listed by states in chapter 12. But neither the directory of locations nor the discussion of geology and prospecting techniques in this volume is exhaustive. Their sole purpose is to give the gem hunter some basic information, to tell him what the American gem materials are and where they have been found. Description of a location in the directory cannot be a guarantee that gem-grade materials will be found there. It merely means that such materials are reliably reported to have been found there and that it is a promising place in which to search.

# 4

# *How to hunt for gems*

In planning a gem-hunting trip, decide where you are going, become familiar with what you will be looking for, and know how and where to look. Some time-tested suggestions may be helpful.

Don't be too ambitious. The attempt to crowd in visits to too many locations, to do in a day what requires a week, is sure to bring disappointment and frustration. Nowadays, a lot of pick-and-shovel work is likely to be necessary to uncover worthwhile gem material, and considerable prospecting may be required before it is even located. Methodical field work is not a waste of time; it yields the best results.

## ASSISTANCE

Advance planning pays off. Visit museums or dealers. That is the easiest way to become familiar with the appearance of the material you will be seeking. Get acquainted with a collector who lives near the place to be visited. His help can be solicited by mail before you go. It will prove invaluable. Advance information about localities and gem materials can be obtained from the state university, state geologist, or a local mineral club.

Once you have reached your destination, you can usually find a fellow collector who will help. Geologists at a nearby college, a filling-station operator, a druggist, the postmaster —all are natural sources of information. Showing a specimen of what you are hunting will elicit more information than many words of description. Landmarks have a way of changing, place names disappear, roads change; and a local collector can save the visitor much time and annoyance.

## MAPS

Maps are essential. Road maps, such as those given away by filling stations and state tourist bureaus, are invaluable for guidance to the general collecting area.

But you will need more detailed maps, such as the topographic quadrangle maps published by the United States Geological Survey. Persons living east of the Mississippi River may obtain these maps from the USGS Map Information Center, Washington 25, D.C.; others may order them from the USGS Map Distribution Center in Denver Federal Center, Denver 25, Colorado. The centers supply on request a free index, from which you can select the specific quadrangle maps that you need.

These centers also offer certain more specialized maps locating mineral deposits. The United States Forest Service, Washington 25, publishes maps of national forest areas.

The Geological Survey's topographical maps record natural features of the earth's surface by means of contour lines. They also include place names, symbols, and man-made features, such as roads and towns, as well as boundaries of civil divisions and parallels of latitude and meridians of longitude.

Understanding contour lines is the key to productive use

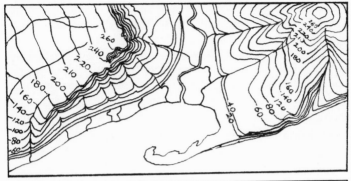

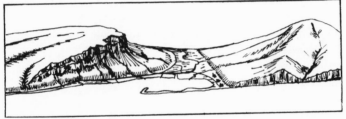

With a little practice you can visualize terrain from a contour map. The contour lines trace land that is at the same level. Notice that the lines are closer where the land slopes more steeply.

of topographical maps. Contour lines show the relief and configuration of land surfaces. Each line connects points of the same elevation above or below sea level. The elevations delineated by the contour lines are spaced at some convenient fixed distance, such as 100 feet apart. Thus contour lines are like steps with risers of uniform height and treads varying in width according to the pitch of the slope. On a steep slope the treads or contours will be close together; on a gentle slope they will be far apart. With practice it becomes easy to visualize the peaks, valleys, and other natural features of a mapped surface.

Topographic maps are of primary value to the gem hunter

intent on finding a described location. Geologic maps, which add further information about rock formations, help guide you to fertile locations.

On geologic maps, colors and symbols identify sedimentary and other types of rocks, as well as faults, direction of pitch and strike, and deformations. Interpretation of such maps requires more practice and more knowledge of geology than other maps. But the rock hunter who can use geologic maps can pinpoint his search in the rock masses in which the gems he is seeking are likely to occur. Herkimer "diamonds," for example, are found only in exposures of the Little Falls dolomite; these would be defined on a geologic map of certain quadrangles in upper New York state. Likewise, petrified bone and wood are associated in the Southwest with such formations as the Morrison and Chinle sandstones.

## TRAVELING

Consider the weather when planning a trip. A desert, such as the Green River country in Utah or much of southern California and Arizona, is no place to visit in the summer. Neither is winter comfortable in Maine or Montana. In hot regions it is more comfortable to hunt for gems in the early morning, while the ground is still cool, and to rest in the shade in the afternoon.

An automobile is a necessity for a trip of any scope. It should be in first-class condition. Gem minerals have a way of being hidden far from the main highways. Present-day cars are not designed for rutted roads or rocky desert tracks; they are too heavy and they are built too close to the ground. A jeep or a four-wheel-drive truck is an ideal vehicle for prospecting far from the superhighways; next best is an old-model car with plenty of daylight under it. Two spare tires and tubes, patches, pump and tools, chains, a roll of chicken wire for traction in sand, spare spark plugs, a tow rope or chain, a spare fan belt, and a jack of the bumper type are essential items. Carry a change of crankcase oil, extra gasoline, and water for the radiator. Spout-type cans are best. Drinking water can be kept cool in gallon jugs wrapped in wet burlap. Canned fruit juices are also convenient thirst quenchers.

Instead of abusing your own car on mountain roads, it is often sensible to hire a car and even a driver for the rough going. A guide-driver is especially advisable if the collecting trip is to be made into an area, such as an Indian reservation, where strangers might be unwelcome.

## PERSONAL EQUIPMENT

For the actual digging, take along a prospector's pick. It can be bought at a large hardware store. You will also need a large cold chisel, a pickax and a sledge hammer, a crowbar, and a shovel or trenching tool. Take bags, boxes, and newspaper for wrapping specimens, and labels (the new write-on adhesive tape is good). A carpenter's apron, which has big pockets, is a convenient collecting bag. A knapsack, candle, flashlight, and magnifying glass belong in the kit. Clothing should cover your whole body to protect against sunburn, insect bites, and scrapes. Women should wear slacks. Stout shoes are essential for both men and women. High boots, though heavy, are advisable for wet and snaky spots. They are more comfortable if two pairs of hose, one light and one heavy, are worn inside them. Work gloves save the hands when you are climbing over rocks or wielding a pick. Don't forget hat, sunglasses, suntan lotion, a first-aid kit, and some dry concentrated food.

## THE PROSPECTOR'S CODE

One thing that must not be left at home is common courtesy. Many areas still rich in gem materials have been closed to collectors because someone was careless, hoggish, or dirty.

For your own good and for the good of others:

1. Always ask permission to enter private property, even an unfenced range, a deserted cabin, or a mine dump. Be ready to sign a waiver absolving the owner from responsibility for accidents.
2. Be careful with fire. Wet down camp fires when leaving, and crush your cigarette butts.
3. Clean up your camp site. Either bury all debris, cans, and garbage, or take it away with you.
4. Don't contaminate wells or creeks.
5. Fill in holes that you dig. Stock may be injured by falling into pits.
6. Leave gates as you find them, open or closed.
7. Don't trespass on growing crops or drive across grasslands, especially if the ground is soft. Try to stay on roads in farming country.
8. Do not meddle with tools or machinery.
9. Leave firearms and blasting materials at home unless you know how to use them, have a reason for using them, and have permission from authorities and property owners to use them.

California mineral clubs are fostering a movement to restore the beauty of the outdoors. On field trips, clubs pick up litter left by thoughtless persons. Stops are made along the highways to gather up bottles, cans, and paper, which are then disposed of at home.

Courtesy also includes moderation; the gem hunter should take only what he needs, leaving some for the next fellow. So-called truck collectors, who haul away everything in sight, have given everyone else a bad name. Grade your specimen on the spot by chipping away a small corner of it. If you don't want it, leave it for someone else who may prize it. Nodules and geodes should not be broken in the field. Take them home intact and saw or break them where the fragments will not litter the landscape.

The field manners of some collectors have been so bad that many excellent locations have been closed. "The flower agate locations south of La Junta have been fouled up by rockhounds who left gates open and cut fences to the point where the ranchers are liable to welcome you with a gun," writes a Colorado collector. "As far as Texas is concerned," says a Texan, "the legislature, prodded by ranchers and leasers of state land, has passed a trespassing law that has virtually killed the ambition of any rockhound. . . . The law makes it illegal to even enter another's property without having written permission . . . to camp, cook a meal, or rest."

And from a New Hampshire state bulletin: "A number of mines are posted and permission to collect must be obtained. . . . With mineral collecting one of the fastest growing hobbies, care and courtesy are a 'must' if New Hampshire mineral collecting grounds are to remain available to the amateur."

A New Mexico mineral club reports the closing of the Diamond A ranch near Engel to collectors because unauthorized digging interfered with ranch operations. A Coloradan voices his annoyance with the gem hunters who haul away large amounts of gem material to break up and polish in tumbling barrels. He refuses to divulge the location of any of his pet collecting spots lest some of these "rockhogs" read of them. Nevada and Utah have both announced a policy of welcoming the collector who is content with a small amount of material, but of protecting their petrified wood on state lands and posted public areas against truckload collectors.

Unrestricted collecting is facing a challenge almost everywhere. Not only have many private areas been closed because of carelessness by rockhounds, but some governmental action is being taken. The Department of Interior has sponsored a law to conserve petrified wood on public lands. It would prohibit removal by commercial interests or the destruction of petrified logs for the manufacture of abrasives or souvenirs.

Collectors would still be allowed to take reasonable amounts for their own use.

Perhaps more serious is a federal proposal—the "Wilderness Bill"—to create roadless areas on twenty-two million acres of federal lands. This exclusion of vehicles would make gem hunting very difficult.

Clubs can delay this trend toward regulation by educating their members in conservation, although it is probably too late to prevent governmental interference. But there are several ways to preserve some freedom in collecting. One is commercial operation of collecting sites. At the Woodward ranch in Texas and the Horse Canyon agate deposit in California, for example, a charge is made to collect and a limit is set on the amount that may be taken away. A second alternative is for mineral clubs to file claims on sites so that they can regulate collecting there. A third alternative is to encourage park districts, forest preserves, or other public agencies to acquire areas for collecting as they now acquire land for other recreational uses.

## HAZARDS

Aside from these problems, prospecting, like any outdoor activity, has physical hazards as well. Rocks can fall from a shattered quarry wall, a cliff, or an overhang. Someone collecting on a rocky slope above you may start a rock slide or roll a large rock on you. Open mine shafts and water-filled pits are obvious dangers. When working in areas where open shafts exist, it is wise to supervise children and pets closely, or, better yet, leave them behind.

The greatest risk the collector runs is that of getting lost. It is a sound rule, unless you are an expert with the compass or know the locality thoroughly, to stay within sight of your car. It will provide shelter, supplies, and a landmark for searchers. Furthermore, it is a wise precaution to leave word where you will be prospecting and when you expect to return, so that a search can be started.

Old hands offer these suggestions for driving in the desert: Use second gear in soft sand. If you get stuck, do not dig sand away from the wheels—this only softens it and makes the wheels sink deeper. Instead try these remedies:

1. Tamp the sand down hard in front of the wheels.
2. Lay chicken wire under the wheels.
3. Place burlap bags, filled half full of sand and tied, under the wheels.
4. Let air out of the tires until they are about half deflated. You can reinflate them later with a carbon-dioxide gas "bomb" or spark-plug pump or a regular tire pump (available from auto accessory stores).

Campers in desert regions are advised to avoid dry stream beds and canyons where they may be trapped by flash floods. Safety goggles protect the eyes when the collector is breaking up boulders or is doing other heavy rock work.

In only a few places in the United States are wild animals a danger. Poison oak and ivy are prevalent, however, and learning to identify them is elementary education for the outdoors. Prompt use of soap and water after exposure will be adequate for most persons.

Rattlesnakes are the most widespread of all poisonous snakes. Most bites are on arms and legs. Modern treatment emphasizes lying still so that venom will circulate as slowly as possible. Tourniquets and cutting the wound and sucking it should be avoided. Getting the patient to a doctor is the most urgent consideration. Even better is to be careful and avoid being bitten.

Snakes have no mechanism for controlling their body temperature, so they avoid heat by coming out only at night in the desert, and they hibernate in cold weather. It is wise to keep your bed off the ground, especially in the Southwest, not only to avoid having a snake as a bed mate, but also to avoid scorpions. These small, straw-colored, virulent desert dwellers hide in shoes, clothing, and papers; shaking such articles before using them will dislodge the unwelcome guest.

Usually a snake will avoid human beings unless it is accidentally cornered and strikes to protect itself. For safety's sake, keep your hands and feet out of holes, crevices, and other places which cannot be clearly seen. Wear stout shoes, thick wool hose, heavy trousers, and gloves. Look closely at the ground, move slowly, and make some noise to avoid unwelcome encounters. In known snake country, it is well to turn over rocks with a stick or a long scoop now made for that purpose.

Besides rattlesnakes, coral snakes, copperheads, and water moccasins are regarded as venomous. The Gila monster is venomous but is generally too lethargic to be dangerous, and the black widow spider is usually thought to be harmless despite its reputation.

## TECHNIQUES

Finding gem material takes some science, some skill, some perspiration, and some luck. The first axiom is to look wherever rock is exposed, whether in a road or railroad cut, a quarry, mine dump, excavation, gravel pit, beach, river bar, or stony field. Sometimes it is profitable to examine streams and washes for fragments of gem materials and then trace them back to their source, much as a gold seeker pans the streams back toward the mother lode.

The second axiom is to look for the rocks and other conditions associated with the gem material. Oregon thunder eggs, for example, are in volcanic beds; tourmaline, beryl, and kunzite occur near the quartz segregations in the feldspar mass of pegmatite dikes. Garnets and corundum settle with other heavy materials to the bottom of gravel beds. The expert agate hunters of Minnesota say that big ones are found only where the stones are large, usually in gullies and on the gravelly uplands, not in the streams. In desert regions, agates and other silica minerals often can be distinguished from the other rocks by a white coating caused by weathering under arid conditions. Where much of the surface material has already been picked up, watch for a corner of rock sticking inconspicuously from the ground. It may be a winner that has been overlooked. Often, when looking for agates in gravel, it is useful to notice whether quartz and jasper pebbles appear in the gravels. If not, it is unlikely that agates will be found there.

A third axiom is that the best collecting time on open ground and beaches is in the spring or after storms, when fresh material is exposed. On the other hand, a storm may wash away the beach pebbles or cover them with sand.

Much good gem material comes from mine dumps and there are tricks to lightening the labor of working at such sites and to working them most effectively. The best specimens are usually in the oldest part of the dump, which is buried under newer debris. Dig in from the side to reach the old part and to avoid working over the top material. Dig where there is tree or shrub growth, as that will be an older, undisturbed part. Break up boulders; they may contain unscrutinized material. When you find a good piece, study the level in the dump and the associated rocks, and look elsewhere for the same combination. And it is often profitable to rework a spot where someone else has hit pay dirt.

To summarize, when you hunt gem material, know what you're looking for. Know how to recognize it when you find it. Give yourself plenty of time. Go prepared for the kind of work you'll have to do. Respect the rights of the man who owns the land you're hunting on and of those other gem hunters who will follow you.

Remembering these points, and putting them into practice, you'll find gem hunting a fascinating and exciting hobby.

# 5

## *Characteristics of important gem stone materials*

**Table B.**

| Name and Specific Gravity | Hard-ness | Composition | Color or Pattern |
|---|---|---|---|
| Agate 2.6 | 7 | Cryptocrystalline chalcedony | Varicolored in bands or patterns |
| Alabaster 2.3 | 2 | Hydrous calcium sulphate | Variegated patterns |
| Amazonite 2.5 to 2.6 (ăm′-à-zŭn-ite) | 6 | Microcline feldspar | Leek green often dappled with white |
| Amber 1.0 to 1.1 | 2+ | Fossil tree resin | Yellow, reddish, brown |
| Amethyst 2.6 (ăm′-ê-thĭst) | 7 | Variety of crystal quartz | Purple or lavender |

The descriptions in these tables are of gem varieties found in the United States that are generally considered to be worth collecting and cutting.

| Diaphaneity and Luster | Fracture and Cleavage | Other Characteristics | Associated Rocks |
|---|---|---|---|
| Translucent to opaque; vitreous luster | Conchoidal | Patterns include iris, eyes, bands, fortification, moss, dot, flower and plume; also sagenitic | Nodules and veins in volcanic and sedimentary rocks; also in gravels |
| Opaque; grainy | | Form of gypsum; satin spar is another variety | Sedimentary rocks |
| Opaque; pearly luster | Perfect cleavage | Well-developed crystals, often banded by twinning | Pegmatite |
| Transparent to translucent; sub-vitreous luster | Conchoidal | As lumps and masses | Marl and clays |
| Transparent; vitreous luster | Conchoidal | Color often in zones | Lining nodules; massive in veins |

**Table B.** (cont.)

| Name and Specific Gravity | Hard- ness | Composition | Color or Pattern |
|---|---|---|---|
| Apatite 3.2 (ăp'-à-tite) | 5 | Calcium fluo- phosphate | Yellow, green, blue, pink, purple |
| Aquamarine 2.6 to 2.9 (ăk-wà-mà-rēn') | 8 | Crystal variety of beryl | Blue green |
| Aventurine 2.6 (ă-ven'-tchu- rĭn) | 7 | A variety of quartz | Green, brown, yellow, red, spangled with mica |
| Azurite 3.8 (ăzh'-ū-rite) | 3+ | Hydrous copper car- bonate | Deep blue |
| Benitoite 3.6 (bĕ-nē'-tō-ite) | 6+ | Barium tita- nium silicate | Sapphire blue and white crystals |
| Beryl 2.6 to 2.9 (bear'-ĭl) | 8 | Beryllium aluminum silicate | Varieties: aquamarine is bluish green; emerald, grass green; goshenite, colorless; heliodor, yel- low; morgan- ite, pink; also asteriated |

| Diaphaneity and Luster | Fracture and Cleavage | Other Characteristics | Associated Rocks |
|---|---|---|---|
| Transparent; vitreous luster | Conchoidal | Yellow crystals often called asparagus stone | Pegmatites and ore veins |
| Transparent; vitreous luster | Conchoidal; basal cleavage | Crystals are prisms, often very large | Pegmatites |
| Translucent to opaque; pearly luster | Hackly fracture | Massive | Pegmatite |
| Translucent to opaque; sub-vitreous luster | Conchoidal | Crystals or botryoidal masses; usually with mala-chite | Copper ores |
| Transparent; vitreous luster | Conchoidal | Wedge shaped crystals in natrolite | California, only lo-cality |
| Transparent to translucent; vitreous luster | Conchoidal; basal cleavage | Crystals are prisms | Pegmatites and schist; limestone |

Table B. (cont.)

| Name and Specific Gravity | Hard-ness | Composition | Color or Pattern |
|---|---|---|---|
| Bloodstone 2.6 | 7 | A jasper | Dark green with red spots |
| Calcite 2.7 (kăl'-site) | 3 | Crystalline calcium carbonate | Colorless, pale brown, yellow, red |
| Carnelian 2.6 (kär-neal'-yăn) | 7 | Variety of chalcedony | Red-brown, often from heat treatment |
| Chalcedony 2.6 (kăl-said'-ō-nĭ) | 7 | Cryptocrystalline variety of quartz | White, vari-colored, and often patterned |
| Chiastolite 3.2 (kī-as'-tō-lite) | 7 | Aluminum silicate | Gray, cross-shaped black inclusions in cross section |

| Diaphaneity and Luster | Fracture and Cleavage | Other Characteristics | Associated Rocks |
|---|---|---|---|
| Opaque | Conchoidal to hackly fracture | Also called St. Stephen's stone and heliotrope | Igneous rocks and in gravels |
| Transparent to opaque | Pronounced cleavage | Onyx is massive, striped variety. Marble and travertine other forms. Fizzes with acid | Sedimentary rocks |
| Translucent; vitreous luster | Conchoidal | Sard is brown. Sardonyx is sard or carnelian, striped with white or black | As nodules, usually in desert areas |
| Translucent; waxy to vitreous luster | Conchoidal | Agate, carnelian, sard, jasper are some varieties | Seams or lining of cavities in sedimentary and volcanic rocks |
| Opaque; waxy luster | Uneven fracture | Cigar-shaped prisms; a variety of andalusite | Schists; metamorphic rocks |

**Table B.** (cont.)

| Name and Specific Gravity | Hard-ness | Composition | Color or Pattern |
|---|---|---|---|
| Chlorastrolite 3.2 (klōr-as'-trō-lite) | 6 | Silicate of calcium and aluminum | Dark green eyes ringed in white or pale green; chatoyant |
| Chrysoberyl 3.5 to 3.8 (krĭs'-ō-bear-ĭl) | 8½ | Beryllium aluminate | Yellow, green; alexandrite is green-red; cat's-eye is chatoyant |
| Chrysocolla 2.6 (krĭs-ō-kŏl'-a) | 7 | Quartz colored by copper silicate | Greenish blue |
| Chrysoprase 2.6 (krĭs'-ō-praise) | 7 | Quartz colored by nickel mineral | Apple green |
| Citrine 2.6 (sĭt'-rĭn) | 7 | Crystalline quartz | Yellow to red-brown |
| Coral 2.6 | 3+ | Organic aragonite | Red, pink, white, black |
| Corundum 3.9 to 4.1 (kō-rŭn'-dŭm) | 9 | Aluminum oxide | Ruby red, sapphire blue; many other colors, also asteriated and cat's-eye |

| Diaphaneity and Luster | Fracture and Cleavage | Other Characteristics | Associated Rocks |
|---|---|---|---|
| Opaque | Fibrous fracture, brittle | Amygdaloids or beach pebbles | From basalt and gravels of Lake Superior district |
| Transparent; vitreous luster | Conchoidal | As crystals | Schists and pegmatite |
| Translucent to opaque; vitreous luster | Conchoidal | Massive, enamel-like surface | Copper deposits |
| Translucent to opaque; vitreous to waxy luster | Conchoidal | Prase is dull sage green; plasma dull dark green | In veins with nickel deposits |
| Transparent | Conchoidal | Often from amethyst by heat treatment | From cavities in igneous and sedimentary rocks |
| Translucent; dull luster | Hackly fracture | Branching formation | From salt water coral formations |
| Transparent to translucent; sub-adamantine luster | Conchoidal | Plate-like or blunt, six-sided crystals | Metamorphic and igneous rocks |

**Table B.** (cont.)

| Name and Specific Gravity | Hardness | Composition | Color or Pattern |
|---|---|---|---|
| Datolite<br>2.9 to 3.0<br>(dăt-ô-lite) | 5+ | Calcium borosilicate | White, copper red, yellow, green |
| Diamond<br>3.5 | 10 | Carbon | Colorless, blue, yellow, pink, brown, black |
| Dumortierite<br>2.6<br>(dū-môr'-tǐ-ĕr-ite) | 7 . | Complex aluminum borosilicate as inclusions in quartz | Blue, violet, pink |
| Emerald<br>2.6 to 2.9 | 8 | Variety of beryl | Grass green |
| Enstatite<br>3.1 to 3.5<br>(ĕn'-stȧ-tite) | 5+ | Magnesium and iron silicate | Hypersthene (bronzite) variety is iridescent brownish green |
| Feldspar<br>2.5 to 2.8 | 6 | Silicates of aluminum with potassium, sodium or calcium | Moonstone is shimmering white; amazonite, green; labradorite, gray with play of colors; sunstone is red spangled |

| Diaphaneity and Luster | Fracture and Cleavage | Other Characteristics | Associated Rocks |
|---|---|---|---|
| Opaque | Subconchoidal | Massive, porcelainlike | Michigan copper mines |
| Transparent; adamantine luster | Octahedral cleavage | Cubic or octahedral crystals with rounded edges | Peridotite and gravels |
| Translucent to opaque; sub-vitreous luster | Fibrous fracture | Usually massive | In schists and gneiss |
| Transparent; vitreous luster | Conchoidal fracture; basal cleavage | Crystals are prisms | Limestone, schists and pegmatite |
| Transparent to opaque | Hackly fracture | Usually massive | Igneous rocks |
| Transparent to opaque; vitreous to pearly luster | Perfect cleavage | Crystals or massive | Principal constituent (with quartz) of igneous rocks |

Table B. (cont.)

| Name and Specific Gravity | Hardness | Composition | Color or Pattern |
|---|---|---|---|
| Flint 2.6 | 7 | Earthy variety of chalcedony | Various pale colors, black |
| Fluorite 3.0 to 3.2 (flōō'-ō-rite) | 4 | Calcium fluoride | Green, blue, purple, red, brown, colorless |
| Garnet 3.4 to 4.3 | 6+ to 7½ | Silicates of aluminum, with magnesium, manganese or iron, or of calcium with iron, aluminum or chromium | Pyrope is wine red; almandine, violet red; spessartite is orange to brownish red; grossularite, green or yellow; andradite, green; rhodolite is red-purple |
| Hematite 4.9 to 5.3 (hĕm'-á-tite) | 5+ | Iron oxide | Black or steel gray |
| Idocrase 3.4 (ī'-dō-krāz) | 6+ | Complex calcium aluminum silicate | Yellow, green, brown or blue |

| Diaphaneity and Luster | Fracture and Cleavage | Other Characteristics | Associated Rocks |
|---|---|---|---|
| Opaque | Conchoidal | Rarely of gem quality | Nodules in limestone, and chalk |
| Transparent; vitreous luster | Perfect cleavage | Cubic crystals | Veins in pegmatite and limestone |
| Transparent to opaque; vitreous to resinous luster | Conchoidal to uneven fracture | Pyrope almost never crystals; almandine is the "carbuncle," often asteriated; grossularite is known as essonite or cinnamon stone; when green, as Transvaal jade; crystals are 12-sided | Pyrope in volcanic rocks; others in metamorphic rocks, and in gravels. Spessartite in pegmatite |
| Metallic luster | Hackly fracture; streak red | Massive, some from Minnesota is chatoyant | Iron mines |
| Transparent to opaque; vitreous to greasy luster | Splintery fracture | Massive form known as California jade; blue known as cyprine. Also known as vesuvianite | Metamorphic rocks |

**Table B.** (cont.)

| Name and Specific Gravity | Hardness | Composition | Color or Pattern |
|---|---|---|---|
| Iolite<br>2.6<br>(ī'-ō-lite) | 7+ | Hydrous magnesium (iron) aluminum silicate | Light to smoky blue |
| Jade<br>(nephrite)<br>2.9 to 3.2 | 6+ | Silicate of calcium, magnesium and iron; an amphibole | Green, brown and black |
| Jade<br>(jadeite)<br>3.3 to 3.5<br>(jād'-ite) | 7− | Sodium aluminum silicate; a pyroxene | Green, gray white, less commonly blue, red, lavender |
| Jasper<br>2.6 | 7 | Impure chalcedony | Varicolored; usually patterned |
| Jet<br>1.1 to 1.4 | 2+ | Carbon, a form of coal | Black |
| Kyanite<br>3.5 to 3.7<br>(kī'-à-nite) | 4+ to 6+ | Aluminum silicate | Spotty blue or green |

| Diaphaneity and Luster | Fracture and Cleavage | Other Characteristics | Associated Rocks |
|---|---|---|---|
| Transparent; vitreous luster | Conchoidal | Also called cordierite or dichroite; crystals are white or blue in one direction, dark in the other | Gravels and metamorphic rocks |
| Translucent to opaque; sub-vitreous luster | Splintery fracture | Compact and massive; very tough | With diorite and serpentine in metamorphic rocks |
| Translucent to opaque; sub-vitreous luster | Granular fracture | Compact and tough; best green is the "imperial" jade | In metamorphic rocks |
| Opaque; vitreous to dull luster | Conchoidal | Massive, with eye, moss, dot or stripe patterns | Veins, nodules in igneous rocks |
| Opaque; resinous luster | Conchoidal | Feels warmer than glass or plastic | Coal mines |
| Transparent to translucent | Perfect cleavage | Bladed crystals harder in one direction than in other | Metamorphic rocks |

Table B. (cont.)

| Name and Specific Gravity | Hard-ness | Composition | Color or Pattern |
|---|---|---|---|
| Labradorite 2.7 (lăb′-rà-dôr-ite) | 6 | Variety of feldspar | Gray with blue, green and golden play of color |
| Lapis lazuli 2.5 to 2.9 (lă′-pĭs lăz′-ū-lĭ) | 5+ | Mixture of lazurite with calcite, pyrite, etc. | Deep blue |
| Lepidolite 2.8 (lê-pĭd′-ō-lite) | 7 | Quartz containing a lithia mica | Lilac-gray |
| Malachite 3.9 to 4.0 (măl′-à-kite) | 3+ | Hydrous copper carbonate | Light to dark green; often banded or orbicular |
| Moonstone 2.6 | 6 | Orthoclase, albite, or oligoclase feldspar | Colorless with blue or milky "moon" |
| Obsidian 2.3 to 2.6 (ŏb-sĭd′-ĭ-ăn) | 6 | Volcanic glass | Black, green, brownish red, or gray |
| Olivine 3.3 (ŏl′-ĭ-veen) | 7 | Magnesium iron silicate | Peridot is bottle green; chrysolite is yellowish green |

| Diaphaneity and Luster | Fracture and Cleavage | Other Characteristics | Associated Rocks |
|---|---|---|---|
| Translucent to opaque | Perfect cleavage | Massive. A transparent yellow form has no play of color | Igneous rocks |
| Opaque; vitreous luster | Hackly fracture | Massive; the best is nearly free of white and contains specks of pyrite | Metamorphic limestone |
| Pearly luster; opaque | Uneven fracture | Massive | Pegmatite |
| Opaque; silky luster | Conchoidal to uneven fracture | Massive; often botryoidal, and mixed with azurite | Copper deposits |
| Transparent to translucent | Perfect cleavage | Best has strong shimmering color play | Pegmatites |
| Transparent to translucent; vitreous luster | Conchoidal | Massive; lacks crystal structure | Volcanic rocks |
| Transparent; vitreous luster | Conchoidal | Crystalline, but usually as pebbles | Dark volcanic rocks |

Table B. (cont.)

| Name and Specific Gravity | Hard-ness | Composition | Color or Pattern |
|---|---|---|---|
| Onyx<br>2.6<br>(ŏn'-ĭks) | 7 | Variety of chalcedony | Varicolored in layers or bands; often dyed |
| Opal<br>1.9 to 2.3 | 6+ | Hydrous silicon dioxide | Precious opal has colorless, gray or black body with varicolored fire |
| Pearl<br>2.6 to 2.7 | 2+ | Aragonite and organic matter | White, pink, blue, green, or black |
| Peridot<br>3.3<br>(pĕr'-ĭ-dŏt) | 7 | Variety of olivine | Bottle green |
| Petrified wood (bone)<br>2.6 | 7— | Variety of chalcedony or opal | Varicolored, often showing wood grain |
| Phenacite<br>2.9<br>(fĕn'-à-site) | 7+ | Beryllium silicate | Colorless or pale yellow or red |
| Prehnite<br>2.8 to 3.0<br>(prăn'-ite) | 6+ | Hydrous calcium aluminum silicate | Pale green |

| Diaphaneity and Luster | Fracture and Cleavage | Other Characteristics | Associated Rocks |
|---|---|---|---|
| Translucent; vitreous luster | Conchoidal | Cryptocrystal-line. Banded calcite is also known as onyx | Igneous rocks |
| Transparent to opaque; vitreous luster | Conchoidal | Amorphous, in veins, often as fossils | In lavas or hot spring de-posits |
| Translucent; pearly luster | Shell has splintery fracture | Abalone and pearl shell cut for jewelry | From pearl oyster |
| Transparent; vitreous luster | Conchoidal | Crystals usually water-worn | Volcanic rocks |
| Opaque | Conchoidal to splintery | Often limbs or trunk masses | In volcanic ash or lava |
| Transparent; vitreous luster | Conchoidal | Crystals look like quartz | Pegmatite or metamor-phic rocks |
| Translucent; vitreous luster | Uneven fracture | Botryoidal masses | With zeolites in dark vol-canic rocks |

Table B. (cont.)

| Name and Specific Gravity | Hard-ness | Composition | Color or Pattern |
|---|---|---|---|
| Quartz 2.6 | 7 | Silicon dioxide | Rock crystal is colorless; amethyst, purple; citrine, yellow; smoky quartz, brown; chrysocolla, blue; chrysoprase, green; rose quartz, pink |
| Rhodochrosite 3.4 to 3.7 (rō-dō-krō'-site) | 4 | Manganese carbonate | Pink to red |
| Rhodonite 3.5 to 3.7 (rō'-dō-nite) | 6 | Manganese silicate | Red, rose or pink, often veined in black |
| Rose quartz 2.6 | 7 | Variety of quartz | Rosy pink, often asteriated |
| Ruby 3.9 to 4.1 | 9 | Variety of corundum | Pink to red; often asteriated |
| Sagenitic quartz 2.6 (săj-ê-nĭt-ĭk) | 7 | Quartz containing needles of rutile, tourmaline, actinolite, or hornblende | Colorless or smoky; often called rutilated quartz; Venus or Thetis hair stone |

| Diaphaneity and Luster | Fracture and Cleavage | Other Characteristics | Associated Rocks |
|---|---|---|---|
| Transparent; vitreous luster | Conchoidal | Crystals are 6-sided with pointed terminations | In cavities of many kinds of rocks |
| Translucent to opaque | Uneven, granular fracture | Usually massive | With manganese deposits |
| Translucent to opaque; resinous luster | Uneven fracture | Compact masses | Manganese ores |
| Translucent; vitreous luster | Conchoidal | Massive; deep color rare | Pegmatites |
| Transparent; sub-adamantine luster | Conchoidal | Crystals are plates or keg-shaped | Schists; limestone or igneous rocks |
| Transparent; vitreous luster | Conchoidal | Crystals shot through with green, golden, red or black needles | In cavities in many types of rocks |

Table B. (cont.)

| Name and Specific Gravity | Hard-ness | Composition | Color or Pattern |
|---|---|---|---|
| Sapphire 3.9 to 4.1 | 9 | Variety of corundum | Colorless, blue, yellow green, violet; also often asteriated |
| Scapolite (wernerite) 2.6 to 2.7 (skăp'-ō-lite) | 6 | Complex silicate | Colorless, yellow, pink and gray |
| Serpentine 2.5 to 2.6 (sûr'-pĕn-tēn) | 5 | Hydrous magnesium silicate | Green, white, yellow, often mottled or striped |
| Sillimanite 3.5 | 6+ | Aluminum silicate | Blue, white, yellow |
| Smithsonite 4.3 to 4.5 | 5+ | Zinc carbonate | Blue, green, yellow, pink |
| Smoky quartz 2.6 | 7 | Variety of quartz | Yellow, brown to black |
| Sodalite 2.2 | 6 | Sodium aluminum silicate | Colorless to deep blue with white veins |

| Diaphaneity and Luster | Fracture and Cleavage | Other Characteristics | Associated Rocks |
|---|---|---|---|
| Transparent; sub-ada-mantine luster | Conchoidal | Crystals often parti-colored | Schists, lime-stone or igneous rocks |
| Transparent to opaque; vitreous luster | Conchoidal to hackly fracture | Sometimes cat's-eye | Pegmatites or metamor-phic rocks |
| Translucent to opaque; greasy luster | Splintery fracture | Massive; variety names such as wil-liamsite, ricolite, bowenite, verd an-tique | In magnesian rocks |
| Opaque; silky luster | Uneven to hackly fracture; tough | Fibrous, often chatoyant | As stream pebbles |
| Translucent; resinous luster | Uneven fracture | Compact masses, often botryoidal | Zinc ores |
| Transparent; vitreous luster | Conchoidal | Sometimes known as cairngorm | Pegmatite, igneous rocks |
| Translucent to opaque; sub-vitreous luster | Uneven fracture | Massive, mot-tled with orange cancrinite | Igneous rocks |

**Table B.** (cont.)

| Name and Specific Gravity | Hard-ness | Composition | Color or Pattern |
|---|---|---|---|
| Spodumene 3.2 (spŏd'-ū-mēn) | 7− | Lithium aluminum silicate | Yellow, kunzite pink; hiddenite, green |
| Staurolite 3.6 (stôw'-rō-lite) | 7+ | Iron aluminum silicate | Reddish brown |
| Sunstone 2.6 | 6 | Variety of feldspar | Reddish, spangled with inclusions |
| Thomsonite 2.3 | 5+ | Hydrous calcium aluminum silicate | Orbicular patterns in red, green, black |
| Topaz 3.5 | 8 | Aluminum fluosilicate | Colorless, wine yellow, golden, blue or red |
| Tourmaline 3.0 to 3.1 (tŏŏr'-mȧ-lĭn) | 7+ | Complex sodium, aluminum borosilicate | Rubellite is red; indicolite, blue; achroite, colorless; usual color of gem material, deep green |

| Diaphaneity and Luster | Fracture and Cleavage | Other Characteristics | Associated Rocks |
|---|---|---|---|
| Transparent; vitreous luster | Perfect cleavage | Some massive spodumene is cat's-eye | Pegmatite |
| Opaque; dull luster | | Crystals twinned in cross form known as fairy stones | Schists |
| Opaque | Perfect cleavage | Massive; imitated with glass "goldstone" | Igneous rocks |
| Opaque; subvitreous luster | Splintery fracture; brittle | Nodules in amygdaloids; a zeolite | Basalt |
| Transparent; vitreous luster | Perfect basal cleavage | Prisms with many-faced terminations | Pegmatite and rhyolite |
| Transparent; vitreous luster | Subconchoidal to uneven fracture | Crystals long, with rounded, triangular cross section, and striated along length; also often particolored, as pink center with green edges | Pegmatite and metamorphic rocks |

**Table B.** (cont.)

| Name and Specific Gravity | Hard-ness | Composition | Color or Pattern |
|---|---|---|---|
| Turquoise 2.6 to 2.8 | 6 | Hydrous copper aluminum phosphate | Sky blue to green |
| Unakite 2.9 (ū'-na-kite) | 6+ | Mixture of minerals | Pink feldspar and green epidote in quartz |
| Variscite 2.5 (văr'ĭs-ite) | 5 | Hydrous aluminum phosphate | Dark to pale green |
| Zircon 4.0 to 4.7 | 7+ | Zirconium silicate | Colorless; red-brown is jacinth; yellow, jargoon; green, blue |
| Zoisite 3.3 (zois'-ite) | 6 | Hydrous calcium aluminum silicate | Thulite is bright pink; saussurite looks like jade |

| Diaphaneity and Luster | Fracture and Cleavage | Other Characteristics | Associated Rocks |
|---|---|---|---|
| Opaque; waxy luster | Conchoidal | Amorphous; nodules in claystone or veins in rock | Usually in desert regions |
| Opaque | | Massive, may have quartz or jasper ground-mass | In granite, mostly in eastern U.S. |
| Opaque; sub-vitreous luster | Conchoidal | Nodules and masses | Shales and slates, mostly in Utah |
| Transparent; adamantine luster | Conchoidal | Crystals; blue and white often by heat treat-ment | Granites and gravels |
| Vitreous to greasy luster | Uneven fracture | Massive | Metamorphic rocks |

# 6

# *Gem materials in their full natural color*

On the following pages you will see gem minerals as they really look. The color photographs show the materials as they occur in nature unless the captions note that they have been polished. Some specimens have been sliced to display their characteristics better.

All photographs were made of material supplied through the courtesy of the Chicago Natural History Museum, the American Museum of Natural History or from the private collections of the author and others.

WHITE DIAMOND crystal in matrix. Such crystals are octagonal in form and unique in their greasy, hard luster. Diamonds from Arkansas are usually far smaller.

TOPAZ crystals from the Thomas Mountains in Utah. These were dug from rhyolite, but crystals on the surface have been bleached white by the desert sun.

RUBY crystal (right) in calcite matrix. Rubies occur in Georgia, Idaho and North Carolina.

BLACK OPAL from Virgin Valley, Nevada. Opal usually is found in desert regions.

EMERALD crystal (left) in matrix. Emeralds are six-sided and grass-green. Excellent emeralds, often translucent to opaque, have been found in North Carolina.

SAPPHIRES in the U. S. can be found in the Missouri River below Helena, Montana, and in Georgia, Idaho and North Carolina.

EMERALD CRYSTALS in white quartz, with black tourmaline inclusions. (Found at Silver Ridge near Spruce Pine, North Carolina.)

CUYUNITE, from Minnesota's iron range, a hard, brilliantly patterned material, is often chatoyant.

CARNELIAN, a red form of quartz, is a favorite cutting material. Specimen is polished and back-lighted.

THOMSONITE (an aluminum, calcium and sodium silicate) shows orbicular pattern and matrix of basalt.

RED CINNABAR (mercury sulphide) in opalite, occurs north of Steamboat Springs area in Nevada.

MOSS AGATE (polished) with a border of silvery marcasite from the fields near Nipomo, California.

CHRYSOPRASE (below), a quartz stained green by a nickel mineral.

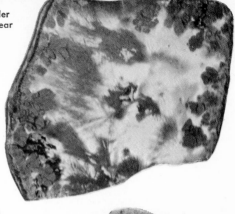

RHODONITE slice of unusual pink hue (right) from the Sunnyside Mine, San Juan County, Colorado.

MOTTLED AGATE from Chihuahua, Mexico, is typical of the many attractive patterns in agate that can be found in Mexico.

DOUBLE-FLOW OBSIDIAN from Glass Buttes, Oregon, is a volcanic glass vividly striped by nature.

AGATE THUNDER EGG from Prineville, Oregon (left), halved and polished. Right, sagenitic or moss agate nodule from Deming, New Mexico.

RHODONITE, most attractive of the red-pink gem materials, is usually veined with black. This is from Siskiyou County, California.

GREEN AMAZONITE FELDSPAR (below), grouped around smoky quartz crystal, can be found in Florissant, Colorado, area.

LABRADORITE, the feldspar of peacock colors, is found in Labrador (the best specimens) and Arkansas, New Mexico, Utah and Vermont.

PERIDOT crystals from the San Carlos Indian Reservation, Arizona, where they occur in volcanic rock debris.

VARISCITE, from Lucin, Utah, offers a unique combination of green and yellow to the gem cutter.

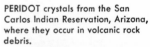

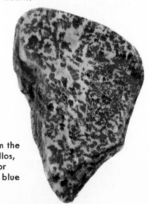

TURQUOISE (left) from the old mines at Los Cerrillos, New Mexico. Fine color material is almost sky blue and dense.

JASPER-AGATE, a slice of an unusual blue and red variety from Oregon, with one face polished.

RED AGATE in a grape or reniform mass from the Henry Mountains of Utah.

POPPY JASPER, a brilliant, red-spotted variety from the noted Morgan Hill locality in California. Note contrast between sides of specimen and polished face.

ALMANDINE GARNET found in cavities in rhyolite at Ruby Mountain, near Nathrop, Colorado. Strong light brings out red translucency.

GOLDEN APATITE crystal, in matrix, from Durango, Mexico. This brilliantly clear material is too soft for gems exposed to much wear.

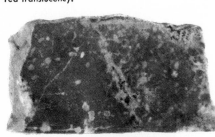

LAPIS LAZULI, like this polished slice from Colorado (left), is finest of the massive, blue gem minerals (best is from Iran).

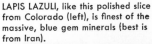

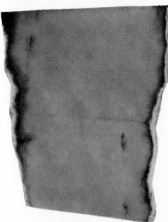

PETOSKEY STONES are a fossil coral from reefs of limestone off the eastern shore of Lake Michigan.

NEPHRITE JADE slice from south of Lander, Wyoming, where large, fine-colored masses were once plentiful.

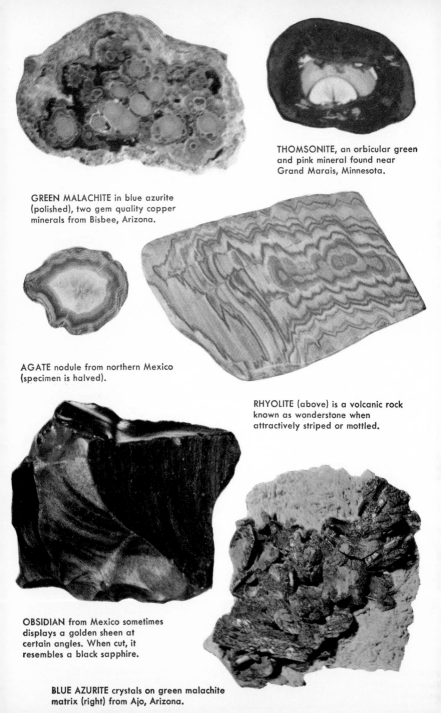

THOMSONITE, an orbicular green and pink mineral found near Grand Marais, Minnesota.

GREEN MALACHITE in blue azurite (polished), two gem quality copper minerals from Bisbee, Arizona.

AGATE nodule from northern Mexico (specimen is halved).

RHYOLITE (above) is a volcanic rock known as wonderstone when attractively striped or mottled.

OBSIDIAN from Mexico sometimes displays a golden sheen at certain angles. When cut, it resembles a black sapphire.

BLUE AZURITE crystals on green malachite matrix (right) from Ajo, Arizona.

CHRYSOCOLLA from Globe, Arizona, is quartz stained sky blue by a copper mineral. Once common, it is now scarce.

FLUORITE crystals from Rosiclare, Illinois, with calcite crystal in center. Although soft, fluorite is often cut and even faceted.

SNOWFLAKE OBSIDIAN from Utah presents snowy white dots in glossy black volcanic glass.

AMETHYST crystal mass from Thunder Bay region of Ontario, where—as is often the case—amethyst is associated with silver mines.

PETRIFIED WOOD slice from Petrified Forest area in Arizona. Surface is polished.

PETRIFIED WOOD (polished) from Texas has faithfully preserved structure of a tree that grew millions of years ago.

TOURMALINE (light greenish-blue) from Newry, Maine, in white feldspar matrix, above. Below, large tourmaline crystal displaying the characteristic bi-coloration of the mineral.

CLEAR QUARTZ with inclusions of golden needles of rutile (titanium oxide) is known as sagenitic quartz or hairstone.

SMITHSONITE (above) is at its best in these blue-green mammillary masses from the Kelly Mine near Magdalena, New Mexico.

RED AGATE, and snowy quartz. This slice shows one of many gem forms of this plentiful mineral.

ORBICULAR AGATE (above), or eye agate, from Mille Lacs, Minnesota, area was brought down by glaciers and is known as Lake Superior agate.

SODALITE from Hastings County, Ontario, Canada, is deep-blue mottled with flesh-colored pink and white inclusions. One face of this specimen has been polished.

DATOLITE in the massive form, as this polished slice shows, is colored pink to brown by minute inclusions of metallic copper.

# 7

# *Black light for your minerals*

Drab rocks can be awakened to glow with incomparable colors by a magic lamp that thousands of hobbyists are using today. The lamp radiates invisible ultraviolet light and the phenomenon this ray produces is known as *fluorescence*.

To understand fluorescence, you need to understand something about light. Light rays visible to the human eye are only part of a great electromagnetic spectrum (see page 63), a vast pattern of radiant energy vibrations ranging from very short cosmic rays to long, alternating current rays. Visible light consists of the colors seen in the rainbow. Ultraviolet light lies just outside this visible light band and is commonly called *black light*.

To identify wave lengths in the various bands of light, the Angstrom unit is used. The ultraviolet band is divided into three parts—far ultraviolet from 2,000 to 2,800 *au* (Angstrom units), middle ultraviolet from 2,800 to 3,200 *au*, and near ultraviolet from 3,200 to 4,000 *au*. Above this band is visible violet. The lens of the human eye transmits only wave lengths between 4,000 *au* and 8,000 *au*, which is why *true* black light is invisible.

Actually, commercially available black light lamps transmit from 40% to 60% of the visible light produced at the source, and this much visible light heightens the fluorescent effect of most substances used for commercial or hobby applications. But in laboratories, where close identification of materials by their degree of fluorescence is necessary, lamps which block out almost all the visible rays are used. Far UV (ultraviolet) radiations are exceedingly active—in addition to causing fluorescence in many materials, they will kill airborne bacteria; middle UV radiations produce vitamin D in the body and too long exposure to it will burn the skin; near UV is the wave length that induces fluorescence in at least 3,000 substances.

When radiation penetrates a mineral, the short wave lengths of ultraviolet light impart a great deal of energy to the atoms. The atoms absorb energy and then give it up. The energy is given up in the form of light waves, but visible light waves this time. The color will depend on the atomic makeup of the mineral, and it has no relation to the native color of the mineral in normal light. If the nature of the mineral is such that its atoms take some time to settle down again, it glows with visible light after the exciting ultraviolet light is removed, and it is then said to be phosphorescent.

Minerals usually must contain a trace of some other compound, commonly a metallic salt, before they will fluoresce. This foreign compound is called an activator and the host material the base. For instance, the activator may be a manganese salt and the base zinc orthosilicate, as in the mineral willemite. Freedom of the base from other substances, the heat at which base and activator were fused together, and harmony between the crystal structure of the two materials are some conditions that determine how fluorescent a substance is. This is true, also, of artificial minerals and compounds prepared for fluorescent lamp coatings. The activator must be present in just the right amount. Calcite from Franklin, New Jersey, fluoresces a fiery red from specimens containing 3½% manganese. If less than 1% or more than 5% manganese is present, the calcite is not fluorescent. It is obvious, therefore, that only certain mineral specimens from certain favorable locations will possess this rare property.

Many substances react most favorably under certain wave lengths of UV light (see page 63). A mineral may make its best display under *far* UV (short wave), another only under *near* UV (longer wave lengths). A few glow one color under short wave, another color under long wave, and some are stimulated to phosphoresce. For instance, calcite from Miles, Texas, fluoresces pink under 3,650 *au* and shows a blue fluorescence and phosphorescence under 2,537 *au*.

There are many black light sources which the hobbyist can use. One is a viewing box with an opening at the top and a special filter glass window in the side which admits only the UV rays of the sunlight. Another is a special filter for a three-cell flashlight which passes a small amount of UV radiation. The fluorescent response of most minerals to these sources is naturally somewhat weak. For a little better response, there are the 2½-watt argon bulb and the 250-watt Purple X bulb, both relatively low-cost items. But the amateur mineralogist who wants a strong response from his fluorescent minerals should pay a little more to secure one of the commercial black light lamps which contain mercury and a small amount of argon gas inside a glass or fused quartz tube. When current is applied in this type lamp, it ionizes the argon and discharges across the tube, vaporizing the mercury. The mercury then radiates bands of light especially strong in the UV region. By controlling pressure within the tube and by using different types of glass for the tube and jacket, varying radiations can be produced. With low pressure the principal radiation is at 2,537 *au*—short-wave UV; medium pressure gives longer wave lengths common in the popular "black light" bulbs; higher pressure is used in lamps producing visible light.

Many of the lamps used for mineral displays provide long-wave UV radiations in the region of 3,200 to 4,000 *au*, with peak intensity at 3,650 *au*. Fluorescent paints, dyes, and fabrics sensitive to this long-wave radiation are used by theatrical and display designers; many minerals will also respond well to long wave. But the most spectacular minerals, such as the Franklin calcites, react best to short-wave mercury vapor and quartz lamps radiating light at the 2,537 *au* band.

Two manufacturers have brought out lamps that radiate both long- and short-wave ultraviolet light, either by building two tubes into one unit or by equipping the unit with a so-called broad spectrum tube that radiates in both regions. Such lamps replace the two lamps formerly needed to get response from all minerals, and are both less expensive and easier to use.

Most famous source of fluorescent minerals is Franklin, New Jersey. From its zinc mines come calcite which fluoresces a fiery red, willemite (zinc orthosilicate) which displays a brilliant green, and calcium larsenite (a calcium-lead-zinc silicate), which has a yellow fluorescence. A similar calcite comes from Langban, Sweden. Wyoming contributes the Sweetwater moss agates, Specimen Hill chalcedony and Eden Valley petrified wood, which owe their reactivity to traces of uranium minerals. Texas supplies a calcite which is pink under long-wave ultraviolet and blue under the short waves. A few diamonds fluoresce blue, and some of the rarer ones fluoresce green, orange, yellow, or red. Table C lists prominent fluorescent minerals, their maximum color of response, and localities where they have been obtained.

Fluorescence is widely employed in other commercial forms such as detecting counterfeit money or postage stamps, exposing alterations in oil paintings and forged documents, and revealing flaws in castings which have been soaked in an oil carrying a fluorescent dye. In fact, fluorescence follows mankind from the cradle, when the baby may be stamped

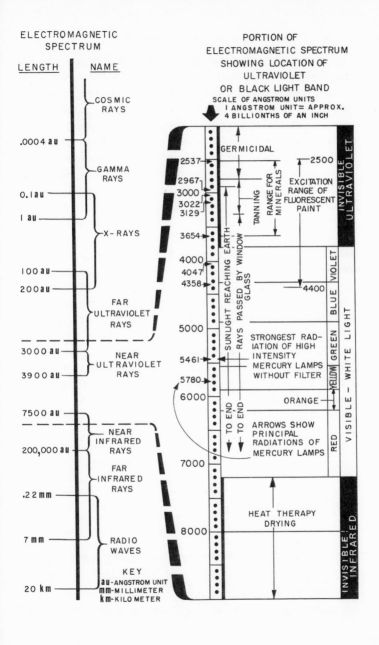

with fluorescent ink in the hospital for identification, to the grave, when a fluorescent embalming fluid may be used.

The hobbyist is not restricted to minerals. He can experiment with fluorescent woods, such as sumac, black locust, and Oregon graperoot; petroleum jelly (blue-green), several kinds of plastics, cheap glassware (yellow-green), false teeth (yellow-white), quinine in acid solution (bright blue), fresh eggs (scarlet), or stale eggs (purple), a number of dyes, waxes, and leathers. UV light makes real teeth and fingernails fluoresce white and shows up freckles. Gardenias or other cut flowers, placed with their stems in water containing the dye fluorescein, will take up the dye in their petals, which will then fluoresce a brilliant green. Rhodamine and eosin dyes can also be used.

Fluorescing minerals can be photographed in color. Exposure varies so greatly that most photographers use a trial and error test sequence to arrive at the proper aperture and time. Photographs taken for one magazine article were made at *f.* 22 on Ektachrome color film Type A with a Wrattan 2A filter, and the exposure time varied from 12 minutes for a brilliant piece of hydrozincite to 20 times that long for a chalcedony geode.

### Table C. Fluorescent Minerals

Their color and wave length of response, and where they may be found

---

ADAMITE: Mexico—green (short wave)

AGATE: Sweetwater Valley, Wyo.—yellow-green—all wave lengths; Goldfield, Nev.—yellow-green; Prescott, Ariz.—cream; San Diego, Calif.—yellow-green

ALUNITE: Marysville, Utah—light blue (long wave)

AMBER: Baltic Sea—greenish yellow; Maryland—green (long wave); Texas—yellow; Washington—yellow

AMETHYST: North Carolina—deep blue

ANDALUSITE: Oreville, S.D.—pinkish (long wave)

ANDERSONITE: Hillside Mine, Ariz.

ANGLESITE: Phoenixville, Pa.—yellow (long wave); Black Hills—yellow

APATITE: Bohemia—white (short wave); Brinton's Quarry, Delaware Co., Pa.—orange; Hull, Que.—yellow; Ontario—dark green

APOPHYLLITE: Paterson, N.J.—yellow

ARAGONITE: Crestmore, Calif.—yellow; Death Valley, Calif.—light green; La Junta, Colo.—cream-white; Livingston, N.M.—red; Platte Mound, Wis.; Chuckawalla Mts., Calif.—white; Vernonia, Ore.—cream; Franklin, N.J.—pale blue

AUTUNITE: Chesterfield, Mass.; Rumford, Me.; Alexander Co., N.C.; Grafton, N.H.; Branchville, Conn.; Black Hills; Wash.—all yellow-green (all wave lengths)

AXINITE: Franklin, N.J.—red

BARITE: Franklin, N.J.—gray-blue; Palos Verdes, Calif.—yellow (also phosphorescent); S. Dakota—brown

BENITOITE: San Benito Co., Calif.—blue (all wave lengths)

BERYL: Elba, N.Y.—bluish white; Gillette Quarry, Haddam Neck, Conn. (morganite)—orange

BUSTAMITE: Franklin, N.J.—orange

CALCITE: Franklin, N.J.—red—2,925 to 3,128 *au;* Bagdad, Ariz.—deep blue; Deming, N.M.—green; Casa Grande, Ariz.—blue; Bisbee and Nogales, Ariz.—red; Granby, Mo.—light green; Keller, Wash.—pink; Picher, Okla.—deep green; Terlingua, Tex.—pink at 3,650 *au,* blue by short wave; Texas calcite containing petroleum—yellow to orange; Barrego Valley, Calif.—rose; Brewster, Tex.—blue; Hollywood Hills, Calif.—red; Miles, Tex.; Paicines, Calif.—white; Randsburg, Calif.—orange; Eagle Ford, Tex.—cream and purple; Lovington, N.M.—green; Cumberland, England—pinkish; Rosiclare, Ill.—cream

CALCIUM LARSENITE: Franklin, N.J.—yellow (short wave)

CALOMEL (MERCURY CHLORIDE): Terlingua, Tex.—orange to pink (long wave)

CERUSSITE: Good Springs, Nev.—blue (short wave); Salt Lake City—orange (long wave)

CHALCEDONY: Aguila, Ariz.; Barstow, Calif.; Tampa Bay, Fla.; Wasco County, Ore.—yellow-green (all wave lengths)

CHLORAPATITE: California—orange

CLINOHEDRITE: Franklin, N.J.—orange by short wave—pink by long wave

COLEMANITE: Death Valley, Calif.—white

COQUINA (SHELL): Florida—white

CROCOITE: Tasmania and Ural Mts., Russia—brown

Table C. (cont.)

---

CUPROSCHEELITE: Milford, Ore.; Plumas County, Calif.—yellow (short wave)

CURTISITE: Scaggs Springs, Calif.—yellow-green

DIAMOND: Arkansas, South Africa, Brazil—most commonly blue, but other colors are known

DIASPORE: Chester, Mass.—pale yellow

DIOPSIDE: Franklin, N.J.—blue

DOLOMITE: Baden, Germany—weak green (short wave); Bloomington, Ind.—gray-green

DUMORTIERITE: San Diego County, Calif.—gray; Lyons, France—blue

EPSOMITE: Death Valley, Calif.—pale blue

FELDSPAR: Amelia, Va.—amazonite, gray-green; Franklin, N.J.—orthoclase, blue; Gillette Quarry, Haddam Neck, Conn.—albite, orange; Broken Hill, Australia—amazonite

FLUORITE: Castle Dome, Ariz.—blue—3,650 *au;* Clay Center, O.—cream; Keller, Wash.—blue; Duncan, Ariz.—green; Durham, England—blue; Cave-in-Rock, Ill.—white and purple; Franklin, N.J.—green; Westmoreland, N.H.—violet; Trumbull, Conn.—blue-white

FLUOROAPATITE: Strafford, N.H.—orange

GAY-LUSSITE: Washington—pink

GLAUBERITE: Borax Lake, Calif.—blue

GYPSUM: Grand Rapids, Mich.—green (long wave)

HACKMANITE: Bancroft, Ont.—orange, yellow or pink (long wave) (Short-wave radiation changes color of rock temporarily from gray to purple, which fades out in daylight.)

HALITE (SALT): Amboy, Calif.—red; Kansas—green

HARDYSTONITE: Franklin, N.J.—green (long wave), yellow (short wave)

HEMIMORPHITE: Good Springs, Nev.—green; Adelanto, Calif.—green (both short wave); Superior, Ariz.—cream

HEXAGONITE: Edwards, N.Y.—red

HIDDENITE (SPODUMENE): N. Carolina—weak red or lilac

HOWLITE: Lang, Calif.—orange (long wave)

HYDROZINCITE: Good Springs, Nev.; Utah; Keeler, Calif.—blue by short wave, yellow by long wave; Dragoon, Ariz.—blue; Franklin, N.J.—blue

KUNZITE (SPODUMENE): Pala, Calif.—reddish yellow; Portland, Conn.—deep red

KYANITE: Tyrol—greenish white

LARSENITE: Franklin, N.J.—blue

LAZURITE: Chile—blue

LEADHILLITE: Arizona—yellow (short wave)

LEPIDOLITE: Keystone, S.D.—pale green

MANGANAPATITE: Portland, Conn.; Center Strafford, N.H.; St. Mary's Lake, B.C.; Valyermo, Calif.—bright orange; Franklin, N.J.—orange

MARGAROSONITE: Franklin, N.J.—violet

MARIALITE: Ludwig, Nev.—rose pink

MEYERHOFFERITE: Death Valley, Calif.—yellowish

NASONITE: Franklin, N.J.—blue

NORBERGITE: Franklin, N.J.—pale yellow

OPAL: Bagdad, Ariz.; Barstow, Calif.; Beaver, Utah; Bishop, Calif.; Connell, Wash.; Fulton, Nev.; Lind, Wash.; Salmon, Idaho; Stone Mountain, Ga.; Coso Hot Springs, Calif.; 29 Palms, Calif.—all green; San Luis Potosí, Mex.—hyalite opal—green (all waves); Alpine, Tex.; Big Fork, Mont.; Lovington, N.M.; Virgin Valley, Nev.—common opal—green; Eden Valley, Wyo.; Goldfield, Nev.; Huntsville, Tex.—opalized wood—green

OZOKERITE: Utah, Brazil—yellow-brown

PECTOLITE: Paterson, N.J.—yellow; Franklin, N.J.—yellow

PHENACITE: Minas Geraes, Brazil—blue

PHOSGENITE: Monte Poni, Sardinia—brownish red

POWELLITE: Beaver, Utah; Bishop, Calif.; Lordsburg, N.M.; Randsburg, Calif.—yellow; Nogales, Ariz.—white

QUARTZ: Red Desert, Wyo.—blue white

RHODOCHROSITE: Franklin, N.J.—pale pink

ROEBLINGITE: Franklin, N.J.—pale pink

RUBY: Siam—weak red; Burma and N. Carolina—strong red; Ceylon —yellow (see Synthetics)

SAPPHIRE: Ceylon—yellow or orange; Montana—blue or lavender

SASSOLITE (BORIC ACID): Tuscany, Italy—blue

SCHEELITE: Inyo, Kern, and San Bernardino Counties, Calif.; Mill City, Nev.; Lucia, Utah—blue (short wave)

SCHROECKINGERITE (DAKEITE): Wamsutter, Wyo.—yellow green (all waves)

SELENITE: Hay Springs, Neb.—pale yellow; Lovington, N.M.—yellow

SEPTARIA: Utah—orange

SODALITE: Hastings Co., Ont.—white; Moultonboro, N.H.—orange red

SPHALERITE: Iturbidie district, Mexico; Tsumeb, Southwest Africa—orange; Trona, Searles Lake, Calif.—blue; Arizona—orange; Franklin, N.J.—pale orange

**Table C.** (cont.)

---

SPINEL: Vesuvius and Ceylon—red spinel fluoresces strong red

SUSSEXITE: Franklin, N.J.—pink to red

SVABITE: Franklin, N.J.—orange

SYNTHETICS: Ruby—strong red at 3,000 *au;* Sapphire—orange to red, strongest in white variety; spinel—red

TARBUTTITE: Rhodesia—orange

THAUMASITE: Paterson, N.J.—white (short wave)

TORBERNITE (AND METATORBERNITE): yellow-green (all waves)

TOURMALINE (RED VARIETY): Pala, Calif.; Newry, Me.—lavender (long wave)

TREMOLITE: Jefferson Co., N.Y.—orange-pink; St. Lawrence Co., N.Y. —red; Franklin, N.J.—orange

URANOPHANE: Grafton, N.H.—green

WAVELLITE: Mt. Holly, Pa.—blue

WERNERITE (SCAPOLITE): Grenville, Que.—yellow

WILLEMITE: Casa Grande, Ariz., Franklin, N.J.—green

WOLLASTONITE: New Jersey—orange spots; Riverside, Calif.—golden

WURTZITE: Utah—golden

ZIPPEITE: Bohemia—yellow-green

ZIRCON: Placer Co., Calif.; Henderson Co., N.C.; Oregon; Idaho; Montana; Wyoming; Ontario in placer sands—orange; Brazil—orange; Siam—yellow

Many natural petroleum derivatives—pitch, bitumen, asphalt, as well as oil—fluoresce; so do some coals.

---

# 8

## *Judging quality and value*

Not many hobbyists get rich from their finds, or even cover expenses. Few expect to. But this does not prevent a lively interest in the cash value of gem minerals. Partly it's plain curiosity, but only partly, for gem hunters trade with other amateurs, and occasionally sell their surplus to dealers. Some skill at judging quality is essential if rough materials are to be finished for display or made into jewelry.

Experience alone will develop the ability to evaluate gems in the rough. You have to practice, first estimating quality and then checking your judgment by cutting the rough into gem stones. You soon learn to watch for defects peculiar to certain types of stone and to judge specimens in the light of their fitness for lapidary purposes.

### VALUES OF QUARTZ MINERALS

Nine-tenths of the stones that the amateur works with belong to the quartz family, of which agate is the most versatile and favored member. Agate sells in the rough for one to three dollars a pound, although especially beautiful pieces, such as Oregon flower agate, often sell far above that level.

Lake Superior and Montana moss agates are unsurpassed, but they are prone to cracks and flaws that mar their fine patterns. Mexican and Oregon agate nodules have not suffered as much from buffeting of streams and the action of frost, but many are hollow and others show dull coloring or patterns. Only sawing can determine their worth, so agate nodules are a gamble—but a fascinating one. As in any patterned material, there is much waste in agate when it is cut. All these elements must be considered in your evaluation.

Much more costly are chrysoprase, chrysocolla and cabochon-quality amethyst, smoky quartz, and citrine. They bring from forty cents to one dollar an ounce. Good color is the most important quality, but the rough should be translucent and free from major blemishes and cracks. Judging color in the large piece of rough can be deceptive. Rose quartz, especially, may have vigorous color in the chunk but yield only a pallid gem when cut up.

Other valuable materials are bloodstone that is well marked with small, bright red spots and carnelian of a rich, red-brown hue. Good material which is sound and fracture free may bring as much as six dollars a pound.

Most jaspers are the poor relations of the quartz family, although a few stand out for unique pattern or color. They sell in the rough for less than one dollar a pound. They and their relatives, the petrified woods, frequently have so porous a texture that they are valueless for cutting. A homespun test can be used to check for porosity. Just lick a sawed or chipped surface. Any porous spots quickly become dull, as the moisture soaks in. Solid material remains shiny.

Pale, dull-patterned, or very dark gem materials rarely possess value unless some unusual quality, such as the black and white contrast of snowflake obsidian, redeems their drabness. Obsidian varies greatly in the degree to which it can be polished; some has a pitchy texture that refuses to take a satisfactory finish. Too much pattern is as bad as too little; some Texas plume, for example, is so dense that the patterns become blurred and lost.

Rutilated quartz, aventurine, and rose quartz of average quality retail for about two dollars a pound. Especially desirable pieces, such as rose quartz of deep color and translucence that fit it for faceting, may be much higher. Coarse rutile inclusions in quartz may create cavities that retain polishing compounds and disfigure the finished stone.

### JADE

The feldspar family has one weakness—easy cleavage. Deposits that have been blasted or exposed to weathering are likely to be shattered. Often a handsome, large specimen will yield only a multitude of small pieces. Amazonite, labradorite, and sunstone, the major gem varieties, retail for as much as six dollars a pound. Moonstone is obtainable only in small pieces and will bring even higher prices.

Nephrite jade of top quality should have a rich, translucent green color and should be fairly free from black inclusions. Most American nephrite is too dark, too gray and pale, or peppered with too many spots to be attractive. Top quality Wyoming jade is expensive, but satisfactory material has been coming from the Fraser River in Canada, from Alaska and occasionally from California. It may be had for as little as five dollars a pound.

Much Alaskan jade has a pronounced grain that causes it to chip in grinding and some will not take a good polish. Only the test of the grinding wheels will evaluate it properly. Monterey jade from California is often disfigured by schistose spots. Black jade from Wyoming, however, is free from almost all defects and is easy to cut and polish.

Garnets are almost always small and brittle, often with cracks and disfiguring inclusions. Almandine and pyrope garnets—the red gem varieties—may be too dark. Those that do not show rich, bright color when examined under—not against—a shaded light are too dense to make a gem.

The most attractive rhodonite is deep pink veined with black. It sells for two to three dollars a pound. Unakite and sodalite of good color and pattern are in the same range.

Banded or orbicular malachite, now mostly obtained from Africa, is among the more expensive materials. It sells for twelve to fifteen dollars a pound, and is so heavy that a pound does not bulk large. South American lapis lazuli brings half as much, but top grade American and Afghanistan lapis—deep blue, solid, and spangled with specks of pyrite—sells for several dollars an ounce. Top grade turquoise, too, is costly at ten dollars and more an ounce. Much porous and off-color turquoise is waxed, oiled, or treated with plastic to "improve" it. Such sophisticated material is useful for cutting into finished gems and ornaments if it is honestly priced.

Opal is the aristocrat of the cabochons, and it is priced accordingly, although Australia continues to produce a lot of surprisingly good stones for a few dollars an ounce. Most Australian white opal is seam material which shows its best fire on the side; a thick piece that can be sawed parallel to the side will yield the flashiest stones and is worth more. Pieces cut so that the top or bottom of the seam material is used for the top of the finished stone show less intense fire. This is not true of Mexican or American opal, which is of the nodular variety. Virgin Valley opal, for all its rare black beauty, has a bad reputation for crazing after it is cut.

Rough that is expected to yield cat's-eye and star stones is difficult to evaluate until the pattern is oriented and exposed in the cutting process. Garnet, sapphire, and tourmaline that are fibrous enough to make such stones, yet are attractively colored, are rare and costly.

## GRADING STONES

Material of faceting quality, suitable for cutting into jewelry stones, is much more expensive than cabochon rough.

Close evaluation of the yield in finished gems becomes essential. Flaws that would be ignored in cabochon rough become glaring in a faceted stone and make the rough undesirable at any price (except for a gem such as emerald, which is rarely found free of defects). You can detect inclusions, cracks, and incipient cleavages by studying the stone under the edge of a lampshade, holding the piece so that it is illuminated but does not reflect light into your eyes. Defects will show up as the stone is slowly turned.

For economy, the shape of the rough piece should be close to that desired in the cut gem. Long, thin, irregularly shaped pieces are extravagant when judged by what can be made from them. It is more economical to buy several small pieces of rough to cut several small stones, as for a bracelet, than to buy one large piece and divide it.

Color zones, characteristic of sapphire and amethyst, are a serious defect unless the rough can be manipulated to place a spot of color at the bottom of the gem, where it will suffuse the stone.

Cabochon-quality rough is usually sold by the ounce or pound, or, if it is slabbed, by the square inch. Faceting material of high quality is sold by the gram or carat. (There are 28.35 grams to the avoirdupois ounce, five carats to the gram.) Faceting-quality tourmaline, topaz, aquamarine, amethyst, citrine, and kunzite bring from fifty cents to six dollars a gram.

## ARTIFICIAL COLORING

Much has been done in recent years to alter the color of gem materials by heat treatment and atomic bombardment. Aquamarine is customarily heated to drive off any tint of yellow and improve its blueness. Some amethyst made green by the same treatment has been on the market in the last few years, and most citrine is derived from amethyst and smoky quartz by careful heating. Carnelian's color deepens when the rough is baked, and both the blue and white zircons of commerce are the result of careful heating of brown stones from southeast Asia.

Atomic bombardment of yellow diamonds changes them to green, brown, or even light blue, while kunzite's lilac becomes an impermanent blue-green and some colorless topaz comes out of the atomic pile a rich yellow. Atomic treatment is also said to intensify the color of many sapphires.

As no gem hunter can hope to visit all the collecting areas in person, he can diversify his materials by exchanging with other collectors or by buying from dealers. Names of the latter may be obtained from the American Gem and Mineral Suppliers Association, P.O. Box 274, Costa Mesa, California, or from the advertisements in magazines listed on page 278.

Mineral conventions, such as those held annually by the American Federation of Mineralogical and Geological Societies and by its six regional federations and those held by individual clubs, offer almost unlimited opportunity to swap with other collectors from all parts of North America, to patronize dealers who have display booths at the conventions, and to learn about new gem materials, new products, and new methods.

# 9

## *Collectors and collections*

Precious stones have been actors in some of the most lurid scenes of history. The Koh-i-noor diamond, before it came to rest in the British crown, passed from hand to hand as the prize of 650 years of violence. It was taken from the Mogul emperor in Delhi, India, in 1739 by the founder of Afghanistan. His grandsons fought over it until the victor fled to Lahore. There the rajah extorted it from him as the price of hospitality. In 1849 the British East India company seized it and gave it to Queen Victoria.

Another ornament of the British crown, the Black Prince's ruby, sealed the death of the king of Granada, who was killed for it by the king of Castile. He gave it to the Black Prince, son of Edward III of England. A later king, Henry V, wore it on his helmet on the famous day at Agincourt when England broke the power of feudal France. It helped deflect a nearly fatal sword blow at Henry's head. The stone, a spinel, has been polished but left in its natural shape.

Jewels have been the last resource of fugitives from war and revolution for ages. Napoleon pledged the Pitt diamond, now in the Louvre in Paris, to raise money for his wars. After World War I, the Russian Communists sold many of the Imperial treasures to strengthen the financial position of their country.

## THE GREAT COLLECTIONS

It was not until the 19th century that gems began to be collected for their scientific interest rather than their beauty and cash value. As mineralogical science developed, wealthy Europeans created a vogue for assembling cabinets of minerals. Philadelphia was the first center of collecting in this country. One of the first gem and mineral collections there was formed by J. R. Cox of the University of Pennsylvania and was later owned by Professor Joseph Leidy of the University, founder of paleontology in America.

A wealthy machine-tool manufacturer in Philadelphia, Clarence S. Bement, created the outstanding cabinet of his time by purchasing collections abroad and in the United States. J. Pierpont Morgan bought the Bement specimens and gave them to the American Museum of Natural History in New York.

Philadelphia was also the home of the notable Vaux family. William S. Vaux gave his collection to the Philadelphia Academy of Natural Sciences; his son George bequeathed his to Bryn Mawr college; and his grandson, George, Jr., augmented the gifts of his father at Bryn Mawr.

Of equal stature among these princely collectors was Colonel Washington A. Roebling, builder of the Brooklyn Bridge, who brightened years of invalidism in Trenton, New Jersey, by assembling the great collection which he gave to the National Museum of the Smithsonian Institution in Washington, D.C.

Buying with a lavish purse, under expert advice, in a time when major European collections were being dispersed and when the demands of industry were opening mines all over the world, these men brought together treasures that are the foundations of the displays of uncut and cut gems in the American Museum of Natural History and the National Museum.

The National Museum dates the formation of its gem collections to 1884, when it was authorized to buy material for an exhibit at New Orleans. Ten years later the valuable and well-chosen gems assembled by Isaac Lea, Philadelphia publisher and naturalist, were given to the museum by his daughter; her husband supplemented these with his own collection. Since then, Colonel Roebling and many later donors have added rich gifts, the most recent being the Hope blue diamond.

The collection of the National Museum is impressively displayed in a modern room. Among the most notable pieces are the 316-carat star sapphire, Star of Artaban; a star ruby of 50 carats; a 40-carat chrysoberyl cat's-eye; the largest cut alexandrite, of 66 carats; a 94-carat sherry-colored topaz that was a favorite of Colonel Roebling's; a 310-carat peridot, the largest cut peridot in existence; the largest cut benitoite; the famous Roebling black opal from Virgin Valley, Nevada; and the largest quartz crystal sphere, 12⅞ inches in diameter.

American gem stones are especially well represented among the exhibits. For example, a case of American rough diamonds includes stones from Arkansas, California, Indiana, Kentucky, North Carolina, Oregon, Texas, and West Virginia, the latter being the Punch Jones stone.

The most complete display of rare gems in the United States is at the American Museum of Natural History in New York. It owes much of its outstanding American material to George Frederick Kunz, who was vice president of Tiffany & Co., the famous New York jewelers. He encouraged his company to form a collection of American gems for exhibition in Paris in 1889. J. Pierpont Morgan bought that collection for the museum. Eleven years later Dr. Kunz again exhibited in Paris—and took a grand prize for the Tiffany collection of precious stones from world-wide sources. And once more Morgan bought the prize-winning collection for the museum. He also donated the Bement minerals, which in-

cluded many famous gem specimens. Morgan Memorial Hall
was set up in the museum to house the gifts of its benefactor.
After that time substantial gifts and endowments were added
by William Boyce Thompson, copper and sulphur-mining
magnate.

Among notable American specimens in the museum are
American fresh-water pearls, diamonds from Wisconsin and
Alabama, some of the finest known tourmalines from Maine
and southern California, and, appropriately, many examples
of two gems named for the men most closely associated with
the collection, the lilac spodumene, kunzite, and the pink
beryl, morganite. Morgan Hall contains such unique displays
as a magnificent cabinet of sapphires given by Morgan's son,
J. P. Morgan: the 100-carat DeLong star ruby; the 536-carat
Star of India, largest known blue star sapphire; a carved morganite crystal 6 inches high; a 600-pound gem-quality topaz
crystal; a fine 71-carat red spinel; a 9.29-carat hiddenite;
and the largest cut blue zircon, of 208 carats.

## SMALLER MUSEUMS

Three university museums in the East also offer the
hobbyist first-rate collections for study: the Mineralogical
Museum at Harvard University in Cambridge, Massachusetts,
is the show window of a great research department with well-
housed and well-displayed collections; the Peabody Museum
of Natural History of Yale University at New Haven, Connecticut, also is a center of research; and the collection at
Wesleyan University, Middletown, Connecticut is good.

In the Midwest, the Chicago Natural History Museum's
Hall of Gems is outstanding. Its excellently displayed collec-
tions include all the principal gem minerals of the world. Its
New England aquamarines and its topaz suite, especially the
Ural Mountain specimens, rank among the best in the world.
In an adjoining room is the notable Laufer collection of jade.

Cranbrook Institute of Science, in Bloomfield Hills, a suburb of Detroit, also has a good collection in quarters well designed for viewing.

Two smaller museums of high quality are the Lizzadro Museum of Lapidary Arts in Wilder Park in Elmhurst, a suburb of Chicago, where a center has been created for hobbyists; and the Walker Art Center in Minneapolis, which houses T. B. Walker's collection of two hundred pieces of jade, principally from the 17th, 18th, and 19th centuries.

The best displays on the West Coast are the Warner collection of the California Institute of Technology at Pasadena, and the California Division of Mines Collection in the Ferry Building in San Francisco. Both are exceptionally strong in the gem minerals of that state.

Canada's most diversified gem collection is in the Royal Ontario Museum of Geology and Mineralogy in Toronto.

## AMATEUR COLLECTORS

Present-day interest in gem collecting goes back to the first amateur club formed in New York in 1886, and the Mineralogical Society of Pennsylvania formed about the same time. A magazine, the *Mineral Collector,* served the interests of these pioneer clubs, but the real growth of the hobby may be dated by the first appearance of *Rocks and Minerals* magazine in 1926. Five years later a club group was formed in Joliet, Illinois, and in the same year the Mineralogical Society of Southern California was organized in Pasadena. Today there are more than six hundred mineral and gem clubs.

Such clubs grow out of the needs of the beginner who comes home from a vacation trip with a bag full of stones. What can he do with them? Most likely he will buy some machinery, or get acquainted with someone who already has the equipment, and cut his finds to bring out their full beauty. Amateurs have invented machinery for cutting gems and have provided a market for companies that manufacture it. Many have developed skill equal to that of the old-time professional lapidaries.

Gem cutting is divided into two major branches: faceting and the fashioning of cabochons. Ordinarily only transparent material free from disfiguring flaws is faceted. Such material is less abundant than the equally colorful nontransparent materials—the agates and jaspers—that are used for cabochons. Faceting, consequently, is generally regarded as the advanced step in amateur gem cutting.

## CABOCHONS

Cabochons are fashioned in four major operations. The large piece of rough material is clamped in a vise, and a circular saw blade containing diamond grit imbedded in its edge revolves against the stone, sawing it into slabs usually $\frac{1}{4}$ to $\frac{3}{16}$ inch thick. Chosen areas are marked on a slab with a template and an aluminum pencil. These blanks are cut out by holding the slab against a smaller diamond saw.

If blanks are large enough, they are grasped in the fingers and ground to the marked shape on a wet abrasive wheel. The base is made to conform to the pencil line, and the top is ground to a dome or some other chosen shape. If the blank is too small to hold, it is mounted on the end of a stick with sealing wax. This supporting stick is known as a dop. The shaped stone is now given a smooth surface by successive sandings with abrasive cloth of finer and finer grades, up to 600 grit. This is usually done on a wheel covered with the cloth or on a wet belt sander.

When the surface is satiny and free of defects after sanding, it is ready to polish. This is done on a rotating wheel covered with leather, or made of wood or hard felt, using a slurry of a polishing agent, such as tin oxide or fine aluminum oxide. The stone is pressed against the damp wheel, and within seconds, if it has been carefully prepared, it takes on a mirror finish which reveals all the innate beauty of the gem.

Ornamental objects, such as book ends or lamp bases, are formed by sawing to shape, sanding, and polishing in the same way. To polish large flat surfaces, special equipment—a power buff made of carpeting, a rotating flat plate, or vibrating plates—has been developed. It has become fashionable to make table tops of gem materials, with the pieces laid close together in mortar and polished like a single slab. Transparencies consisting of unpolished slabs cemented between glass plates and viewed against a lamp form another means of displaying the color and pattern of gem materials.

Tumbling has become one of the most popular ways of fashioning gems because it eliminates most of the handwork of forming and polishing and because it makes available a lot of material formerly too shattered or flawed for cutting. The rough pieces, usually all about the same size and hardness, are placed in a rotating container with water and abrasive. As the container turns slowly, the stones slide on one another, grinding away rough edges. When the rough grinding is completed, the process is repeated with finer abrasive, and then finally with polishing agents. In the conventional tumbler, the whole cycle will require four or more weeks. The result is a large supply of irregularly shaped, highly polished stones. If they have been well chosen in the beginning and preshaped to fit small, bell-shaped mounting caps, they can be made into attractive costume jewelry.

## FACETING

Until the amateurs took up faceting about thirty years ago, this delicate work was done with tools as primitive as those used in the Middle Ages. High skill alone enabled the professional faceter to do wonders. His only equipment was a horizontal rotating lap wheel and a dop jammed into a hole in a block of wood to give the proper angle for the facet. But amateurs compensated for their lack of this skill by devising machinery that would give even more precise results.

The stone to be faceted is roughed into shape on a grinding wheel. Then it is cemented to a metal dop which fits into a fixed metal post. The angle at which the stone touches the horizontal grinding wheels can be set with a protractor. It is possible to place the facets exactly where they belong to bring out maximum fire and brilliance in the gem. A device that allows some free-hand manipulation while retaining the advantages of the faceting machine is also on the market.

## DISPLAYS

Most cut gems find their proper place in jewelry, and many amateurs have become skillful craftsmen. But since there is a limit to the amount of jewelry that a family or its friends can wear, many collectors exhibit unmounted stones in a number of ways. In regions of abundant gem resources, such as the Far West, many collectors take pride in comprehensive displays of cabochons. Many faceters enjoy the challenge of cutting uncommon gem materials, which, either because of rarity, softness, or fragility, are not suitable for use in jewelry. Others cut or collect special types, such as star stones, opals, jade, or tourmaline.

Collections are displayed in many ways. A case of shallow drawers such as an antique spool cabinet suits a small collection. For a larger one, a case designed for architectural drawings is satisfactory. In such cabinets, typical rough material, the sawed slab, and the finished gem can be laid out together to tell the entire story of the gem.

The mineral federations have fixed on display case standards of twelve square feet of surface, the case usually being three feet from front to back, four feet long, and not more than one and a half feet deep. Often it is a rectangular box of wood topped by plate glass. The case may be shallower at the front than the back, to set the glass at a reflection-free angle and to accommodate specimens of various sizes.

Smaller cases of the same design are useful for specialized collections. Even smaller lots of gems may be displayed safely and yet be handled in Riker mounts, which are shallow black cardboard boxes with glass lids. They are filled with cotton and held together with pins.

# 10

## *Diamonds in the United States*

The vast forces of nature, which produced diamonds as a by-product of the molding of continents and oceans, did not spare North America. Diamonds have been found in the United States all the way from North Carolina to California and from Georgia to Wisconsin. Some are found in the rock in which they were created by volcanic fires. Others have washed out of the rock formations of the east and west coast mountains, while the diamonds of the Midwest region of the United States were carried there by great glaciers that crunched down from Canada.

The Great Lakes region is the largest diamond field in the United States and it undoubtedly contains a thousand stones for every one that has been recognized. Thousands of years ago this area was planed smooth by a succession of glaciers that advanced and retreated; the southern limit of this glaciated region is marked roughly by the Ohio and the Missouri rivers. As the glaciers retreated they left behind great moraines or dumps of boulders, gravel, and clay which the ice had carried along. Diamonds are found in the moraines at the outer limits of the glacial advance in an area 600 miles long and 200 miles wide, which trends in a northwest-southeast direction from above Milwaukee, Wisconsin, to Cincinnati, Ohio.

There is strong evidence that the diamonds were carried down by the thick ice sheet from a source near the summit east of James Bay and south of Hudson Bay in Labrador. Only by coming from near the glacier's summit, whose location is known to geologists, could diamonds have been brought down by the various lobes into which the glacier was divided. The theoretical Canadian deposit, however, has never been found. A recent search by a Canadian consulting firm licensed by the Ontario government concentrated in an area 100 miles north of Cochrane.

Perhaps fifty diamonds have been found in the Great Lakes region, and undoubtedly only the difficulty of recognizing them in this thinly scattered field has kept others from being discovered. An uncut diamond has none of the luster and the transparency of the cut jewel. It is usually a frosted, greasy looking, rounded crystal, shaped like a fat double pyramid with the bases together. Because diamonds are so much harder than any other stone, they can wander far without becoming worn. The distinctness of their rounded crystal faces helps to distinguish them from quartz, a softer mineral.

The largest glacial diamonds have been found near Milwaukee. Others have been found in central Indiana, near Cincinnati, and at Dowagiac, Michigan. Few have been reported in recent years, perhaps because of the decline in placer mining for gold in this region, and also because income tax laws penalize such publicity. Table D indicates authenticated finds in this Midwestern states region.

The Eagle diamond had a curious history. Its finder, not knowing it was a diamond, sold it for one dollar to a Milwaukee jeweler, who learned later that he had bought a diamond and sold it to Tiffany & Co., only to be sued by the original finder. The courts decided that the jeweler had acted in good faith.

Wisconsin diamonds have a characteristic dodecahedral shape. African rough diamonds are usually octahedral in form.

### Table D. Diamond Finds in Midwestern States
### (For Finds in Indiana, see Table E)

| Place | Date | Weight | Description |
|---|---|---|---|
| Eagle, Waukesha County, Wis. (while digging well on Thomas Devereaux farm) | 1876 | $15\frac{12}{32}$ cts. | Slightly distorted crystal with yellowish cast |
| Plum Creek, Rock Elm Twp., Pierce County, Wis. | 1880 | 10 stones largest $\frac{3}{4}$ ct. | From stream bed, with platinum and gold in mining operations. Stones tinged yellow and green |
| Saukville, Ozaukee County, Wis. (on Conrad Schaefer farm) | 1881 | $6\frac{13}{32}$ cts. | Distorted white crystal |
| Theresa, Dodge County, Wis. | 1886 | $21\frac{4}{16}$ cts. | $\frac{1}{2}$ white $\frac{1}{2}$ cream colored |
| Oregon, Dane County (found by boy in clay bank on Devine farm) | 1893 | $3\frac{14}{16}$ cts. | Distorted and pitted white stone |
| Dowagiac, Cass County, Mich. | 1894 | $10\frac{14}{16}$ cts. | |
| Milford, Clermont County, Ohio | 1897 | 6 cts. | A white stone of fine quality |
| Burlington, Racine County, Wis. | 1903 | $2\frac{1}{16}$ cts. | A white twin crystal |

The largest number of Midwestern diamonds has been taken from glacial drift in Brown and Morgan counties in Indiana, south and southwest of Indianapolis, probably because gold panning has been carried on for years in the creeks there. These creeks wash down and concentrate the heavy

Dots show where diamonds have been discovered in Midwestern states.

material, including diamonds, in the glacial debris and leave it deposited in joints in the bedrock over which they flow. The diamonds here are associated with sapphire, garnet, black sand, and, occasionally, native copper and chlorastrolite carried down from the Lake Superior region. Recorded finds of Indiana diamonds number more than twenty (see Table E).

In the Appalachian region, diamonds have been reported from Virginia, West Virginia, North Carolina, Georgia, Alabama, Kentucky, and Tennessee. These mountains are so ancient, so eroded, and have undergone such extensive geological changes that one can only guess at the origin of the Appalachian diamonds. They were probably of volcanic

### Table E.   Indiana Diamond Locations

| Place | Date | Weight | Description |
|-------|------|--------|-------------|
| Goss Creek (tributary of Little Indian Creek), Morgan County | About 1863 | 3 cts. | Good quality with a greenish cast |
| Lick Creek, Brown County | 1882 | | Yellowish white of good quality |
| Lick Creek, Brown County | About 1882 | ⅛, ³⁄₁₆, ⁵⁄₃₂ ct | Pink, yellow, and brownish, respectively |
| Gold Creek, Morgan County | | 11⁄₁₆ ct. | A blue stone |
| Brey, Morgan County (on Dr. Clark Cook farm) | | 2 tiny stones ⅛ ct. or less | Pinkish |
| Branch of Gold Creek, Morgan County | 1900 | 4⅞ cts. | Greenish yellow, with a small flaw |
| Salt Creek, Brown County | | 3.06 cts. | |
| Morgan County | | 3.64 cts. | |
| Brown County (owned by state) | | 1.05 cts. | |
| Gold Creek, Morgan County (all found by Dr. Kelso of Mooresville) | 1904 | 1¼ cts. ⁶⁄₂₅ ct. ¾ ct. | |
| Morgan County | 1908 | 1.00 ct. | |
| Peru, Miami County (found in field by farmer) | 1949 | 3.93 cts. | |

In addition, a veteran gold panner of Brown County, James Merriman, is said to have found eight small stones in Salt Creek.

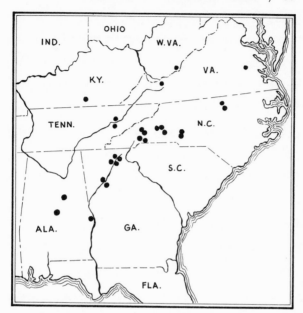

Dots show where diamonds have been discovered in Southern states.

origin and were carried by rivers throughout an area at least 600 miles long and 200 miles wide.

Most of the stones were found in the course of gold mining. Consequently two of the most active mining states, North Carolina and Georgia, have supplied most of them. Records are incomplete, but Table F lists some of the recorded finds.

Table F.   North Carolina and Georgia Diamond Locations

| *Place* | *Date* | *Weight* | *Description* |
|---------|--------|----------|---------------|
| | NORTH CAROLINA | | |
| Brindletown Creek, Burke County | 1843 | 2 stones | |

Table F. (cont.)

| | | | |
|---|---|---|---|
| Twitty gold placer, Rutherford County | 1845 | 1⅓ cts. | Clear, flawless, and faintly yellow |
| Placer on Levinthorpe property, Rutherford County | | .84 ct. | |
| Placer, Cottage Home, Lincoln County | 1852 | ½ ct. | Greenish, clear |
| Todd's Branch, Mecklenburg County | 1852 | 2 stones one of 1 ct. | Fine crystal |
| Portis Mine, Franklin County | 1853 | 2 stones | One of fine water |
| Muddy Creek headwaters, McDowell County | | 2 or 3 small stones | |
| McDowell County | 1877 | 2⅜ cts. | White, flawed |
| Dysortville, McDowell County | 1886 | 4⅓ cts. | Greenish, twin crystal |
| King's Mountain, Cleveland County | 1893 | ¾ ct. | Canary yellow |
| **GEORGIA** | | | |
| Branch of Muddy Creek, Williams' Ferry, Hall County | 1843 | | |
| Horshaw Mine, Nacoochee Valley, White County | 1866 | Less than ⅛ ct. | Opaque |
| White County | | 1 ct. | Fine quality |
| Daniel Light farm, ¾ mi. NE of Morrow, Clayton County | 1887 | 4¼ cts. | Slightly yellow |

Table F. (cont.)

| | | | |
|---|---|---|---|
| 11 mi. NE of Macon, Twiggs County | | Several | |
| Stockeneter branch at the Glades, 13 mi. NE of Gainesville | | Several | |
| Near Atlanta | 1889 | | Defective and poor color |

In addition, diamonds have been reported from placers in Lumpkin, Dawson, and perhaps in Habersham, Banks, Forsyth, Gwinnett, Cherokee, Bartow, Haralson, Carroll, Paulding, and Cobb counties in Georgia.

A 4.27 carat diamond was found about 1900 in Shelby County, Alabama, 30 miles south of Birmingham, and one of 2⅖ carats was found in 1905 on the Isbell property of Prescott Siding in St. Clair County, 20 miles northeast of Birmingham. One found in 1901 in Lee County, Alabama, not far from Columbus, Ga., weighs 4¼ carats. All Alabama stones are of good quality and have a greenish cast.

The two most famous American diamonds are the "Punch" Jones, of 34.46 carats, found by William P. ("Punch") Jones in a vacant lot at Peterstown, West Virginia, in 1928, and the Dewey, of 23¾ carats, dug up by a well excavator at Manchester, Virginia, in 1854. The former, which was uncovered by a pitched horseshoe during a game, was not identified as a diamond until 1943. It is of good color and apparently is free of imperfections. The surface is covered with tiny circular marks, believed to have been caused by blows from other stones when they were all tossed together in a stream. The Dewey diamond is transparent, has a slightly greenish cast and one large flaw. It was cut to a stone of 11.69 carats. It is presumed that the "Punch" Jones diamond was carried down by Rich Creek; the Dewey, by the Jones River. In 1913 a diamond was cut in New York that was reported to have come from a cornfield at Pounding Mill, Tazewell County, Virginia.

Rivaling these two is the 27.21-carat diamond which Mrs. Pellie Howard of Searcy, Arkansas, about 50 miles northeast of Little Rock, sent to Tiffany & Co. in 1946 for identification. She said she found it while chopping cotton. The stone, which is of good quality and faintly yellow in color, was bought by Tiffany.

A 3-carat stone, bought by a Knoxville, Tennessee, jeweler in 1889, and one of 1.69 carats bought by the same jeweler in 1900, are the only ones reliably reported from Tennessee. The former is supposed to have been found in the Clinch River in Roane County, the other on the bank of Flat Creek in Luttrell, Union County. A light yellow stone, weighing .78 carat, was reported found in 1888 on the Henry Burris farm, near Cabin Fork Creek in Adair County, Kentucky. It is also likely that diamonds have been found in South Carolina.

The West Coast, one of the most intensively mined areas in the United States, has yielded a great many diamonds. In California, diamonds were found soon after placer mining began with the gold rush. One was reported in 1849, a crystal the size of a small pea and of a straw-yellow color, and since then about 500 have been found, mostly from the counties north and east of Sacramento. Most of these have been small and off-color and of a pale yellow tinge, but several have been more than 2 carats and of good quality, and one was of $7\frac{1}{4}$ carats. California diamonds have been found only in placer gravels and black sands and concentrates. It is presumed that they came from the igneous rocks from which the serpentines of the Sierra Nevada were derived. Discovery of a serpentine "pipe" resembling the vertical pipes penetrating the horizontally bedded rocks of diamond-bearing districts in South Africa led to sinking of a shaft near Oroville, but no diamonds were found. Table G, made by Joseph Murdoch of

Table G. California Diamond Locations

| Place | Date | Number | County | Largest Size |
|-------|------|--------|--------|--------------|
| Jackass Gulch, near Volcano | | 60–70 | Amador | 1.57 cts. |
| Rancheria, near Volcano | | 1 | Amador | |
| Loafer Hill, near Oleta | | 1 | Amador | |
| Indian Gulch, near Fiddletown | 1855–67 | 5 | Amador | |
| Plymouth | 1934 | 1 | Amador | 2.65 cts. |
| Cherokee Flat | 1853 on to 1918 | 300 | Butte | 2.25 cts. |
| Oroville | | 10 | Butte | |
| Yankee Hill, near Oroville | 1861 | 1 | Butte | 1½ cts. (cut) |
| Thompson's Flat, near Oroville | 1915–16 | 11 | Butte | 1 ct. |
| Smith River | | | Del Norte | Microscopic stones |
| Smithflat | 1859–1912 | 47 | El Dorado | 1.88 cts. |
| Foresthill | Before 1867 | 40–50 | El Dorado | 1.5 cts. |
| Unrecorded | Before 1873 | 12 | El Dorado | |

Table G. (cont.)

| | | 3–4 | El Dorado | 1.25 cts. |
|---|---|---|---|---|
| White Rock Canyon, Cedar Ravine, near Placerville | | 3–4 | El Dorado | 1.25 cts. |
| Webber Hill | | 3 | El Dorado | |
| Lower Trinity River | | | Humboldt | |
| French Corral | | 2 | Nevada | 7.25 cts. |
| Gopher Hill and Upper Spanish Creek | | 2 | Plumas | |
| Sawpit Flat | | | Plumas | |
| Nelson Point | | 1 | Plumas | |
| Near Junction of Trinity and Klamath rivers | | 1 | Trinity | 2 cts. |
| Alpine Creek | 1895 | 1 | Tulare | Many minute stones |

the University of California at Los Angeles, for the California Division of Mines, summarizes California finds.

Operations at the Rock Flat gold placer 5 miles east of New Meadows, Adams County, Idaho, have yielded three small stones, grayish in color, the largest ⅛ carat. Several years ago the finding of a 19½-carat diamond at this mine was reported, but the authenticity of the report is very doubtful. Microscopic fragments are also found in Owyhee County and in the sands of the Snake River. Placer miners in southwest Oregon have found perhaps 100 small stones, mostly flawed and yellowish, including a 3-carat stone from Josephine

County and a 2½-carat stone from Malheur County, and a few tiny ones have been reported from Oregon and Washington beach sands. A 4-carat stone was found in Skamania County, Washington, in 1932. A scattering of other reported discoveries included a 2¼-carat stone from Montgomery County, Texas, another found in 1911 in Foard County, Texas, and a tiny diamond from near Syracuse, New York. More doubtful are ones reported from Santa Fe, New Mexico; Yankton, South Dakota; the Santa Maria River, Arizona; Cleveland, Ohio; and San Juan County, Colorado.

Montana has reported at least five diamond discoveries, including one found in 1883 at Nelson Hill, Deer Lodge County; a .22-carat stone found the next year in the same place; and three small stones sent to New York by A. F. White of Butte.

The nation's most spectacular diamond occurrence, however, is in the hills of southwestern Arkansas. Two and one-half miles southeast of Murfreesboro (which is southwest of Little Rock and Hot Springs) on a 72-acre tract lie the only deposits of diamond-bearing rock in the Western Hemisphere. These are almost precisely like the geological formations in South Africa that during the past 100 years have sent a flood of diamonds to world markets.

Geologists believe that more than 200 million years ago a rock known as peridotite was squeezed under great pressure and heat from deep within the earth, like toothpaste from a tube, creating the vertical pipes from which the Arkansas and South African diamonds come. This rock, a bluish green material containing fragments of shale and sandstone engulfed as it reached the surface, weathers at the surface to a yellowish, slick mass.

John W. Huddleston, an unlearned but shrewd farmer who suspected that there was copper in the yellow and blue ground near Murfreesboro, traded a mule as down payment on it. According to one account, he was plowing to plant his turnip greens in August, 1906, when he turned up first one, then a second shiny stone. Suspecting that they were diamonds, he took the stones to Murfreesboro; from there they were sent to New York and their nature authenticated. The two stones, of 1.35 and 2.75 carats, are still preserved in the Pike County bank in Murfreesboro.

Huddleston's good fortune was soon known, and a group of business men bought his farm for $36,000. The subsequent history of the attempts to operate the tract as a diamond mine is one of 40 years of bickering, bald-faced thefts and breach of trust, mismanagement, law suits and shots in the night, arson and intimidation. The property in recent years has come into three hands—35 acres owned by a corporation of which Mrs. Ethel Wilkinson of Logansport, Indiana, has control; 32 acres controlled by the Howard Millar family; and 5 acres owned by Glenn L. Martin, airplane manufacturer.

Perhaps 100,000 diamonds have been found in the Arkansas mine. The largest, weighing 40.23 carats, was found in 1924. It was cut to a rosy tinted stone of 14.35 carats.

Since 1950, the Wilkinson and Millar interests have operated together to open 32 acres of the area, known as the Crater of Diamonds, to the public for a fee. Visitors are permitted to hunt for rough diamonds and they have been lucky enough to find something like 1,000 stones. Diamonds under 5 carats become the property of the finder; for those above 5 carats the owners of the land receive a 25% royalty.

Mrs. Arthur L. Parker, of Dallas, made the most spectacular find, a stone of finest color 1½ inches long, ⅝ of an inch thick, and ¼ of an inch wide. It weighed 15.31 carats and has been cut to an 8.28-carat marquise. Another Texan, Mrs. Don Macrae of Irving, in May, 1957, found a 3.11-carat diamond near the spot where Mrs. Parker found hers.

Since then, four diamonds of more than 3 carats and one of 6 carats, found by Niels Bach of Ludington, Michigan, in 1960, have been reported. Railroads have run all-expense excursions to this gemmological tourist attraction, and a 75-acre tract a short distance south of the Crater of Diamonds has been opened to gem hunters for a fee.

The Arkansas stones have included a number of superb canary and pink-colored diamonds. The white ones are noted for their exceptional freedom from color, like the so-called river stones of Africa. Arkansas diamonds have an unusually high luster in their natural state, resembling the Brazilian gems, and show complex crystallization, which makes the crystals very rounded. They are said to be harder than the African stones. The white stones make up 40% of the total, the yellow and canary 22%, the brown 37%, and bort 1%. About 10% of the white stones are gem quality.

Rough diamonds are valued by the same criteria as cut stones—color, flawlessness, and weight. The finest color is a total absence of color, or at least of any yellowish tinge. A diamond of the first water (the professional phrase) is as clear, colorless, and sparkling as a drop of spring water. Such quality is the rarest attribute of a diamond. Next most desirable quality is comparative flawlessness, which means the absence of imperfections visible to a trained eye through a 10-power magnifying glass. Weight, of course, is important, too, in valuation, because small diamonds are much more common than large ones. Consequently, the value of a 10-carat stone is much greater than the total value of ten 1-carat stones.

The quality of rough diamonds is estimated by experts who chip a tiny window so that they can see behind the dull, rough skin into the stone. They decide in the same way how the stone shall be cut to eliminate flaws and give the greatest marketable weight in finished gems.

# 11

## *Pearls in the United States*

Among the varied U.S. gem sources are its streams and rivers which have produced rare and valuable pearls that rival the best from the Orient. Some worth thousands of dollars have been found in the Middle West in the last 100 years; they can still be found today. Quantities of these gems have been dug from the graves of the ancient Indian mound builders, and in 1542 De Soto found the natives of the Southeastern states rich in them. But modern systematic search for them dates back only to 1857, when a pearl for which Tiffany & Co. paid $1,500 was taken from the river at Paterson, New Jersey.

News of this good fortune started a "pearl rush" to the rivers of the East which quickly spread west. Pearls of remarkable luster and in a great variety of colors were found in southwestern Wisconsin and in the Illinois River by about 1900, and silvery pearls were found in the Wabash River. The search for pearls was rapidly taken up in Tennessee and Arkansas. The first important pearl found in Arkansas was a 27-grain gem from the White River in 1888, and good pearl fishing grounds were developed at Bald Knob, Cypress Bayou, and in the Black, St. Francis and Cache rivers.

By 1908, Midwestern streams were producing nearly

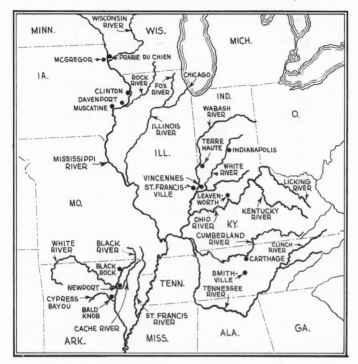

Dots show where fresh-water pearls have been found.

$500,000 in pearls annually, mostly from tributaries of the Mississippi. Soon, however, intensive fishing depleted the shallower streams, and industrial wastes and sewage destroyed many shellfish. And when Japanese cultured pearls depressed the market for genuine pearls, pearl fishermen turned to gathering shells for the button factories, principally in Muscatine, Iowa. They began to fish in the Mississippi and in its deeper tributaries, and the search for pearls became incidental to the shell industry. Today the Tennessee River and its tributaries are the major sources of fresh-water shell and pearls, although some still come from Arkansas and Okla-

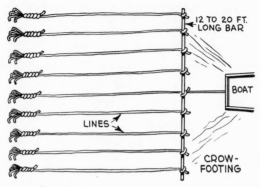

Crowfooting method of harvesting mussels from river bottom.

homa. A veteran Perrysville, Indiana, pearl hunter found a $300 pearl in the Wabash River in 1961; one worth $400 was taken in 1953 and one almost as good later in the same year. In 1955 the United States produced $64,000 worth of gem pearls and 16,183 tons of shell.

Of the nearly 100 varieties of American mussels, about 25 have the pearly shell lining characteristic of pearl mollusks. In the Middle West the most plentiful of these is the niggerhead, almost round and black and rough on the outside, which forms large beds. A good-sized niggerhead is 4 inches across. The best pearl mussel is the three-ridge, named for a characteristic of the shell. Sand shells, found singly in mud banks and on beaches, are 5 to 6 inches long when mature, and very narrow. The buckhorn is long, narrow, and has a rough brown exterior. The butterfly, a mussel whose shell is marked with dotted stripes, produces excellent pearls. Some other varieties are the pimpleback, monkey face, pigtoe, washboard, mucket, maple leaf, grandmaw or pocketbook, eggshell or glass back, warty back and creeper.

Most pearl and shell fishermen are farmers, woodsmen, or trappers who make a part-time occupation of pearling from

June to October. In Arkansas, about 1,500 families take part each year. The method most commonly used for taking mussels from the river bottom is called *crowfooting*. This is done with a 12- to 20-foot-long iron bar, to which are attached lines ending in crowfeet made of heavy twisted wire bent back into four prongs like a bird's foot. This rig is dragged behind a boat. (See drawing.) The mussels, which lie half open against the current as they feed, close on the prongs, and the rig is pulled periodically into the boat. With such an outfit, 200 to 800 pounds of shell can be harvested in a day.

A "hogger," who wades in the shallow water at night hunting the mussels with a flashlight, can bag 25 to 100 pounds. A net is often used to scoop up the shell from soft, muddy bottoms, or they can be taken with a long rake in swift water, or with shell tongs (two rakes hinged and used like tongs) in deep water. Diving with a helmet and an inflated suit is the most costly method, and is resorted to only in very deep water. The fishermen steam their catch for 20 minutes in a vat to open them, examine the mussel for pearls, cut out the meat for fertilizer, and clean and sack the shells for the button-factory auctions.

The best pearls come from shells taken from swift-running streams with clean, sandy bottoms. Fishermen always expect to find a good pearl in an old, deformed shell but often are disappointed. Some idea of the good hunting grounds may be gleaned from the pearl-buying centers of past years. These include Prairie du Chien, Wisconsin; McGregor, Clinton, and Muscatine, Iowa; Newport, Black Rock and Bald Knob, Arkansas; Clinton, Carthage and Smithville, Tennessee; St. Francisville, Illinois; and Vincennes and Leavenworth, Indiana. Today, Davenport is the principal point to which Midwestern pearls are sent on their way to the jewelry market.

As the Midwestern pearl-shell catch has diminished in recent years, such conservation methods as licensing of fishermen, minimum limits on the size of shells that may be taken, and "resting" of streams have been put into force. The fresh-water pearl-button industry has been challenged recently by plastics, and a decline in the demand for shell would lead to less fishing and to conservation of a dwindling natural resource.

Pearl hunting in other parts of the United States is not systematically pursued any more, except in California, where the abalone gives interesting green and blue pearls, and in Florida, where beautiful deep pink pearls are found in the conch shell.

Abalone blister pearls are sought on the Pacific Ocean side of Baja California, Mexico. In the southern part of the long peninsula, around Punta San Francisquito on the Gulf side, the western wing shell and a heavier shell known as Pinctada mazatlania are gathered for their pearls, which are often pink or black. La Paz is the center of this pearl trade. The local pearls are also imitated by cutting spheres from the shell.

A Salisbury, Maryland, jeweler, Hans Schilling, has made a collection of more than 600 pearls from cherrystone clams found off the Delaware and Maryland coasts. The best are button-shaped and they range in color from milky white through cream and orange to mauve and purple and, rarely, black. Some are as large as a half inch across. The pearls, which lack the fine iridescence of gem pearls, are a by-product of commercial shell fishing, and most of them are found by shuckers preparing the clams for restaurant use. Mr. Schilling estimates only one clam in five million contains a desirable pearl.

A valuable pearl has a regular shape, a definite color or tint, an even, clear skin without blemishes, and the real pearl luster. The most valuable are usually spherical or egg-, pear-, drop-, or button-shaped. Fresh-water mussels are noted for the variety of odd-shaped pearls they form, such as the long, dog-toothed hinge pearls, and others resembling a wing or a petal. Irregular pearls of an attractive shape are known as baroques, shapeless ones as slugs, and tiny ones as seed pearls.

Pearls usually are the color of the lining of the shell of the mussel or oyster in which they form, and, especially in fresh-water varieties, exhibit an astonishing spectrum which includes rose, cream, white, black, gray, bronze, and shades of lavender, blue, yellow, mauve, orange, brown, and green. The first four mentioned are the most desirable.

Unlike most other gems, the pearl is of organic origin. Around a foreign particle—a sand grain or a tiny parasite—the mussel secretes layer after layer of a substance which is about 6% conchiolin (an organic material like tooth enamel), 2% water, and the rest calcium carbonate (the same substance as limestone or marble). The thin, semitransparent layers, arranged and crinkled like the leaves of a well-formed cabbage, break up the light that falls on them, reflecting back the peculiar iridescence or *orient* which is the pearl's unique glory. Gems with the thinnest, most symmetrically arranged layers have the finest luster. By careful peeling, layers can be removed from a pearl until a blemish is eliminated or a layer of good luster exposed.

Weights of pearls are expressed in pearl grains, of which there are four to the metric carat, so that the grain is 50 milligrams. Because large pearls are rare, pearl values increase rapidly with size. The usual method is to grade the pearl according to shape, color, luster, and perfection, then assign a unit value, which is the value it would have if it weighed 1 grain. This unit or base value is multiplied by the square of the number of grains the pearl weighs to give its value. For example, if the base value were $1, a 2-grain pearl would be worth $4, a 5-grain pearl $25.

High prices and the steady demand for fine pearls have inspired efforts to cultivate them. The Chinese practiced this art in the 14th century, when they learned that small beads or lead images of Buddha inserted into the body of the mussel would become coated with pearly nacre within a few months. In the last 50 years, experiments in pearl culture have been carried on in the Gulf of California and at Cedar Rapids, Iowa. In Iowa, holes were bored in the shells of fresh-water mussels and pellets of mother-of-pearl inserted into the living tissue. Although the experiments in this country were said to be successful, they did not lead to any commercial development, probably because of high labor costs.

Pearl culture was brought to its present state in Japan, where a high degree of skill, infinite patience, and low labor costs are favorable circumstances. By the method usually credited to the late Kokichi Mikimoto, a piece of the mantle of a living pearl oyster is removed and used as a bag to hold a bead made of Mississippi Valley fresh-water pearl shell. This bead measures from 80% to 90% of the linear diameter of the cultured pearl. The bag is inserted into the tissue of a three-month-old pearl oyster. The oysters are kept in the ocean in baskets, inspected annually, and cleaned to speed their growth. They are allowed to grow for three to eight years. But only about 5% yield perfect pearls big enough for an expensive necklace, the rest being baroques or defective.

More recently, the Japanese have begun to grow another type of pearl in fresh water in Lake Biwa, northeast of Kyoto. Not only are these fresh-water pearls, but they do not have a nucleus. They are started by inserting bits of mantle from another oyster into the pearl oyster. The oysters are hung in wire baskets and the pearls removed when they are less than two years old. The pearls become oval if they are allowed to grow older and larger, and even the young ones are not perfectly round. Work is also being done on growing larger pearls with nuclei.

A fine necklace of cultured pearls may cost as much as $25,000, or as little as $50. Only an expert can tell cultured pearls from natural pearls, and the expert will usually rely on X-ray photographs and the endoscope, a tiny probe with a mirror on the end which is inserted into the hole drilled into a pearl for stringing. It can "see" the mother-of-pearl core of the cultured gem. Both natural and cultured pearls are worlds above the imitations, which are made of glass beads lacquered with a preparation of fish scales called *pearl essence,* or of hollow glass balls filled with the essence and wax.

# 12

## *Directory and maps of gem-hunting locations*

It is the purpose of this volume to discuss the gem materials available (chiefly in the United States), and to offer suggestions about the best means of prospecting for them, and to tell the amateur where to look for them. It is not its purpose to enable the collector to gather commercial quantities of gem rough. It is always possible to strike a rich new location, of course, but generally speaking a gem hunting trip should be looked on as recreation. It should not be expected to return a financial profit.

This directory of locations has been made up from state and federal reports, from other published materials, from personal communications from collectors, from museum lists and from other reliable sources. New gem locations are discovered every season; old ones become exhausted. Constant revision of such a list as this is therefore necessary. The current Rand McNally Road Atlas has been taken as the standard reference, and with few exceptions the following locations appear in it.

It is not always possible, however, to pinpoint locations,

especially in the West, where the absence of man-made landmarks prevails over vast areas. Other areas have deliberately
been kept vague or even secret by their discoverers to prevent
commercial collectors from stripping them. A number of
eastern locations have been included only because mining
may again be resumed at them, making possible the discovery
of gems as a by-product.

Many areas have been closed, either by state or federal
authorities, or by private owners who have other uses for
their land or who have been annoyed by thoughtless collectors. Storm and fire also occasionally make localities inac-
cessible. For these reasons, it is wise to make prior inquiry
about locations before undertaking a long trip to them.

MAP SYMBOLS

| | |
|---|---|
| 357 ................... U.S. ROUTES | ✗ .......................... MINES |
| ⑨ ⑫③ ........... STATE ROUTES | ✈ ....................... AIRPORTS |
| _ _ _ ............ STATE LINES | +++++ ........... RAILROAD TRACKS |
| ★ 2 MI. ★ DISTANCE BETWEEN POINTS | 🚗 ............. PARKING PLACES |
| 🏠 ....................... HOUSES | ☀ ............... GEM LOCATIONS |
| ⚒ ......... FACTORIES, MINE BUILDINGS, ETC | |

**DIRECTIONS ARE IN ABBREVIATED FORM,
AS IN N FOR NORTH, NW FOR NORTH-
WEST, S FOR SOUTH, ETC. * DENOTES MAP**

## *United States*

### ALABAMA

A coastal plain formed of sedimentary rocks and sand
and gravel makes up the lower half of the state. The northern
half rests on sedimentary beds, rich in coal and iron, while
a small wedge-shaped area of about six counties in east central

Alabama offers an area of metamorphic rocks to the gem hunter.

*Blountsville, Blount County*
AGATE NODULES: W 2 miles.
*Hanover, Coosa County*
YELLOW BERYL, AQUAMARINE:
In mica pegmatites, especially near Hissop.
*Lineville, Clay County*
TURQUOISE: In railroad cut at Erin NW on Hwy 49; and also S of Pleasant Grove church on the Hobbs farm.
*Phil Campbell, Franklin County*
CARNELIAN: In gravel pits 2 miles N of town on Hwy 43.

# ALASKA

The largest of the states resembles the western United States in topography. A chain of mountains borders the Pacific, including active volcanoes, separated by a basin from another mountain chain which includes Mt. McKinley, highest in North America. These mountains are formed of sedimentary rocks intruded by igneous rocks. Northeast of these ranges lies an arctic plain like the great plains of the West. South of the main plateau of Alaska lies a panhandle with many islands, and the Aleutian chain stretches west almost to Asia. The geology of Alaska is complex and is made more difficult for the gem prospector by frozen ground, vast distances, and lack of transportation.

*Admiralty Island*
AGATE NODULES: On beaches from Gambier Bay to Wilson Cove and near Point Gardner.
*Fairbanks*
FOSSIL IVORY: In gold dredge gravels.
*Juneau* (Indian reservation)
GRAY SAPPHIRE, STAR RUBY: In Copper River gravels.

*Kenai* (On Cook Inlet)
AGATES: On beaches.
*Kobuk River*
DARK GREEN AND GRAY JADE:
Boulders in Dahl Creek about 150 miles inland and inland from Kotzebue Sound.
At headwaters of creek at 5,000 ft. level.
GRAY JADE: At Shungnak River,

14 miles W of Dahl Creek.

BEST GREEN JADE: Fairly free of black spots. At Jade Mountain, 30 miles NW of Dahl Creek, and in Jade Creek.

*Kotzebue Sound*

FOSSIL IVORY: In scarp on S side of sound.

*Platinum*

FOSSIL IVORY: Near Cape Newenham on Bering Sea.

*Popof Island*

CHALCEDONY PEBBLES: On beaches near Sand Point.

*Port Heiden*

AGATES: On beaches all the way to Port Moller. At Unga Island.

*Point Barrow*

AMBER: In beach deposits.

*Sitka*

RHODONITE: At head of Silver Bay on Baranof Island.

*Wrangell*

ALMANDINE GARNET (mostly specimen grade): Near mouth of Stikine River.

## ARIZONA

The Colorado plateau, with its sandstone formations containing fossil wood and bone, extends over the northern third of Arizona. It is set off sharply from the rest of the state by an escarpment, the Mogollon Rim. South of the Rim lies a semi-desert region of plains broken by low mountains, from which chalcedony minerals erode. The east central and southern areas are a major copper mining district.

*Ajo, Pima County*

CHALCEDONY ROSES: Hwy 85 N for 20 miles, then right on road 7½ miles to far end of Black Mesa.

CHALCEDONY: S of road.

SHATTUCKITE: In veins at New Cornelia Mine.

*Alpine, Apache County*

MOSS AGATE: Go NW on U.S. 260 27 miles to sawmills, then E into Escudilla Mountains, and collect on N side.

PLUME AGATE: Take national forest road NE to state line to collect.

*Ash Fork, Yavapai County**

AGATE: Hwy 66 W for 5 miles, then left on dirt road at first cattle guard on left side of road for mile, then take left fork across a wash (which contains agate),

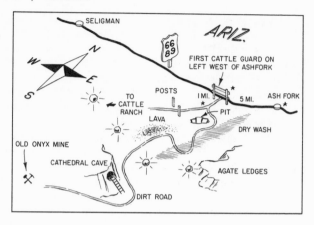

and agate will be found along roadside where road passes under ledges from which agate is weathering. Continue to Cathedral Cave. About 500 ft. from cave entrance are ledges containing white agate spotted with colors. (Beyond cave about ¾ mile is abandoned onyx mine.)

*Bisbee, Cochise County*

SHATTUCKITE: At Shattuck Mine.

TURQUOISE: at Lavender Pit.

*Boulder City (Nevada)*

BLACK AGATE, BROWN JASPER: In Mohave County 3 miles SE of Hoover Dam and W ¼ mile to hill.

*Bouse, Yuma County*

SEAM AGATE: In black volcanic butte, one mile E of Bouse.

*Camp Wood, Yavapai County*

AGATE, JASPER: NW 26 miles.

*Casa Grande, Pinal County*

AGATE, JASPER: South past Chuischu 12 miles. E to Wild Horse Pass.

*Cibola, Yuma County*

CHALCEDONY, PETRIFIED WOOD: In river gravels 7 miles N of town.

*Clifton, Greenlee County* *

RED JASPER, VEIN AGATE, BRECCIA AGATE: Take road NE from Clifton, following San Francisco River. Cross on steel bridge, turn left and go 2 miles to Limestone Canyon on right.

PURPLE AGATE: Three miles farther up Limestone Canyon, Mulligan Peak area to right can be reached on foot; N of peak.

NODULES: W of peak. Similar material is also found beyond on side of Granite Mountain.

CHALCEDONY, JASPER: At Crystal Mountain, trail to right around peak.

JASPER, BLUE AND BLACK AGATE: In nodules and boulders. Above Bobcat Canyon, cross river at Colorado Gulch and take road on right at cattle guard to Ash Spring Canyon. Found 2 miles from cattle guard.

NE of Ash Spring Canyon agate lies in foothills of Sunset Peak.

Nearer Clifton, west of the river, jasper and agate oc-cur in Rocky Gulch and Weaver and Potter Canyons.

BLUE AGATE, CARNELIAN: N from Clifton on U.S. 666; found in first canyon to left a mile S of the Apache National Forest.

FIRE AGATE: Farther N road to left marked Upper Eagle, if followed to bottom, will lead to deposit.

OBSIDIAN NODULES (APACHE TEARS): Three miles farther N, road to right goes to Fritz ranch 16 miles.

CARNELIAN, CHALCEDONY: Continue N on U.S. 666. The 6K6 ranch sign points to this area 2 miles away.

OPALIZED WOOD: Exposed by road cuts. Farther N at Engineer Springs, 3 miles beyond Rose Peak lookout, old road to left for ½ mile.

AGATE: SE of Clifton on Hwy 75 and 4 miles up cemetery road in Wards Canyon.

S on Hwy 75, Mule Creek road leads E to Davis ranch road, which is first road to right past tank in canyon, to dig for agate nodules.

OBSIDIAN NODULES: At state line on Mule Creek road;

lie scattered on hillsides.

FIRE AGATE, CARNELIAN: About 15 miles S of Clifton on Hwy 75, the Apache Creek area E of highway is celebrated. (Note: Many of these Clifton areas lie on rough roads and are on private property. Permission should be obtained to collect.)

*Congress, Yavapai County\**

PINK AGATE: Under bridge of Burro Creek which lies 47 miles NW on Hwy 93.

BLUE AGATE, JASPER: In canyon above bridge.

In lava outcrop along highway E of bridge.

OBSIDIAN NODULES, OBSIDIAN, BANDED AGATE: N of bridge 5½ miles and beyond another bridge a lava and limestone ridge meet, forming a collecting area.

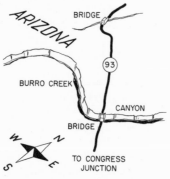

BRIDGE

ARIZONA

93

BURRO CREEK

CANYON

BRIDGE

W N E S

TO CONGRESS JUNCTION

QUARTZ CRYSTALS: Found on Gypsy ranch, reached by taking Hwy 93 N to ranch sign and turning N 2 miles to diggings along road.

*Courtland, Cochise County*

TURQUOISE: At Turquoise Ridge ¾ mile NW.

*Dragoon, Cochise County*

CHALCEDONY, CHRYSOCOLLA: At Arizona Mines, 3 miles N.

*Florence Junction, Pinal County*

CARNELIAN, CHALCEDONY ROSES: Take blacktop road W of town, go N and W for 5 miles, then N on faint road past corral.

*Ft. Defiance, Apache County*

PYROPE GARNET, PERIDOT. (See Buell Park under New Mexico.)

*Fredonia, Coconino County*

PETRIFIED WOOD, AGATE: To SW in area of Pipe Spring National Monument.

*Ganado, Apache County*

PETRIFIED WOOD: At Nazlini Canyon, N of Ganado.

*Gila Bend, Maricopa County*

OBSIDIAN: Go 10½ miles S on Hwy 85, then left 36 miles on jeep road to Javelina camp. NW at base of mesa.

GEODES IN WASH: NE at base of mesa. (Get permission from Lynn Cool in Gila Bend.)

GEODE, AGATE: Go 24 miles S on Hwy 85, then 7 miles E on jeep road to area on W side of Hat Mountain. N in Sauceda Mountains.

AGATE, BANDED: Go 14 miles W on U.S. 80, N on dirt road 5 miles, then NW 4 miles around red butte, where material is loose on ground.

*Globe, Gila County*

CHALCEDONY, MOSS AGATE, PINK JASPER: Go SE on Hwy 70 7 miles and take road to Coolidge Dam. Take winding road in front of dam to bridge and gravel pits for agate.

Search in hills along big bend in river and below for agate and jasper.

YELLOW AND BROWN ANDRA-DITE GARNET: Take dirt road S 10 miles E of dam to Stanley Butte, then go 1½ miles S to shack for garnets in vugs in gneiss.

SERPENTINE, GOLDEN AND GREEN: On mine dumps at Apache town 35 miles NE on Hwy 77.

PERIDOT: In basalt and stream gravels S on Hwy 70.

E on dirt road to Peridot and Tolkai (on San Carlos Indian Reservation; ask permission).

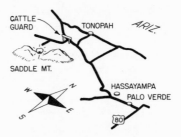

CHRYSOCOLLA, RED QUARTZ: At Old Dominion Mine.

VARIEGATED JASPER: W to Hwy 88, then 21 miles to Young Road, then N 15 miles to windmill, E to dry wash.

*Hassayampa,*
*Maricopa County\**

WHITE CHALCEDONY: Go 20 miles NW from Hassay-ampa to turnoff at a cattle guard onto a dirt road, then S and W 1⅘ miles to a faint road S across flats to base of Saddle Mountain. White chalcedony mixed with brown is found in rhyolite, and quartz crystals.

FIRE AGATE: Is found in a cliff high on E side of the saddle between peaks of mountain, and some in the fan below peak.

CHALCEDONY GEODES: S 8 miles on Gillespie Dam Road, then 21 miles W to Fourth of July Peak. Search in debris on S side of pass.

*Holbrook, Navajo County*
PETRIFIED WOOD: In draws and
banks all around Petrified
Forest National Monu-
ment (no collecting in
park).

*Hyatts Camp, Maricopa County*
LAZULITE: N 1¼ miles on
Phoenix-Cavecreek Road.

*Jerome, Yavapai County*
PINK AGATE: N 9 miles on Per-
kinsville Road, deposit in
place to left of road.

*Kingman, Mohave County*
TURQUOISE: In porphyry cut-
ting schists, 15 miles NW
at Ithaca Peak in Cerbat
Mountains.
AMETHYST: NE of Boulder
Spring, near McConnico
4 miles SW on U.S. 66.

*Lees Ferry, Coconino County*
PETRIFIED WOOD: In Paria and
Colorado Rivers.

*Mayer, Yavapai County*
BROWN AND VARIEGATED ONYX:
NE of town across Big
Bug Creek.

*Mesa, Maricopa County*
CHALCEDONY ROSES: Go 25
miles on Bush Hwy, then
right on Stewart Moun-
tain Lake Road 4 miles
and turn left toward lake.
AMETHYST: On Bush Hwy 3
miles farther to Cotton-
wood Ranch Road and
right to end of road, then

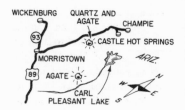

hike to Four Peaks where
amethyst is found.

*Moenkopi, Coconino County*
PETRIFIED WOOD: 9 miles NW
at Willow Springs.

*Morristown, Maricopa County\**
JASPER, AGATE, QUARTZ CRYS-
TAL: Go 25 miles NE to
Castle Hot Springs (where
there is an excellent ho-
tel); in area just above hotel, in creek to S, and in
draws off main canyon in
which stream flows.

From Castle Hot Springs,
Champie Ranch is reached
by road N. Here, agate
nodules may be collected
for a fee. (Area is in
rugged Bradshaw Moun-
tains.)

*New River, Maricopa County*
RED JASPER: S in Skunk Creek.
BLACK AND RED JASPER: In New
River.

*Oatman, Mohave County\**
AGATE AND NODULES: Take
Kingman road NE for
5⅖ miles to curve in Mea-

dow Creek Canyon; some on slopes above canyon, but best material, including chalcedony roses, agate and sard, is just below Hwy at curve and to N of Hwy on buttes and ravines.

FIRE AGATE: Can be collected at Sitgreaves Pass at Ed's Camp (fee).

16 miles to NW at bend in Colorado River near Bullhead City, agate is found as float over a wide area.

*Parker, Yuma County*

CHALCEDONY: Loose on ground along Santa Fe right-of-way E of town.

*Paulden, Yavapai County*

DENDRITIC AGATE: W 3 miles along road.

*Payson, Gila County,*

QUARTZ CRYSTALS: Kohl's Ranch Road, take left fork for 24 miles to Diamond Point for crystals in sandstone, loose in washes.

VEIN AGATE: Road W past newer town and left to fork of North Peak and Cypress thicket roads for agate in the area between the roads.

*Phoenix, Maricopa County*

LAZULITE: In hill on edge of Paradise Valley 12 miles N.

AGATE, ONYX: N one mile to Cavecreek Road and 5 miles E to old house and Maricopa agate bed.

*Quartzsite, Yuma County*

MOSS, PLUME JASPER: E 17 miles on Hwy 60 in area S of road.

QUARTZ CRYSTALS: S 9 miles on Hwy 95, then E 5½ miles to fork, and N to celebrated Crystal Hill area. Crystals, many containing chlorite inclusions, are dug from beds N and S of hill and in hills E of Crystal hill, and loose on flats.

GEODES: Go 19 miles S on Hwy 95, turn E 5½ miles and dig in saddles of hills to SW.

GRAY AND PINK OPAL: Go 22 miles S on Hwy 95 to Cibola Road, then W 4½ miles and S a short distance to butte.

CHALCEDONY ROSES: Go 27 miles S on Hwy 95 and dig in alluvial fan E of road.

*Safford, Graham County*

GREEN MOSS AGATE, RED AGATE, OBSIDIAN NODULES: Take

Hwy 70 to Hwy 666, continue on Hwy 666 8 miles to faint road N to collecting area.

FIRE AGATE: Return to Hwy 666, go 3 miles and turn N through gate at Milepost 141 for 1⅔ miles N and E of parking place.

WHITE CHALCEDONY ROSES, RED AGATE: Are found in draws in hills NW of Hwy 666.

NODULES, PALM ROOT, MOSS AGATE, RED AGATE: Continue on Hwy 666 toward Thumb Butte; where road passes hill.

OBSIDIAN NODULES: Scattered over hills.

AGATE, PETRIFIED WOOD, BONE: Take U.S. 70 3½ miles past U.S. 666 intersection and S to 111 ranch. Collect on hillsides mile S.

*St. Johns, Apache County*

MOSS AGATE: In gravels to S.

AGATE, JASPER: 11 miles S on Hwy 260 at right of highway in blue sandstone.

AGATE: N 5 miles on Hwy 666; collect on both sides of road in weathered hills.

*Salome, Yuma County*

MOSS AGATE, CARNELIAN: To S in Eagle Tail Mountains.

*Show Low, Navajo County*

RED JASPER: Along Mogollon Rim road 47 miles W.

*Superior, Pinal County*

CHALCEDONY ROSES: Go W on Hwy 60-70 to Florence Junction, then 2 miles on old highway to bridge, turn onto dirt road and follow under power line to hills.

OBSIDIAN NODULES: Roads S from Hwy 60-70 to W cut through perlite beds containing Apache tears.

*Topock, Mohave County*

AGATE, BLACK JASPER: Go 5 miles N on road to Oatman, pebbles loose on ground.

*Tucson, Pima County*

BANDED AND MOSS AGATE: Take Hwy 84 N to Cortaro, left across gas pipeline to Wade Road, then right to desert roads to Little Peak area, and hike to Safford Peak.

RHYOLITE (WONDERSTONE): Near Tumamoc Hill and Sentinel Hill 2 miles SW.

*Wickenburg, Maricopa County*

CHALCEDONY ROSES, OBSIDIAN NODULES: Take Hwy 60-70 W to Aguila, then N on dirt road toward E end of Harcuvar Mountains to gem field.

QUARTZ CRYSTALS, AMETHYST: Take Constellation Road NE 6 miles to cattle guard, then left ½ mile to amethyst in hills. Return to

cattle guard, go S ½ mile to collect quartz crystals.

Continue on Constellation Road 4 more miles to top of ridge for quartz crystals.

*Young, Gila County*

SERPENTINE: (verd antique): 10 miles SE between Cherry and Canyon Creeks.

*Yuma, Yuma County**

AGATE: E on Hwy 80 for 4 miles past Ligurta, then N 3 miles on dirt road and follow E along Gila River for 3 miles; turn N into hills and hike on trail 2 miles to Huggins Mountains to find agate in boulders.

PALM ROOT SPECIMENS, JASPER, AGATE: The collecting area NE of Yuma lies in a military reservation; permission to collect should be obtained from the Yuma Test Station. The road to Martinez Lake in the Colorado River turns W from Hwy 95 at a windmill and a branch road leads to the Test Station. In the large area from a mile S of the Yuma Test Station to 10 miles N and from Hwy 95 to the Colorado River, palm root, jasper and agate can be collected lying loose on the ground. This whole general area is very hot and much better adapted to winter than to midsummer collecting.

## ARKANSAS

Southern and eastern Arkansas are sandy river delta and coastal plain, while the northern and western areas are rugged plateaus shared with Missouri and Oklahoma. Most of the plateaus are formed of hard sedimentary rocks, but a small area including Hot Springs and Pike counties is underlain by crystalline rocks. These include the quartz crystal and diamond producing regions.

*Little Rock, Pulaski County*

QUARTZ CRYSTALS: To W in

Ouachita Mountains from Hot Springs to Mount Ida,

notably in the Crystal Mountains E of Norman, at Mountain Valley, Jessieville, Glenwood, and Crystal Springs.

*Malvern, Hot Springs County*

NOVACULITE: On dumps along Rock Island tracks near Butterfield, at Magnet Cove N on U.S. 67.

SODALITE: In syenite quarry on S side of Magnet Cove.

*Mountain Pine,*
 *Garland County*

VARISCITE: At Dug Hill, near Cedar Glades.

*Murfreesboro, Pike County*

DIAMONDS: In peridotite (see chapter on diamonds for details).

*Yellville, Marion County*

YELLOW SMITHSONITE: At Morning Star Mine on Brush Creek.

## CALIFORNIA

California's heart is a great central valley fringed with high mountains. Along the ocean rises the broken coast range, and on the east tower the Sierra Nevadas. These meet in northern California in a welter of glacier-cut valleys dominated by majestic Mt. Shasta and linked to Oregon's Cascade Mountains. In the south the coast range and the Sierra Nevadas swing together below Bakersfield to enclose the valley at that end. Below this point California's arid lands belong to the great basin and, like Nevada, are cut by short ranges. The Sierras tower in sheer cliffs above the narrow strip at their base, formed by the sinking of this part of the great basin. Within a few miles are the highest point in the continental United States, Mt. Whitney, and the lowest, Death Valley.

In the north, volcanic activity is still evident, and the abundant lavas yield obsidian to the gem hunter, while elsewhere metamorphism has created jade and serpentine. In the south, agate materials are plentiful in the arid deserts and eroded mountains, and in the coarse granites of the mountains north of San Diego are treasures of tourmaline, topaz, and beryl.

*Alturas, Modoc County*

OBSIDIAN NODULES: N 15 miles and one mile E of Davis Creek in gravel pits.

*Amargosa, Inyo County*

AGATE: S almost 8 miles on Hwy 127 to Deadman Pass Road. Collect float agate along road.

*Amboy,*
*San Bernardino County*

MARBLE: E to Cadiz on Hwy 40, S to telephone line for 2⅓ miles and E for 2 miles, to collect in quarry to N.

*Antioch, Contra Costa County*

PETRIFIED WOOD: Along Antioch Reservoir to S.

*Applegate, Placer County*

SILICIFIED ASBESTOS: At Best Bet Mine. (Fee; see D. M. Housley, Box 304, Weimar, Calif.)

*Arroyo Grande, San Luis Obispo County*

TRAVERTINE: Take road N to Routzahn County Park, then E along creek almost 10 miles; then hike on S side of creek to veins of travertine in hills.

*Avenal, Kings County*

PETRIFIED WOOD: Near airport.

*Bagdad,*
*San Bernardino County*

OBSIDIAN NODULES: Go ½ mile E on Hwy 40, take road N across railroad tracks and take left fork to power line, then go left ⅔ mile, right under power line and take rough road to collect in hills to N and W.

*Baker, San Bernardino County*

RED AND YELLOW AGATE, PETRIFIED WOOD: Take Hwy 127 N to Milepost 174, turn E 10½ miles, passing Sperry Station ruins and through canyon into open space at Sperry Wash.

AGATE, JASPER: Take Hwy 127 N to Salt Spring, go left on Furnace Creek Road 11⅓ miles, and left 15 miles into Owlhead Mountains.

*Bakersfield, Kern County*

ROSE QUARTZ: At Breckenridge Mountain; go E on Hwy 178, then S on Morning Drive to the Breckenridge Mountain sign, turn E 29 miles and take mine road.

*Bankhead Springs, San Diego County*

RHODONITE: On Hwy 80 go E for 2½ miles to dirt road, and take it N to end.

*Barstow,*
*San Bernardino County\**

JASPER, AGATE: E 2½ miles on Hwy 15, turn S on dirt road ⅓ mile. Mule Canyon Road leaves Hwy 466 E of Barstow and N of military base. As it curves

to the left for a short distance under an overhanging rock, there is a trail into saddle and to left to excellent travertine (under claim and guarded). The road works right to a boulder in the wash and a canyon N which leads to hills, and several hills back is a sagenite agate deposit.

PETRIFIED PALM ROOT: Mule Canyon Road goes on past this canyon, and on its S side are places to dig for petrified palm root. The road climbs out of the wash and it grows very faint. Park and hike NE over white stone outcrops and to left to agate and petrified palm root diggings.

CHALCEDONY NODULES: NE on Fort Irwin road and 1½ miles W of Tiefort village. (Permission needed from Commandant, Fort Irwin Military Reservation.)

JASPER: On Fort Irwin Road 8 miles N, then 2 miles N on Superior Valley Road to faint road E for ¼ mile. Collect in wash and on hillsides.

SAGENITE AGATE: On Hwy 15 8 miles E, then N on Calico Road and right to Doran Drive. Hike ½ mile N into Odessa Canyon and one mile N and E to collect in volcanic ash in Green Hill.

*Berkeley, Alameda County*

AGATE NODULES: In schist, take road just north of Claremont Hotel to top of hill, then left on hwy to second turn. Park and climb wall and go down slope to collecting area.

*Bigpine, Inyo County*

QUARTZ CRYSTALS: Go E through Westgard Pass, and continue 12 miles through Deep Spring Valley to cattle guard, turn left along fence and collect in rocky hills.

*Bishop, Inyo County*

OBSIDIAN: At Montgomery Pass; take Hwy 6 for 2 miles past Nevada line, then left through wash and take trail to diggings.

Return to Hwy 6 and turn right to collect at Queen Mountain.

PETRIFIED WOOD: Continue on Hwy 6 through Montgomery Pass to intersection with Hwy 10, turn right and collect in hills S of Hwy 6.

*Blythe, Riverside County*

PYROLUSITE, PSILOMELANE: Take Lovelin Blvd. 21 miles NW to Inca Siding, cross tracks, turn left ¼ mile and then right for 9 miles to Arlington Mine.

*Bodie, Mono County*

LAZULITE: Mile W of Green Lake in Green Creek Canyon.

*Camarillo, Ventura County*

SAGENITIC AGATE: E 3 miles on Hwy 101, turn N to county park and hike mile up private road to diggings.

*Carlsbad, San Diego County*

AGATE, JASPER PEBBLES: On beaches S to Cardiff-on-the-Sea.

*Cedarville, Modoc County*

AGATE, OPALIZED WOOD: One mile S and 4 miles W in Deep Creek area. Also 20 miles S.

*Chilcoot, Plumas County*

QUARTZ CRYSTALS: Take Hwy 70 to U.S. 395, N on U.S. 395 7 miles and E 1½ miles to Crystal Peak.

*Clio, Plumas County*

FIRE OPAL: In ironstone 3½ miles N at Laura quartz mine.

IDOCRASE (CALIFORNITE): E 7 miles.

*Coalinga, Fresno County*

JASPER, PETRIFIED WOOD: Hwy 33 S 3½ miles, turn off at largest bridge across Jacolitos Canyon and continue W up canyon; look in creek bed.

JADEITE BOULDERS: Northwest 34 miles in Clear Creek, San Benito County,[*] are jadeite boulders, light green banded with white. Same material exists as lenses in serpentine in the walls of the canyon, and as veins of dark green jadeite with white centers.

SERPENTINE: On the Aurora

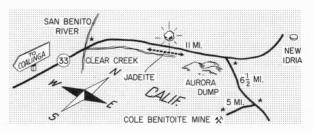

Dump is cutting quality serpentine. (Get permission at the New Idria store.)

BENITOITE: Hunt benitoite at Cole Mine. (Fee.)

*Cobb, Lake County*

QUARTZ CRYSTALS: Hunt in road cuts on Hwy 291 and at Manke ranch, NW of Cobb.

*Covelo, Mendocino County*

NEPHRITE JADE, JADEITE: NE 15 miles on top of Leach Lake Mountain.

Also in N fork of Eel River, reached by road N to Mina to where it crosses river.

*Crescent City,*
*Del Norte County*

AGATE, PETRIFIED WOOD, JADE: In beach gravels at foot of Pacific Avenue.

*Davis Creek, Modoc County*

OBSIDIAN: Take Hwy 395 11 miles N, turn E for 5 miles to Royal Purple Mines. (Fee; write Ray Griffith, New Pine Creek, Ore.)

*Desert Center,*
*Riverside County*

AGATE NODULES, SEAM AGATE: E 22 miles on Hwy 10, then S on Army Road 6 miles to right fork, continue 9 miles to fork, and left to Chuckawalla Spring. Collect geodes in hills below camping place and in Augustine Pass area to W, and seam agate SE at Graham Pass.

*Earp, San Bernardino County*

JASPER, AGATE: Take Wall Canyon Road N for 1 mile, collect on E side of road.

*El Centro, Imperial County*

PETRIFIED WOOD, JASPER, AGATE: On Hwy 8, 48 miles E, take dirt road N to old army camp to collect NE and S of camp.

*Eureka, Humboldt County*

NEPHRITE JADE, JADEITE PEBBLES: On beaches from Patrick Point State Park, 28 miles N on U.S. 101, to Dry Lagoon, 8½ miles farther N.

Also 40 miles E in Trinity River.

*Exeter, Tulare County*

ROSE QUARTZ: At Gasenberger ranch 8 miles SE.

*Fairfield, Solano County*

BANDED ALABASTER: E for 5 miles, at Tolenas quarry.

*Fallbrook, San Diego County*

QUARTZ CRYSTALS: Go 2 miles NE of De Luz school, to dig in granite ledge 700 feet S of Murrieta-Fallbrook road.

*Fiddletown, Amador County*

RHODONITE.

*Fresno, Fresno County*

AGATE, JASPER: In Panoche Pass; take Hwy 180 W to road through Panoche hills.

*Furnace Creek, Inyo County*

TRAVERTINE: Take Hwy 190 N for 13¾ miles to abandoned quarry W of road; also collect in ravine near road ½ mile farther N.

*Georgetown, El Dorado County*

WHITE GROSSULARITE GARNET, PREHNITE, IDOCRASE (CALIFORNITE): 2½ miles SE in serpentine along Traverse Creek.

*Goffs, San Bernardino County*

GREEN OPAL, PETRIFIED WOOD: Take Lanfair Lane, a dirt road, 10½ miles NW to Hackberry wash.

*Halloran Spring, San Bernardino County*

TURQUOISE: In area about 10 miles NW of Halloran Spring in group of old claims in the Turquoise Mountains, including Toltec and others.

*Happy Camp, Siskiyou County*

RHODONITE: Go 9 miles N to Mt. Thompson, collect on E side between Indian and Thompson creeks.

IDOCRASE: Take road N and then left across bridge where S fork joins Indian Creek; continue mile across second bridge to ranch house, where road ends. (Get permission; hike up creek a mile.)

NEPHRITE JADE: At Chan jade claim.

*Hemet, Riverside County*

SMOKY, ROSE QUARTZ: At Juan Diego flat; take Hwy 74 E 4 miles, then S 17 miles and turn left to Juan Diego flat.

SMOKY QUARTZ, PINK BERYL: Are found at the Williamson mine just S of Juan Diego flat at Coahuila Mountain.

*Hinkley,*
*San Bernardino County*

CHALCEDONY NODULES, GREEN OPAL: At Opal Mountain and Black Canyon. Go

6½ miles N and take right fork 4 miles to a left fork, continue on left fork 6½ miles into canyon, dig for nodules on Black Mountain to S; continue to summit, collect cherry opal at Opal Mountain to NE; continue left and then right for almost three miles to small white hill in Black Canyon and dig green dendritic opal.

*Hornbrook, Siskiyou County*

MOSS AND DENDRITIC AGATE: E on road along Klamath River 11 miles.

AGATE, PETRIFIED WOOD: N of river as far as Copco and into Oregon.

*Independence, Inyo County*

QUARTZ CRYSTALS: Take Hwy 395 N for 5⅓ miles, then new road N for 3 miles to Colosseum Road. Take that E for 1 mile, then keep generally E under power line and across old railroad for 5 miles. Go past national-forest sign 1½ miles, to dig in hillside.

*Johannesburg, Kern County*

AGATE, BLOODSTONE: Take road N toward Westend, but take right fork skirting S end of Searles Lake 19 miles to Wingate Pass for vein agate. To S is Brown Mountain, and 4 miles SE is bloodstone.

BLACK MOSS AGATE: At Sheep Spring; go N on U.S. 395 for 14 miles, turn S at road to Freeman for 8 miles and E to Sheep Spring to collect in hills to E.

BLUE CHALCEDONY AND NODULES: Go E from Johannesburg(*) on a fair road to Granite Wells, then NE nearly 12 miles to road turning S that is beyond a narrow ridge visible to the S known as Battleship Rock. Curve around rock to a canyon and take a branch road into it. Leave car and find specimens in volcanic ash.

FIRE OPAL, NODULES: Farther up and higher.

SAGENITE AGATE: In nodules, lies farther up the canyon.

FIRE OPAL, BLUE AGATE NODULES: Back at canyon mouth, take road on W a short distance and turn S again to Lead Pipe Springs, where gems can be dug from red rhyolite, particularly to the SE.

JASPER, AGATE: Back near the road.

AGATE, OPAL: Back to road, next turn S goes to diggings. The road curves N shortly farther W and goes back

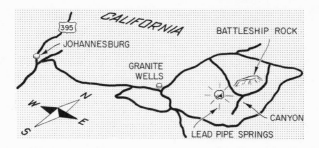

to road to Granite Wells. (Note: Area is Naval Ordnance Testing Station. For permission to collect, write Commandant, N.O.T.S., China Lake, California.)

*Kane Spring, Imperial County*
PETRIFIED WOOD: In clay hills 15 miles W.

*Kramer,*
*San Bernardino County\**
PETRIFIED WOOD, PALM WOOD: From Kramer Junction, go 17 miles W on Hwy 58, then N past some new houses and through gap in reddish hills, keeping left at fork to large dry lake which contains best petrified wood, including palm wood.

BLOODSTONE, AGATE, PETRIFIED WOOD: Go on and keep left toward Castle Butte, where bloodstone, agate, and petrified wood can be dug on east slope and in

area just NE of butte. Right fork before reaching dry lake leads to small dry lake and hills containing wood. A hot, dry locality except in the winter season.

AGATE: A short distance E of the intersection of Hwys 395 and 58 near Kramer lie the Kramer Hills, reached by following a road that parallels tele-

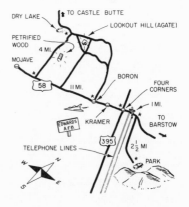

phone lines about 2½ miles S of Hwy 58, turning off to the SE into the hills to park. Collect agate around parking area and to W of phone lines.

BORON WOOD: 11 miles W of Boron a road N leads to a dry lake where the noted Boron wood is dug from the soil. Some is also found on dry lake areas E of the road.

AGATE, NODULES: To the SE of this region lies Lookout Hill, high spot in the area, where agate and nodules of various kinds are to be found.

*LaGrange, Stanislaus County*

AGATE, JASPER: At Dry Creek 7 miles S.

RHODONITE: At Sturtevant ranch, 14 miles NE on Coulterville Road.

*Lake City, Modoc County*

AGATE, PETRIFIED WOOD: In stream gravels from Fort Bidwell to Cedarville.

*Laporte, Plumas County*

QUARTZ CRYSTALS: NE 22 miles at Nelson Point.

*Las Cruces, Santa Barbara County*

PETRIFIED WOOD, AGATE: Take state park road to Jalama Beach.

*Lemoncove, Tulare County*

ROSE QUARTZ: N 5 miles on ridge W of Dry Creek.

RHODONITE: N 3 miles.

*Lindsay, Tulare County*

CHRYSOPRASE, GREEN OPAL: N on SE slopes of Venice Hill.

IDOCRASE: On ridge S of Lewis Creek.

*Little Lake, Inyo County*

OBSIDIAN: Go N for 2½ miles on Hwy 395 to cinder road, E into naval test station, and then 3 miles E into hills. (Open weekends; get pass at China Lake office.)

*Littlerock, Los Angeles County*

AGATE: In Agate Valley, 2 miles W of Little Rock Dam and 3 miles S near quarry.

*Livermore, Alameda County*

CITRINE QUARTZ: At Newman mine to SE near Cedar Mountain.

*Los Angeles, Los Angeles County*

HOWLITE: Take Golden State Freeway NW to Palmdale cutoff (Hwy 14), go on old Sierra Hwy NE to Solemint Junction. Continue NE 6 miles to Davenport Road, then E for 1½ miles and N to dumps of Sterling Mine in Mint Canyon.

AGATE: In beach gravels at El Segundo, Hermosa, and Redondo beaches.

*Los Olivos,*
  *Santa Barbara County*
SAGENITIC AGATE: Take Figueroa Mountain road 8 miles past end of pavement, then trail down hill to collect along creek.
*Lower Lake,*
  *Lake County*
CHRYSOPRASE: E 21 miles to Knoxville and S 3½ miles at Lone Pine chromite mine.
ONYX: N 2 miles of Knoxville at Manhattan mine. (Fee.)
*Lucerne Valley, San Bernardino County*
SERPENTINE (VERD ANTIQUE): N on Barstow Road 12 miles and W 5⅓ miles to faint road, then S 3 miles into Sidewinder Mountains.
RHYOLITE: Go 5 miles E on Old Woman Springs Road to Camp Rock Road, then 14 miles N and NE, turning NW into East Ord mountain area near old gold mine.
*Lucia, Monterey County*
NEPHRITE JADE, RHODONITE: Farthest N location is at Lime Kiln Creek Beach, where jade pebbles are found with rhodonite.
NEPHRITE JADE: To S on Hwy 1 at Plaskett Creek and just S of it at Jade Cove,

and next cove S is another spot.
Farther S is Willow Creek Beach and Salmon Creek even farther S. Some jade is in place and some has been recovered by skin diving. (This is on a military reservation and blasting and camping are prohibited.)
*Ludlow,*
  *San Bernardino County\**
JASPER: Take Crucero Road N 21⅓ miles, take a jeep road left for 12 miles into Cady Mountains. Collect in basin between Flat Top Peak and Mt. Afton, and on Mt. Afton and canyon to N.
JASPER, AGATE: Take any road N of U.S. 40 between Ludlow and the airplane beacon to W and collect in hills and canyons of Cady Mountains 2 or 3 miles N of hwy.
CARNELIAN: Go 9 miles W on Hwy 40 to old hwy, go S for ⅖ mile, hike in and

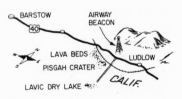

collect on hill and slopes ½ mile W.

CHALCEDONY ROSES: Go 11 miles E on Hwy 40, take road N 3 miles and collect them along road, or go 4 more miles into hills and collect them there.

PINK CHALCEDONY: SE 12 miles to Siberia along railroad and 3½ miles W to gulch near Ash Hill.

OBSIDIAN: S of Hwy 40, for ½ to 1½ miles E.

JASPER, CHALCEDONY: S of Hwy 40 and between Milepost 114 and airway beacon 44-18 (*). Good jasper is also found at Milepost 121.

WIND-POLISHED CHALCEDONY, AGATE PEBBLES: N of Pisgah Crater, imbedded in lava-formed bay.

JASPER, AGATE: W of above area, on surface. Farther E, at Milepost 114, turn from the road S, across the railroad at Lavic Station, and on down to Lavic jasper field. (Area S of railroad is under claim.) About 3 miles farther S, the road leads to a dry lake and a military-reservation sign. Turn E here 8 miles on poor road into mountains for agate.

*Manix, San Bernardino County*

YELLOW JASPER, SEAM AGATE: Take road N almost 9 miles into canyon, then right into side canyon.

AGATE, PETRIFIED PALM WOOD: Go 5 miles W on Hwy 15, collect on both sides of hwy.

JASPER, PETRIFIED PALM WOOD: Take Hwy 15 W for 11 miles and then road N for 6 miles to Alvord Mountains.

*Mesa Grande, San Diego County*

BICOLORED TOURMALINE, MORGANITE, AQUAMARINE: World famous locality for pegmatite gem minerals. On Gem Hill, 2¾ miles NW of Mesa Grande, are the Himalaya and San Diego mines.

PINK AND DARK GREEN TOURMALINE, MORGANITE, AQUAMARINE, CITRINE QUARTZ: NW of Gem Hill 1½ miles at the Esmeralda mine. (This mine and those on Gem Hill are privately owned.)

*Middletown, Lake County*

OBSIDIAN: Take Hwy 125 to Cobb and Bottle Rock Road NW for 3 miles and collect for next 8 miles along road.

20 miles to Randsburg Road, take road up Red Rock Canyon $8\frac{1}{2}$ miles, turn right $2\frac{1}{2}$ miles, then right and S into Last Chance Canyon. Collect in side canyons and red hills to W.

## Mojave, Kern County *

AGATE, JASPER, PETRIFIED PALM WOOD: E on Hwy 58 to Clay Mine Road, N almost to end of pavement (about 3 miles), then W for $\frac{1}{4}$ mile, and collect along ridge and S of ridge.

IRIS AGATE: Go 6 miles S on Hwy 14, then E on to Backus Road, go $1\frac{1}{2}$ miles to Glen Hill.

PETRIFIED WOOD, JASPER-AGATE: N on Hwy 14 for

## Mokelumne Hill, Calaveras County

QUARTZ CRYSTALS: Take Glencoe Road, turn off on road to ghost town of Jesus Maria, then to bridge and $9\frac{1}{2}$ miles through Jesus Maria, park at turn, take trail to right, down slope and to left into gulch.

## Monolith, Kern County*

MOSS AND PLUME AGATE: At Horse Canyon. Go 3 miles E on Hwy 58 to Cache Creek Road and turn N about 9 miles, keeping right. Heavy digging, and

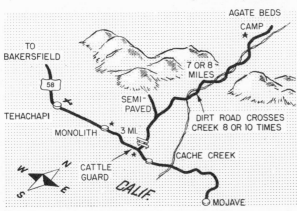

there is fee and limit on amount taken.

*Morgan Hill,*
*Santa Clara County*

ORBICULAR JASPER: At Paradise Valley. (Fee.)

MOSS AGATE, JASPER: Go NW on Hwy 101 to Cochran Road, then E to parking area near Anderson Lake at dam, and hunt along lake. (Get permit from director of parks, Room 724, San Jose.)

*Needles,*
*San Bernardino County*

SEAM AGATE, CHALCEDONY ROSES: Take Hwy 95 S to Lake Havasu Road, then 1½ miles farther. Go W on Turtle Mountain Road 10½ miles, then right 4½ miles on N side of mountains to collect in hills.

AGATE NODULES, JASPER: S on Hwy 95 23 miles to dirt road W.

CHALCEDONY ROSES, CARNELIAN: Along the above road. Continue 11 miles, then S for chalcedony roses and agate to E and S in washes, and S and W to Mohawk Springs.

AGATE, JASPER: S on Hwy 95 19 miles to road E into Chemehuevi Mountains and S into wash. Dig in hills below wash.

BLUE-GREEN AGATE: In rhyo-
lite on above road. (Get directions and permission, Needles Gem Society, 308 D St.)

JASPER, CHALCEDONY ROSES: Go 39 miles S on Hwy 95, then E at milepost 270 for 2 miles to jasper field SE of knoll. Hike half mile NE across basin into canyon for chalcedony roses.

*Nevada City, Nevada County*

OPALIZED WOOD: Hwy 20 E for 5 miles, then 3 miles N to Scott Flat Lake. Collect along shore.

*Newberry,*
*San Bernardino County*

AGATE NODULES: Go 2 miles S on Newberry road, keeping right to end of road. Walk ½ mile W into canyon and collect in blue-white ash in walls.

*Newport Beach,*
*Orange County*

PETRIFIED WOOD, PETRIFIED BONE: Turn W on Cherry Street to sea cliffs, take trail to beach near Arch Rock; collect on beach and in ravines.

*Nipomo,*
*San Luis Obispo County*

SAGENITIC AGATE: In bean fields, or at Freddi's ranch. (Fee.)

*Nuevo, Riverside County*

GARNET, STAR QUARTZ: Go 2

miles N and take road E a mile and then S to Mountain View ranch. Also at Southern Pacific silica quarry nearby. (Get permission.)

*Ogilby, Imperial County*

CYANITE, GARNET, PETRIFIED PALM WOOD, DUMORTIERITE: At Bluebird mine; from Hwy 8 go N to Ogilby sign and then follow mine signs. (Get permission R. K. Foster, Box 575, Winterhaven.)

PETRIFIED PALM ROOT: At Gold Rock ranch N of Ogilby.

AGATE, JASPER: From Ogilby sign, take Ogilby road N nearly to Ben Hulse Hwy, to collect to E in foothills of Black Mountain.

*Oroville, Butte County*

NEPHRITE JADE: At Simmons mine.

*Pala, San Diego County*

TOURMALINE, KUNZITE, BERYL: In pegmatite dikes. World famous locality.· Especially famous for tourmaline are the Pala Chief mine on Pala Chief Mountain; the Tourmaline King and Tourmaline Queen mines on Tourmaline Queen Mountain. These mines and two on Hiriart Hill, 2 miles NE of Pala, the Senpe and the Vanderburg, are noted for mor-

ganite beryl. The Pala Chief, and the Katerina, Vanderburg, and San Pedro on Hiriart Hill are mines noted for kunzite. (All these mines are privately owned.)

*Palmdale, Los Angeles County*

AGATE NODULES: Go 5 miles S on U.S. 14, then SE to Little Rock Dam, and take jeep trail 5 miles to Agate Valley.

*Palo Verde, Imperial County*

JASPER, CARNELIAN, FIRE AGATE: S 11 miles at Palo Verde Pass.

AGATE, PETRIFIED WOOD: 6 miles W of town in old Colorado River terraces.

*Paradise, Butte County*

QUARTZ CRYSTALS: In pockets in quartz veins in Sawmill Peak. Some of crystals contain inclusions.

*Pescadero, San Mateo County*

AGATE, PETRIFIED WHALEBONE: At Pescadero Beach, 3 miles SW.

*Petaluma, Sonoma County*

NEPHRITE JADE: As lenses and veins in serpentine, SW 5 miles and on E side of Massa Hill on Vonsen ranch.

JASPER, PETRIFIED WOOD: 5 miles N of adobe mission.

*Placerville, Eldorado County*

NEPHRITE JADE: Take Hwy 49 N for less than a mile, then

take road right to S fork of American River. Cross bridge, turn right on dirt road along river for 2 miles, and collect in rock along river and in river.

ROSE QUARTZ: E 18 miles in road cut along Hwy 50.

*Porterville, Tulare County*

NEPHRITE JADE: NE 2 miles at commercial workings of Januko Brothers.

CHRYSOPRASE: At Russian Mine on Deer Creek, 9½ miles SE.

*Pozo, San Luis Obispo County*

ALABASTER (ONYX): Go 10 miles from Routzahn County Park into Santa Lucia Mountains and hike E a mile.

*Pulga, Butte County*

IDOCRASE, MASSIVE GROSSULARITE GARNET: In spoil piles from gold dredging in Feather River E of town, and in outcrops ½ mile from river in hills above town to W.

*Ramona, San Diego County*

DARK GREEN TOURMALINE, AQUAMARINE, MORGANITE: Another of the celebrated pegmatite gem-producing districts. At the ABC mine, 3½ miles NE of Ramona.

DARK GREEN TOURMALINE, TOPAZ, SPESSARTITE GARNET: At the Little Three mine, 3¾ miles NE of Ramona in the Hatfield Creek valley.

SPESSARTITE GARNET: In the Spaulding and Hercules mines.

EPIDOTE, GROSSULARITE GARNET: At McFall Mine, 7½ miles SE.

*Randsburg, Kern County*

JASPER: At Rainbow Ridge. Take U.S. 395 N for 3 miles past intersection with Ridgecrest Road, turn S on road along power line slightly more than 5 miles and W into El Paso Mountains to collect. (Get permission from Charles Bishop, Box 354, Red Mountain, Calif.)

RHODONITE: At main street turn S for 7½ miles to Sunshine Mine Road. Turn here, go for 1 mile to end of pavement, continue straight on dirt road for 1 mile. In next ½ mile take two left turns, then turn right to mine dumps. Collect in vein and dumps.

FLOWER AGATE: Take Trona Road 1½ miles N, then go 6 miles E on Steam Well Road and N for 5½ miles from Brown's ranch, to collect in hills.

*Rincon, San Diego County*

TOURMALINE, AQUAMARINE,

MORGANITE: At the Victor mine, 2 miles SE of Rincon.

MORGANITE, AQUAMARINE: At the Clark and Mack mines.

*Rosamund, Kern County*

CARNELIAN, RED AND GREEN JASPER: W 3½ miles and then N 4⅓ miles and left around hill on dirt trail for collecting on N and NW sides of hill.

*Sage, Riverside County*

TOURMALINE: N 2½ miles on Hwy 79 and then E on dirt road to Anita mine.

LEPIDOLITE: At Anita mine.

*St. Helena, Napa County*

ONYX: At Erdahl ranch. (Fee.)

*Saltdale, Kern County*

JASPER, PETRIFIED WOOD: N past road leading into Last Chance Canyon, then E into hills for petrified palm root and jasper. Return to road, go N into Last Chance Canyon for black petrified wood and yellow jasper.

*San Diego, San Diego County**

DUMORTIERITE: Go E on U.S. 8 to Alpine, take Taven Road ½ mile to Arnold Way and go 2½ miles S to Dehesa Road and short distance SW to road S into quarry.

*San Francisco, San Francisco County*

CHALCEDONY PEBBLES, PETRI-

FIED WHALEBONE: At beaches at Bodega Bay, Tomales Bay, Drakes Bay and Duxbury Point, all in Marin County.

*San Jose, Santa Clara County*

DENDRITIC AGATE: Take Coleman Road to end at Guadalupe Mine.

*San Miguel, San Luis Obispo County*

BRECCIATED JASPER: Take Parkfield Road 17 miles, turn N for 9 miles and then go 2 miles E into Stone Canyon. (Get permission from Mrs. Hope Bagby, Hidden Valley Rancho, San Miguel.)

*Santa Barbara, Santa Barbara County*

PETRIFIED WHALEBONE: At Gaviota Beach, 32 miles W on Hwy 101; also Refugio Beach, 20 miles W.

*Santa Cruz, Santa Cruz County*

AGATE, PETRIFIED BONE: N 30 miles on Hwy 1 at Steele Beach.

*Santa Monica, Los Angeles County*

SHELL CONGLOMERATE: Go NW for 30 miles N to Coquina Beach for shells in dark matrix.

*Susanville, Lassen County*

AGATE, BLACK AND WHITE PETRIFIED WOOD: W 8 miles on Hwy 36, then S toward Stephens ranch.

*Tecopa, Inyo County*

PRECIOUS OPAL: Go 3½ miles W to Hwy 127, 2½ miles N on it to ruins of stage station. Collect in gray-green area in hills to W.

*Tennant, Siskiyou County*

OBSIDIAN: NE 4 miles from Medicine Lake at Glass Mountain.

*Tollhouse, Fresno County*

IDOCRASE (CALIFORNITE), GROSSULARITE GARNET: On E side of Watts Valley, 1½ miles S of Hawkins School.

*Trinidad, Humboldt County*

BRECCIATED JASPER: On beach.

*Trona, San Bernardino County*

ONYX: N on Panamint Valley Road to summit, then 3 miles to sharp left turn-off, 2 miles to road to left and through rough country to house and around to right to Onyx Hill for Death Valley onyx.

*Upland, San Bernardino County*

LAPIS LAZULI: 12 miles N in N fork of Cascade Canyon.

*Valley Ford, Sonoma County*

JASPER, AGATE: Take Hwy 1 to Bodega, then 8 miles N to Shell Beach for pebbles.

*Valley Springs, Calaveras County*

MOSS AGATE, PETRIFIED WOOD: At Marie Costa ranch.

VEIN AGATE: At Hooton ranch. (Fee.)

*Victorville, San Bernardino County*

VERD ANTIQUE: N on Hwy 15 to Bell Mountain exit, go NE 3 miles on exit road to dirt road, take it NE 7 miles, then E to quarry on mountain.

*Vidal Junction, San Bernardino County*

RED JASPER, CHALCEDONY: Take road E to Earp, then mile W and 4 miles N to collect in ledges in Whipple Mountains near road, and to W in badlands.

*Warner Springs, San Diego County*

MORGANITE: At Pearson mine, 13 miles NW on Hwy 79 to Oakgrove and E to mine.

MORGANITE, TOPAZ: At Aguanga Mountain, 10 miles NW on Hwy 79 and W to

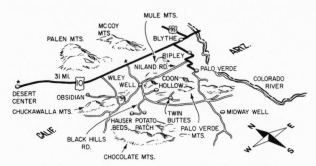

Mountain Lily mine.

TOPAZ, BLUE-GREEN TOURMA-
LINE: At Ware mine near
summit of Aguanga Moun-
tain.

*Westmorland, Imperial County*

OBSIDIAN: To N at Obsidian
Butte.

*Wiley Well Area, Imperial
County*\*

CHALCEDONY ROSES, FIRE AG-
ATE: Take Hwy 10 E
from Desert Center (Riverside County) 31 miles and
turn S after crossing
bridge. Cross Niland Road
at 8 miles and go 3 miles
more to left-hand road
leading into Coon Hollow
in the Mule Mountains.
Specimens along road.

Road E out of Coon Hollow
goes mile to fire agate and
chalcedony diggings.

Other road NE out of Hol-
low goes less than mile into
Mule Mountains and then
hike about a block to bed
of white nodules.

OBSIDIAN NODULES: About 13 1/2
miles W of Wiley Well on
the road along the power
line, turn off N 1 1/2 miles
into sandy flat to hills between Big and Little
Chuckawalla Mountains
for nodules on stony
slopes.

BANDED AGATE, SEAM AGATE,
BLACK CHALCEDONY,
FLOAT AGATE, PLUME
AGATE, CHALCEDONY
ROSES: In Palo Verde
Mountains. Back on Wiley
Well Road, go on S and
then E to Twin Buttes
Road which leads up a
ridge and at 1 1/2 miles it
forks. Right fork leads to
Twin Buttes nodule beds,
a great variety of colors
and materials. Left fork
leads into a mountain ba-
sin where float agate, including some plume, is
found. Rough road goes

on toward buttes to a field of chalcedony roses.

SEAM AGATE, GEODES, AME-THYST: Back on Wiley Well Road N almost to Coon Hollow Road but turn W on Black Hills Road. At 5⅔ miles it splits into three branches. The southernmost branch goes almost 2 miles S, then forks left between two hills where seam agate is found, and into the Potato Patch, a deposit of crystal-lined geodes, and some amethyst, now deep with the debris of digging. Branch veers to W and at 3½ miles reaches old Hauser bed and new bed a half mile farther up canyon for agate-filled geodes lying 3 to 5 ft. below surface.

HAPPY CAMP

BIG LAGOON
ROCKY POINT

WILLOW CREEK

CALIFORNIA

EUREKA

TRINITY RIVER

299

299   REDDING

JADE AREAS OF NORTHERN CALIFORNIA

5

101

NORTH FORK EEL RIVER

MIDDLE FORK EEL RIVER

COVELO

70

OROVILLE

UKIAH

MARYSVILLE

101

99E   PLACERVILLE

50

SACRAMENTO

PETALUMA

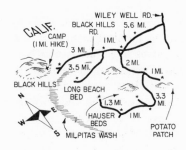

CARNELIAN, RED VARIEGATED JASPER: On faint fork left nearly a mile farther on.

FLOAT AGATE: A mile farther on where road ends.

AGATE, CARNELIAN, JASPER: Next branch N off Black Hills Road leads 3½ miles through flats where these occur as float, and to trail up wash a half mile to blue nodule (Long Beach) bed. Northernmost branch of Black Hills Road(*) goes 3 miles to fork, then left to end of passable road. Hike up wash to geode bed in side of hill.

*Willow Creek,*
*Humboldt County*

JADE: In Trinity River; both up and down stream. Take Hwy 96 N to Orleans area, and look in Klamath River. Road parallels river for 30 miles.

*Winterhaven, Imperial County*

AGATE, DUMORTIERITE: Go 12 miles W on Hwy 8, then 4 miles N to Ogilby and NW and N 9⅓ miles to a dirt road E 7½ miles to dig at Indian Pass.

RED PALM WOOD, JASPER: Return to graded road and go 6½ miles farther to collect E of road.

AGATE NODULES, CHALCEDONY ROSES: Take Imperial Dam Road 2½ miles past Laguna Dam, turn off on road across canal and toward Ferguson Lake, but keep to left on this road, cross ridge into a basin, dig on W side for nodules and on S edge for chalcedony roses. Distance from canal to basin is 10 miles.

*Yermo, San Bernardino County*

PETRIFIED PALM WOOD: Go E on U.S. 15 1⅔ miles past power lines, then turn N ½ mile into hills.

AGATE, PETRIFIED WOOD: Take Hwy 15 E beyond agricultural inspection station to Minneola Road exit. Follow access road N, then E to dump sign. Turn left here, go 1 mile to fork under pole line, then left again up dry streambed to point where road leaves bed. Turn right into hills to collect.

## COLORADO

Colorado is a state of startling physical contrasts: the eastern third is part of the high plains like Kansas and Nebraska; the midstate area is formed of massive mountain chains enclosing fertile basins; the western slope meets Utah in a welter of mesas and plateaus that comprise the wildest part of the state. Sedimentary rocks have been raised or pushed aside by the great igneous intrusions that formed the spectacular Front Range and created Colorado's mineral wealth.

*Alma, Park County*
RHODOCHROSITE: On dumps of Sweet Home mine, 3 miles NW on side of Buckskin Gulch.

*Baxterville, Rio Grande County*
BLUE AND GRAY AGATE NODULES: Go SW on Hwy 160 7¾ miles beyond Wolf Creek Pass and collect in loose rock below road.

*Bedrock, Montrose County*
PETRIFIED WOOD, PETRIFIED BONE: One mile S on south bank of Dolores River.

*Burlington, Kit Carson County*
MOSS OPAL: In S fork of Republican River 20 miles N.

*Canon City, Fremont County*
AGATE: At Curio (Specimen) Hill, 6 miles S; loose in soil or in limestone ledge near top of ridge.

AGATE, PETRIFIED BONE: At Garden Park, 7 miles N in hills on W side of Oil Creek.

BERYL: In Mica Lode, Meyers and School section mines at Eightmile Park.

SATIN SPAR, PETRIFIED BONE: 8 miles N on Shelf Road up Fourmile Creek to mouth of Felch Creek. Collect just W of Fourmile Creek.

GEODES: One mile E on Felch Creek.

AMETHYST: At Twelvemile Park 12 miles NW and one mile S (private claim). Near Parkdale 13 miles W.

ALMANDINE GARNET: On Grape Creek 2 miles SW.

*Colorado Springs, El Paso County*
AMAZONITE, SMOKY QUARTZ, WHITE TOPAZ: In pegmatites at Crystal Park, at foot of Cameron Cone, 2 miles S of Manitou Springs (use toll road on E slope of Pikes Peak). Crystals found for mile NW and SW of park, especially in Bear Creek Canyon and

at Specimen Rock in canyon.

CARNELIAN: At Austin Bluffs, 4 miles N, and mile E of U.S. 85-87. Collect on SW side of bluffs.

PETRIFIED PALM WOOD: At sand pits near Pike View coal mine 7 miles N and ½ mile W of U.S. 85-87.

*Creede, Mineral County*

AMETHYST: As vein material sealed with agate (sowbelly agate), less than one mile N in dumps of Amethyst mine and at Last Chance mine.

GREEN CHALCEDONY, OPAL: Drive to W end of Rio Grande Reservoir to Trail Creek, hike S through rough country to Ute Creek. Collect along creek.

*Del Norte, Rio Grande County*

PLUME AGATE: N on Hwy 112 for mile, then 4 miles W to fork, take right fork 5 miles and collect at Twin Peaks. Agate is to be found over hills to N and W of Del Norte as far as the La Garita area.

*Elbert, Elbert County*

PETRIFIED WOOD: In headwaters of Bijou and Kiowa Creeks, in gravels of rivers to SE, along Hwys 157 and 217, in Union Pacific railroad cut and as far S as Peyton and Calhan. Some from Peyton and Kiowa areas contains carnotite.

*Elizabeth, Elbert County*

PETRIFIED WOOD: At Kit Carson Monument.

*Elk Springs, Moffat County*

AGATE: In gravels at SE edge of town and along Hwy 14 off U.S. 40 for a few miles.

JASPER, AGATE: Take U.S. 40 8 miles W to Hwy 16 and N 19 miles to road junction.

SPOTTED AGATE: Take dirt road from junction 6 miles to cabin.

PETRIFIED BONE: Continue W on U.S. 40 4½ miles from intersection with Hwy 16 and take trail N ½ mile, search on ridges.

AGATE, JASPER, PETRIFIED BONE: N of U.S. 40 in gravels and outcrops within two miles of highway all the way to Blue Mountain.

*Fairplay, Park County*

MOSS AGATE: At salt works SE.

*Florissant, Teller County*\*

AMAZONITE, SMOKY QUARTZ: Take Hwy 67 N to a Y fork. Take left fork 2 miles to pits and other diggings in pegmatite outcrops in the woods. From these diggings, once known as the American Gem Mines,

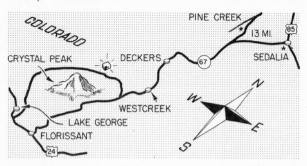

have come spectacular gems. (The area is now made up of private claims and fee is charged.)

Further N along Pine Creek similar outcrops are worked for amazonite.

WHITE TOPAZ: Found in pegmatite near Crystal Peak, especially ½ mile NW of peak.

*Fort Collins, Larimer County*

AMETHYST: On Hwy 287 22 miles NW and W on Hwy 200 to Red Feather Lakes. Deposit is about 5 miles W of that town.

SATIN SPAR, ALABASTER: Take U.S. 287 17 miles N to quarry in Owl Canyon.

ROSE QUARTZ: Between Stove and Box Prairie 25 miles W, in granite.

*Fruita, Mesa County*

OPALIZED WOOD: 2 miles S at Opal Hill, first high hill W of golf course and ¼ mile W of road to Colo-

rado National Monument.

PETRIFIED BONE: 4 miles W.

*Glade Park, Mesa County*

AGATE, OPALIZED WOOD: Take road S toward top of mesa for 8½ miles, take left fork and keep right for 3 miles; collect along road and at house ½ mile farther along road.

*Granby, Grand County*

BLOODSTONE: On ridges in Middle Park near junction of Willow Creek and Colorado River.

*Guffey, Park County*

BLUE AGATE: At 31 Mile Mountain 8 miles W.

*Gunnison, Gunnison County*

LAPIS LAZULI, GROSSULARITE GARNET: At Italian Mountain. Take Hwy 135 19 miles N to mouth of Cement Creek. Follow creek on bad road 12 miles. Mountain is mile NE of end of road. Collect on W side of north mountain near top and just above ledges of slaty black limestone.

BLUE CHALCEDONY: In rhyolite in Gunnison River above Black Canyon.

AGATE: E on U.S. 50 to mile E of Sargents; take dirt road left and hunt in streams.

*Hartsel, Park County*

MOSS AGATE, PETRIFIED WOOD: Along Hwy 9 SE 1½ miles.

*Idaho Springs, Clear Creek County*

RHODOCHROSITE: At Moose Mine. Take Virginia Canyon road to Russel Gulch Road and to Willis Gulch. Mine is ½ mile below head of gulch.

ROSE QUARTZ: In pegmatite at Santa Fe Mountain prospect; 3 miles SE on ridge NE of mountain, and reached by road up Sawmill Gulch from U.S. 6.

*La Garita, Saguache County*

AGATE: Along La Garita Creek.

*La Jara, Conejos County*

TURQUOISE: In old workings 13 miles SE in hills 1½ miles from Rio Grande.

*La Junta, Otero County*

FLOWER AGATE, PETRIFIED BONE: In washes and streams to S.

*Leadville, Lake County*

TURQUOISE: At Turquoise Chief mine, 7 miles NW just below crest of ridge between Turquoise Lake and basin to N.

RHODOCHROSITE: In dumps of John Reed mine, 12 miles NE and E of Hwy 91.

*Manassa, Conejos County*

TURQUOISE: At King Mine (private claim). Take Hwy 142 E for 6⅔ miles; S ⅓ mile to mine dumps at bottom of hill.

*Mount Antero, Chaffee County\**

BERYL, AQUAMARINE, PHENACITE, SMOKY QUARTZ, FELDSPAR CRYSTALS: Stones of gem quality are found in pockets in the pegmatite. Outstanding American source for aquamarine and phenacite, but exposed at more than 13,000 feet to sudden storms. Collecting, usually by blasting, is within 500 feet of top in Mount Antero and nearby White Mountain in pegmatites in granite. Access is by Hwy 162 from Nathrop and up Baldwin Gulch to saddle in mountain which can be climbed to top, or by taking U.S. 285 S 3½ miles from Nathrop and following either of two

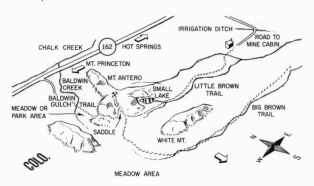

MEADOW AREA

trails up Browns Creek. Either the Little Brown or the Baldwin Gulch trails are about 6 miles and rise about 1,000 ft. to the mile.

BERYL, SMOKY QUARTZ: At the California mine, 2 miles SW of Mount Antero, at 12,500 ft. and reached by either trail. Mine is on S slope of divide between Browns Creek and Baldwin Gulch, on what is known as Carbonate Mountain.

*Nathrop, Chaffee County*

SPESSARTITE GARNET, WINE-COLORED TOPAZ, OBSIDIAN NODULES: Just to N on U.S. 285 at Ruby and Sugarloaf Mountains E of river, and Dorothy Hill W of river.

*Ouray, Ouray County*

YELLOW ANDRADITE GARNET: At Mt. Sneffels, 5 miles SW.

RHODOCHROSITE: At Grizzly Bear mine, to S near Bear Creek Falls.

*Palmer Lake, El Paso County*

PINK SATIN SPAR: 10 miles NW at Perry Park.

*Parker, Douglas County*

PETRIFIED PALM WOOD: One mile S.

*Salida, Chaffee County*

PETRIFIED WOOD, JASPER: In hills to SW on S side of U.S. 50, from Poncha Springs to Sargents.

CHRYSOPRASE, SPECIMEN GAR-NETS: On dumps at Sedalia mine. Take Hwy 180 N for 4 miles, turn right, cross tracks, and turn back $\frac{1}{2}$ mile. Best collecting for garnets is in outcrops near highest dumps.

SAPPHIRE, GROSSULARITE GAR-NET, SAGENITIC QUARTZ:

In schists at Calumet iron mine, in E wall of Railroad gulch. Take Hwy 291 N from Salida, right on Hwy 180 to Hwy 190, then left on Hwy 31 to gulch.

*Sedalia, Douglas County*
TOPAZ, SMOKY QUARTZ: In pegmatite pockets at Devil's Head, just S of peak at top of ridge below highway. Take Hwy 67 SW to Rampart Range Road and S, a total of 21½ miles.

*Silverton, San Juan County*
RHODONITE: On dump on N side of Sunnyside Mill at Eureka, 9 miles NE of Silverton on Hwy 110.

At Gold Prince mine, Terry Tunnel of Sunnyside mine, and Golden Fleece mine at Treasure Mountain.

*Texas Creek, Fremont County*
ROSE QUARTZ: N 6 miles near junction of Echo Canyon and East Gulch in fluorite mine.

*Villa Grove, Saguache County*
TURQUOISE: At Hall mine (private claim). Take U.S. 285 NW 2⅔ miles, then side road 2⅔ miles W to edge of Cochetopa National Forest, and then 2 miles to cabins that are ½ mile below mine.

*Wagon Wheel Gap, Mineral County*
CARNELIAN: At fluorspar mine dumps, S 1⅔ miles.

## CONNECTICUT

A central lowland valley divides eastern Connecticut from the western part of the state. This valley is cut by ridges of trap rock, while the eastern and western uplands are broken by mountain ranges and valleys, affording exposures of crystalline rocks containing gem materials. The trap rocks of the Connecticut valley yield agate and jasper, and amethyst and prehnite in cavities.

*Branchville, Fairfield County**
GOLDEN BERYL, ROSE AND SMOKY QUARTZ, SPODUMENE: The quarry, a short distance NE of Branchville, has long been noted for these gem minerals. Work on the dumps is required to uncover fresh material, however.

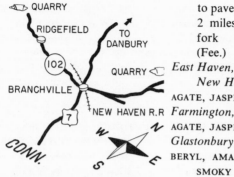

West of Branchville, a short distance out of Ridgefield, is a pegmatite that has been worked, containing some beryl, as well as quartz crystals and rose quartz. It is reached by following Conn. 102 W 1½ miles from the stoplight in Ridgefield, then turning N, crossing a bridge, and taking dirt road to left just beyond bridge. Drive to end, park and hit trail ¼ mile to area of pit and dumps where gem material can be found.

*East Granby, Hartford County*
AGATE, JASPER: As float.
*East Hampton,*
*Middlesex County\**
GOLDEN AND BROWN BERYL, ROSE QUARTZ: In Slocum Quarry. Take Hwy 196 SW to Daniel Road, then to paved road N. Continue 2 miles to fork, take left fork past farmhouse. (Fee.)

*East Haven,*
*New Haven County*
AGATE, JASPER: As float.
*Farmington, Hartford County*
AGATE, JASPER: As float.
*Glastonbury, Hartford County*
BERYL, AMAZONITE, ROSE AND SMOKY QUARTZ: At Old Hale Quarry.
*Guilford, New Haven County*
AGATE, JASPER: As float.
IOLITE: In gneiss at Hungry Horse Hill.
*Middlefield, Middlesex County*
AGATE, JASPER: As float.
*Middletown,*
*Middlesex County*
BERYL, RUBELLITE TOURMALINE: At White Rocks Quarry.

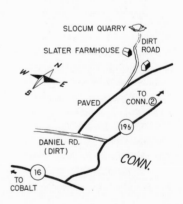

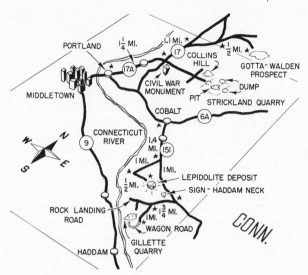

*Milford, New Haven County*

AGATE, JASPER: As float.

*Monroe, Fairfield County*

ROSE QUARTZ: NE of East Village beyond old canal in feldspar quarry.

*New Milford, Litchfield County*

BLUE AND GOLDEN BERYL, SMOKY QUARTZ: NW 5 miles at Upper Merryll in George Roebling (Merryll) Mine.

CYANITE: Take Hwy 67 E to Judd's Bridge, collect one mile N.

*North Branford, New Haven County*

AGATE, JASPER: As float.

*Portland, Middlesex County**

TOURMALINE IN A VARIETY OF COLORS, BLUE, PINK AND GOLDEN BERYL, GARNET, AMAZONITE, THULITE: The Gillette Quarry is a noted source. It is reached from Portland via Conn. 6A, turning S at the hamlet of Cobalt. At about 4 miles, a road right leads at less than 2 miles to one S, which inside a mile leads to the quarry, which is near the Connecticut River. Collect on the dumps. (Permission should be obtained to enter.)

LEPIDOLITE: Another mine is reached by taking Conn. 151 S 3 miles from Cobalt and continuing S as Conn. 151 veers E. At a farmhouse, a dim road leads a half mile to a dump containing large masses of excellent lepidolite.

BERYL, TOURMALINE, SPODUMENE, GARNET, APATITE, SMOKY QUARTZ, CITRINE: The Strickland Quarry, NE of Portland, has produced these, some in varied colors. Take Conn. 17A out of Portland to a brown Civil War monument. Turn right here and keep right until the road ends in a T. Keep straight ahead up a rough road on Collins Hill to the quarry. The pit, when it is dry, is a choice collecting spot and the dumps have yielded many specimens to collectors.

Reached from Portland via Conn. 17 and a back road is the Gotta-Walden Prospect, an abandoned mine in the woods, where golden and green beryl and almandine garnets in mica are to be found.

*Roxbury Falls,*
 *Litchfield County*
GARNET, STAUROLITE: SE ⅘ mile from Hwy 199, turn off E on road to Green farm, garnet in dump, staurolite deposit beyond farmhouse.

*Southbury, New Haven County*
AGATE, JASPER: As float.

*Southford, New Haven County*
BERYL, ROSE QUARTZ: 1¾ miles SW in quarry.

*Torrington, Litchfield County*
AGATE, JASPER: As float.

*Unionville, Hartford County*
FELDSPAR, MOONSTONE, IOLITE: 1½ miles NE in road cut S of Biglow Pond.

*West Redding, Fairfield County*
GROSSULARITE GARNET: SW ⅓ mile in cavities in ridge E of road.

*West Stafford, Tolland County*
QUARTZ CRYSTALS: ¾ mile by road along brook to Diamond Ledges.

*Woodbury, Litchfield County*
BERYL, AGATE, ROSE QUARTZ: In Flanders Quarry.

## FLORIDA

Florida is a peninsula not far above sea level but containing a diversity of natural features, ranging from the hilly area in the northwest to the coastal plain on the east, and marked by many lakes and the huge Everglades Swamp to the south. Underlain by limestone, it lacks the formations that would yield mineral or gem specimens.

*Lakeland, Polk County*
CHALCEDONY, FOSSIL CORAL: On Lake Parker Beach for chalcedony and fossil coral.

On canal near Kathleen, 7 miles E.

*New Port Richey, Pasco County*
AGATIZED CORAL: To S at Bailey's Bluff agatized coral has been reported to have been discovered.

*Tampa, Hillsborough County*
AGATIZED CORAL: In Hillsborough Bay off Ballast Point agatized coral has been reported.

## GEORGIA

With representative rocks of almost every geologic period exposed on the surface, it is not surprising that Georgia exhibits a variety of rocks and minerals. The southern half of the state is part of the coastal plain underlain by sedimentary rocks. North of this is the Piedmont Plateau and, in the extreme northeast, a highlands, both formed of crystalline rocks containing minerals of interest. The extreme northwest corner is formed of ancient, folded, and eroded sedimentary rocks.

*Albany, Dougherty County*
RED JASPER: In Flint River.

*Apalachee, Morgan County*
AQUAMARINE: To W on Adair plantation.

*Athens, Clarke County*
BERYL: In field along Alps Road across from new airport.

*Ball Ground, Cherokee County*
RUTILATED QUARTZ: NE 2½ miles at Cockran Mine.

STAUROLITE: On James Speer property.

ALMANDINE GARNET: In prospects along Hwy 5 toward Canton.

*Blue Ridge, Fannin County*
STAUROLITE: To W at Hackney farm off Copperhill Road.

*Blairsville, Union County*
RUBY: On S side of Track Rock Gap.

*Bremen, Haralson County*

QUARTZ CRYSTALS: W 1½ miles.

*Buford, Gwinnett County*

AGATE, MOONSTONE: On Addison Lowe farm.

*Clarkesville,*
*Habersham County*

AGATE: W 2 miles.

RUBY: At Alex Mountain in Piedmont Orchards, 6 miles NW.

CYANITE: On grounds of North Georgia Vocational School.

*Clayton, Rabun County*

AMETHYST: On dump of the North Georgia Company Mine 4 miles N.

Also at Ledbetter Mine dump, N on Hwy 23 to Rabun Gap and one mile E to S side of Black Creek.

Also at W. T. Smith Mine at junction to road E from Clayton to junction with S.C. Hwy 28.

Also at Wilson farm 4 miles SE.

Also N on Hwy 23 on mine dumps near dam at Mountain City.

Also, take U.S. 76 W, turn N, follow Tallulah River into Towns County, then left on Upper Charlie Creek to diggings.

BERYL, QUARTZ CRYSTALS: E 8 miles, at Mark Beck farm.

CORUNDUM: E to Pine Mountain, then 1½ miles NE to Laurel Creek Mine.

ROSE QUARTZ: E to road N to crossing of Walnut Fork, in dumps of Kell Mine.

*Columbus, Muscogee County*

PETRIFIED WOOD: Near Bull and Randall Creeks.

*Cumming, Forsyth County*

AMETHYST: E 6 miles at the I. H. Gilbert farm.

*Dallas, Paulding County*

ALMANDINE GARNET: On surface near Little Bob Copper Mine 6 miles SE.

*Elberton, Elbert County*

SMOKY QUARTZ: NE 10 miles.

AMETHYST: Take Hwy 17 5 miles NW to Dewy Rose, then go 2 miles N to W. B. Perkins place.

*Griffin, Spalding County*

BLUE BERYL, SMOKY QUARTZ AND ROSE QUARTZ: Take Hwy 92 NW to Vaughn, and go 2 miles NE to T. J. Allen property; collect crystals in pegmatite and loose in soil.

*Hiawassee, Towns County*

PINK CORUNDUM: Often with smaragdite, 2 miles SW at Hog Creek Mine.

Also at Bell Creek Mine 4

miles N at head of Chatuge Lake and in beach deposits and outcrops along Chatuge Lake, especially near Elf.

*Holly Springs, Cherokee County*

APATITE: In talc at Verd Antique Quarry.

*Kingston, Bartow County*

RED AND BROWN AGATE: To S along Etowah River, and near Cleveland crossroads.

*La Grange, Troup County*

QUARTZ CRYSTALS, ROSE QUARTZ, AQUAMARINE: At Foley (Mineral Processing Company) Mine 8 miles S.

*Macon, Bibb County*

AGATE: At Holton Quarry, $7\frac{1}{2}$ miles NW.

BERYL: In Oconee National Forest.

*Madison, Morgan County*

AMETHYST: Take U.S. 278 E to Buckhead and go 2 miles E to Ray farm.

*Maysville, Banks County*

QUARTZ CRYSTALS: In Commerce area along railroad.

*Milledgeville, Baldwin County*

JASPER: At State Farm.

*Monroe, Walton County*

AQUAMARINE: On surface at Malcolm farm; take Hwy 83 SE to Blasingame, then $6\frac{1}{2}$ miles on dirt road.

*Morgantown, Fannin County*

STAUROLITE: Take Hwy 60 N to Mineral Bluff and collect at Windy Ridge.

*Nacoochee, White County*

GREEN APATITE: In cut on N side of Hwy 17 3 miles E.

*Norcross, Gwinnett County*

MOONSTONE: Hwy 141 N to crossing of Chattahoochee; in pegmatite on Green farm. (Ask permission.)

*Powder Springs, Cobb County*

CORUNDUM: S 2 miles on Turner property.

*Roswell, Fulton County*

CORUNDUM: E $3\frac{1}{2}$ miles

*Round Oak, Jones County*

RED JASPER, AGATE, QUARTZ CRYSTALS.

*Summerville, Chattooga County*

AGATE: S 2 miles.

*Tate, Pickens County*

GOLDEN BERYL, AQUAMARINE: In pegmatite on Rock Creek on Ralph Cook farm near Refuge Church.

*Thomaston, Upson County*

CORUNDUM: NE 7 miles at the Kelly place.

FELDSPAR, MOONSTONE, APATITE, TOURMALINE: At Mitchell Creek Mica Mine.

RED AND WHITE AGATE: At Wilmot's Ravine.

CYANITE: Loose in soil $3\frac{1}{2}$ miles SW.

*Toccoa, Stephens County*
QUARTZ CRYSTALS: S 9 miles.
*Villanow, Walker County*
AGATE.
*Warm Springs, Meriwether County*
AGATE: One mile S on Southern Railroad.

*Washington, Wilkes County*
PALE BLUE LAZULITE, CYANITE, RUTILE: These can all be found at Graves Mountain.
*Yatesville, Upson County*
BERYL: $\frac{1}{4}$ mile E at Herron Mine.

## IDAHO

Its diversity of geographical features, ranging from the rugged mountains of the northeast and central parts of the state to the arid wastes of the south and the basalt plateaus of the north, makes Idaho a state rich in mineral and gem resources. The Salmon and Clearwater River regions are one of the last frontiers of collecting in the United States—a wilderness of canyons and forests.

*Avery, Shoshone County*
CYANITE, STAUROLITE: To S.
*Avon, Latah County*
GREEN BERYL: In mica mines, especially the Levi Anderson and Muscovite Mines.
*Bear Lake, Bear Lake County*
JASPER: In Paris Canyon.
*Bliss, Gooding County*
BROWN OPALIZED OAKWOOD: In volcanic ash along Clover Creek.
*Bruneau, Owyhee County*
BROWN PASTEL JASPER, OPAL NODULES, FIRE OPAL: In Bruneau River Canyon to S on Hwy 51.
  In Jacks Creek, Dorsey Creek and forks of Bruneau River. (Rugged. Local guide needed.)
*Camas, Jefferson County*
FIRE OPAL: In rhyolite near source of E branch of tributary to S fork of Camas Creek.
*Challis, Custer County**
RED AND SEAM AGATE, BLACK WOOD: Have been found in valleys near Challis, W 2 miles on Garden Creek Road. S on Hwy 93 through the gorge, agate nodules may be found in small valleys and hills to right and, 2 miles from the

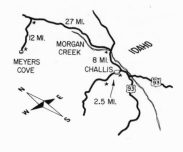

road to the left, black wood has been collected in the hills. On Hwy 93A, 11 miles S of Challis, take Lime Creek Road E for 2 miles, hunt in hills for agate.

AGATE, JASPER, PETRIFIED WOOD: Fifteen miles S on Hwy 93A, just E of highway at Specimen Hill.

A mile farther S a dirt road leads in 2 miles to Malon Gulch where specimens occur in ravines.

SEAM AGATE IN VOLCANIC ASH: N of Challis about 8 miles is turnoff at Morgan Creek almost due N for 27 miles, then sharply left toward Meyers Cove. Look along road to cove.

*Emmett, Gem County*

FIRE OPAL: At Black Canyon Dam. Go toward Horseshoe Bend to small pond

E of road; take trail to canyon and go mile to diggings on left side.

RED AND YELLOW JASPER: To S in Willow Creek.

*Fernwood, Benewah County**

DARK ALMANDINE STAR GARNET: At Emerald and Purdue Creeks in Benewah and Latah counties. The areas are reached from Fernwood by going SE on Hwy 43 (parallels the St. Maries River).

At Emerald Creek turn on to dirt road W and follow along E fork. One collecting area lies along a tributary about 8 miles from road, the other a couple of miles farther along on E fork.

Purdue Creek crosses Hwy 43 a short distance N of Bovill. By following a dirt road and then a trail along a left fork, the star garnet location is reached,

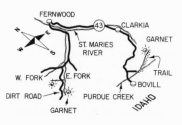

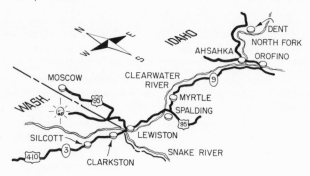

about 4 miles from road. Collect waterworn garnets in the stream gravels near bedrock.

*Firth, Bingham County*

PETRIFIED TEMPSKYA: In Willow Creek.

*Galena, Blaine County*

AMETHYST GEODES: Take U.S. 93 W for 4 miles and dirt road N to Pole Creek.

*Hailey, Blaine County*

AGATE, PETRIFIED WOOD: SW 5 miles to Bellevue and E to Little Wood River.

*Homedale, Owyhee County* (See Adrian, Oregon.)

*Idaho City, Boise County*

ALMANDINE GARNET: In placers.

FIRE OPAL: At Moore Creek.

*Lewiston, Nez Perce County\**

FIRE OPAL: Just N of Lewiston a dirt road turns W from Hwy 95. Take it for 10 miles, then hike up ridge a half mile, turn right and follow along cliffs to diggings.

A mile or so farther along the dirt road and across the Snake River is a big gravel pit at Silcott. Opposite it on N side of river and 900 ft. up, caves are reached by a trail. Diggings are in caves.

AGATE (HELL'S CANYON): Found just below fire opal diggings, on talus slopes.

FIBROUS SILLIMANITE (AS WATERWORN BLUE, YELLOW, GREEN AND WHITE PEBBLES): Found E and N from Lewiston in the Clearwater River and in its N fork as far as Dent. The best hunting is between the Cheerylane and Myrtle bridges and at Big Eddy above Spalding.

AGATE: Found in the same stream areas.

*Lost River, Custer County*

AMETHYST AND QUARTZ CRYS-TALS: In geodes in the Low Hills.

AGATE, JASPER: On the North Fork.

*Mackay, Custer County*

RED AND YELLOW JASPER SPOTTED WITH CHRYSOCOL-LA: Found in Alder Creek district mines.

*Marsing, Owyhee County*

FIRE OPAL: Take Homedale Road, turn left and S to Graveyard Point. Turn left on Canal Road for 2 miles to bridge. Cross and return ¾ mile on other side to diggings.

*Montpelier, Bear Lake County*

QUARTZ: Colored red by hematite and green by malachite at Humming Bird Mine dump in Paris Canyon.

*New Meadows, Adams County*

RUBY, GARNET: Take Hwy 15 7 miles E, the dirt road left, and pan sands of stream at Rock Flat for small stones.

*Panther Creek, Lemhi County*

FIRE OPAL: Six miles from creek's source in porphyry dike 7,000 ft. up and on W side of valley.

*Pierce, Clearwater County*

ALMANDINE (STAR) GARNET: In streams near Headquarters 11 miles N.

*Riggins, Idaho County*

GARNET: For several miles to N in Salmon River.

*St. Anthony, Fremont County*

YELLOW FELDSPAR (ANDESINE) CRYSTALS: At Crystal Butte, 18 miles N, where they have weathered out of lava.

*Setters, Kootenai County*

COMMON OPAL (WHITE, YEL-LOW, BROWN, GREEN): In Spokane Valley.

*Silver City, Owyhee County*

AGATE, JASPER: In ravines and draws in area S for 25 miles from Snake River.

*Weiser, Washington County*

AGATE NODULES: W on Hwy 70 5 miles through Eaton, N on Old's Ferry Road a mile to crossroads, W 2 miles, then right up hill 4 miles into saddle. Nodules are loose in decomposed rock.

Also on road left from Eaton to end of road for nodules in Grouse Creek area.

BLACK AND WHITE OPALIZED WOOD: Take Hwy 95 N

13 miles to Mann's Creek guard station sign, turn NW on dirt road 8½ miles to Fourth of July Creek Canyon. Dig in right bank.

RED AGATE, PETRIFIED WOOD: To SE lies Sage Creek; specimens can be found in its ravines upstream for several miles.

*White Bird, Idaho County*
AGATE: S and E of U.S. 95 6 miles.

*Yellow Pine, Valley County*
WHITE OPAL: Stained red by cinnabar (myrickite), in mercury mines.

## ILLINOIS

Most of the state consists of prairie underlain by sedimentary rocks yielding coal, oil, and glass sand and deeply buried by glacial sand and gravel. The Ozark plateau and coastal plain of the southwestern part of the state, and the unglaciated "driftless" area in the northwest corner contain fluorite, lead, and zinc mines.

*Grand Chain, Pulaski County*
BROWN JASPER: In rail cut mile to NE.

*Hamilton, Hancock County*
BROWN JASPER: Old gravel pit.

*Warsaw, Hancock County**
WATERWORN AGATE PEBBLES: In gravel pits.

QUARTZ CRYSTALS: In geodes in river banks over wide area extending to Kahoka, Mo., Keokuk, Iowa, and to Hamilton, Ill.

## INDIANA

Like Illinois, Indiana rests on the sedimentary rocks laid down by ancient seas, which are rich in fossils but poor in gem minerals. Where the glacial drift that covers most of the state lies on bedrock, streams sort out gold and some minerals such as diamond. Although most of the state is flat, resistant ridges and glacial moraines in the southern half create scenic variety.

*Heltonville, Lawrence County*
GEODES: In Salt Creek and to W toward Guthrie.

*Martinsville, Morgan County*
BROWN CHATOYANT SAPPHIRE: In gravels of Highland Creek 7 miles NW

*Morgantown, Morgan County*
SAPPHIRE, GARNET: In Gold Creek and other small streams through glacial drift and running on bedrock.

*Scottsburg, Scott County*
PETRIFIED WOOD: Can be found in shale beds throughout county.

*Trevlac, Brown County*
QUARTZ GEODES: In Bear Creek. Streams east of Bloomington, Monroe County, and in Brown County and to the south in Washington County contain quartz-filled geodes according to reports.

## IOWA

Iowa is a moderately rolling prairie tableland of glacial materials resting on sedimentary rocks except in the northeast corner, which was not touched by the glaciers so that cliffs and hills make a more rugged topography, and in the extreme west, where moundlike bluffs rise from the Missouri River's flood plain. Geodes eroding from sedimentary rocks and quartz gem materials from the glacial drift can be expected in such circumstances.

*Bellevue, Jackson County**
CARNELIAN, BANDED AGATE, PETRIFIED WOOD: Lake Superior agates from Mississippi River gravels: Take U.S. 52-67 N from Bellevue $\frac{1}{4}$ mile to gravel pit, which is privately owned, operated most of the year. Search big piles

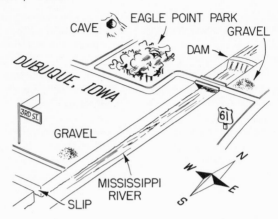

of washed gravel for specimen. Inch to 2-inch agate is large. Occasional big ones go into oversize gravel discard pile near loading dock. Collecting in pits themselves is not very rewarding. (Permission to collect should be obtained at office; collectors should not block track with cars or interfere with machinery or workers.)

Other similar gravel operations may be found up and down the Mississippi River, especially at Muscatine, Burlington, in the Tri-City area, near Clinton, and upstream in Wisconsin. Some plants are on barges pumping the gravel from the river bed.

*Des Moines, Polk County*

PETRIFIED WOOD: In strip coal mines.

*Dubuque, Dubuque County**

AGATE: There are two gravel operations at Dubuque, one just N of the junction of Third Street and the Mississippi River, the other just across the river in Wisconsin. Waterworn Lake Superior agates may be hunted in the stock piles. (With permission.)

SATIN SPAR: On the bluffs above the city, just W of Eagle Point Park in cave. It lies behind a housing development.

*Keokuk, Lee County*
QUARTZ GEODES. (See Warsaw, Ill.)

*Mount Pleasant, Henry County*
AGATE: In gravels of Big Creek and Skunk River and in pits.

*Muscatine, Muscatine County*
AGATE: In gravel pits S of town and E of Hwy 96. Hahn's pit is 2 miles S. Acme and a third pit are 5 miles S. There are other pits along the shore and barges pumping gravels up and down the Mississippi River from Missouri northward.

*Nevada, Story County*
AGATE: In Indian Creek gravels to E.

*New London, Henry County*
AGATE GEODES: From water tower due S for 8 miles, turn left to creek and collect in bed and along banks.

*Orient, Adair County*
AGATE, QUARTZ CRYSTALS, PETRIFIED WOOD: 5 miles N and E in washes and clay hillsides.

*Red Oak, Montgomery County*
AGATE: In vein in limestone of quarry to N agate is found.

*Steamboat Rock, Hardin County*
QUARTZ GEODES: Along Iowa River and also between Chapin and Sheffield along U.S. 65.

## KANSAS

Extensive sedimentary beds underlie Kansas, containing coal, salt and world famous fossils. The surface is formed of sand and gravel derived from erosion of the Rockies and carried eastward by water. These deposits create the gently eastward sloping High Plains, a region where agates and other quartz materials may be expected. East of the High Plains are the Smoky Hills in the north and the Great Bend Prairie. East of them is a strip known as the Flint Hills, north to south across the state, and in the northeastern corner of Kansas is a glaciated region. The prairie surface is diversified by broad plains, isolated hills, and moderate valleys.

*Ashland, Clark County*
MOSS AGATE: To N.
*Bonner Springs, Wyandotte County*
QUARTZ CRYSTALS: In geodes in Lone Star Quarry.
*Carneiro, Ellsworth County*
AMBER: S 5 miles in lignite along banks of Smoky Hill River (now under water).
*Concordia, Cloud County*
WATERWORN AGATE: Can be found in glacial gravels of old river bed.
*Elkader, Logan County*
AGATE: W in river terraces.

*Ellsworth, Ellsworth County*
AGATE, JASPER, PETRIFIED BONE AND WOOD: In gravels N of Kanopolis Lake.
*Ransom, Ness County*
AGATE, PETRIFIED WOOD: To NE in Seybert sand pit.
*Wallace, Wallace County*
MOSS OPAL: In road cut 5 miles to the S.
*Yates Center, Woodson County*
QUARTZ CRYSTALS: In granite 8 miles S.
AMETHYST: In quartzite 4 miles W and 10 miles S.

## KENTUCKY

Rugged eastern Kentucky belongs to the Allegheny plateau, a region of sharp ridges and deep valleys which includes extensive coal fields. The rest of the state is divided between the Highland Rim plateau to the south and the bluegrass region of rolling hills to the north, all sloping gently to the Mississippi River. Like the Plains states, it is underlain by sedimentary rocks but unglaciated and hence more varied in character.

*Louisville, Jefferson County*
AGATE: In Ohio River gravels.
*Sandy Hook, Elliott County*
PYROPE GARNET: At Isonville 6 miles SE.

*Wickliffe, Ballard County*
JASPER: In the gravel pit jasper can be found by the collector.

## LOUISIANA

Much of Louisiana has been built by the Mississippi River from mud and sand carried down from the north. On the west side of the river lie areas of low hills and plains becoming marshes to the south. There are agate-bearing gravel deposits in these hills, 20 to 45 miles W of the river, and petrified wood near Alexandria. No gem materials occur south of an East-West line through Baton Rouge. The East side of the river is low flood plain. The state is not particularly rich in gem materials.

*Monroe, Ouachita Parish*
BANDED AGATE (SOME OF MON-
TANA MOSS AGATE TYPE),
PETRIFIED WOOD, SILICI-
FIED CORAL: Scattered over
wide area to south and
east. To south, some of the
prominent locations are
Pollock, Grant Parish;
Woodworth, Rapides Par-
ish; Turkey Creek, Evan-
geline Parish; and, farther
east, St. Francisville and
Jackson, in Feliciana Parish; and Watson in nearby
Livingston Parish. Farther
west, petrified wood is
found in the Sabine River
from Leesville, Vernon
Parish, N to Shreveport.
In the extreme east these
materials are found near
Bogalusa and Franklinton
in Washington Parish; and
in Tangipahoa Parish
along the Tangipahoa
River from Kentwood
south to Independence.
Most of the gem materials
are found in streams and
in stream gravels accord-
ing to the reports.

## MAINE

Southern Maine is a rolling upland broken by hills and isolated mountains and valleys; the northern part is hilly and often swampy. Glacial action caused many lakes to form behind debris, damming the normal drainage, and stripped the rocks of soil, laying bare the crystalline rocks that are the source of Maine's splendid tourmalines and other gems.

*Auburn, Androscoggin County*
TOURMALINE, LEPIDOLITE, PUR-
PLE APATITE, BLUE BERYL:
At Pulsifer and Wade
Quarry.
PINK BERYL, QUARTZ CRYSTALS:
At Maine Feldspar Mine.
SMOKY QUARTZ: In Littlefield
Quarry.
*Bethel, Oxford County*
AQUAMARINE: At Stearns Mine,
$1\frac{1}{2}$ miles SE of Hunts
Corner.

ROSE QUARTZ, BERYL: At Wardwell Mine.

SMOKY QUARTZ, ROSE QUARTZ: At Scribner Ledge, 3 miles S of Hunts Corner.

SPESSARTITE GARNET: At Bethel Mica Mine.

*Bowdoinham, Sagadahoc County*

GREEN BERYL: At Coombs Mine.

*Brunswick, Cumberland County*

BERYL: At LaChance Mine 4 miles S.

*Buckfield, Oxford County*

BERYL: At Fletcher Mine 2 miles SW on Hodgson Hill and 2½ miles SW at Robinson Dudley Mine.

PINK AND BLUE BERYL, ROSE QUARTZ, TOURMALINE: At Paul Bennett Quarry 3 miles W on back road to Mount Mica.

BERYL: At Irish Mine 3 miles SE.

*Byron, Oxford County*

RED JASPER: In Swift River.

*Canton, Oxford County*

AMETHYST: In brook at Ragged Jack Mountain.

*Deer Isle, Hancock County*

LAVENDER GRANITE: On Moose and Crotch Islands.

*Denmark, Oxford County*

AMETHYST, SMOKY QUARTZ: In Warren Quarry on W side of Pleasant Mountain.

*Dixfield, Oxford County*

BERYL: On south slope of Hedgehog Hill.

*Fryeburg, Oxford County*

GARNET, SMOKY QUARTZ: To S on E side of Stark Mountain at Eagle Granite Quarry.

*Georgetown, Sagadahoc County*

BERYL, ROSE QUARTZ, TOURMALINE: At Consolidated Quarry 3 miles S.

*Hebron, Oxford County*

GOLDEN AND BLUE BERYL, ROSE QUARTZ: 1½ miles N at Hibb's Mine.

GREEN BERYL, TOURMALINE: At Mills Quarry 2½ miles N on Number 4 Hill.

*Litchfield, Kennebec County*

SODALITE: At Spear's Corner.

*Machias, Washington County*

JASPER PEBBLES: At Jasper Beach.

*Minot, Androscoggin County*

AMETHYST, QUARTZ CRYSTALS: At Phillips Mine.

TOURMALINE, APATITE: Take Route 11-121 E to Haskell's Corners; turn left and go 2 miles to dirt road to right and continue on it to quarries on side of Mt. Apatite.

*Mount Desert, Hancock County*

AMETHYST, SMOKY QUARTZ: At Hall's Quarry.

*Newry, Oxford County*

BERYL AND BICOLORED TOUR-
MALINE: To NE at Dun-
ton-Neville Mine.

ROSE QUARTZ: At Plumbago
Mountain; spodumene in
lower pit at mountain.

*North Lovell, Oxford County*

GOLDEN BERYL: 4 miles NW on
E side of Durgin Moun-
tain and 3 miles NW at
Sugar Hill.

BLUE BERYL: 3 miles N at
Chapman Hill.

*Norway, Oxford County*

TOURMALINE: At B.B. No. 7
Mine at Nobles Corner 8
miles NW.

TOURMALINE, ROSE QUARTZ: N
2 miles at Tubb's Ledge.

*Paris, Oxford County\**

ROSE QUARTZ: At James Bow-
ker farm.

At Colby Ledge.

At Hooper's Ledge on Paris
Hill.

At Stearn's farm.

ROSE QUARTZ, BERYL: At God--
dard's Ledge.

*Sanford, York County*

BROWN IDOCRASE: In pit and on
dump. Go 1½ miles E on
School Street at Goodhall
farm.

*South Paris, Oxford County\**

GOLDEN AND BLUE BERYL: At
Andrews Ledge.

At Sugar Hill.

AMETHYST: At Foster Hill.
At Harding's Hill.

CITRINE: At Blueberry Mountain. The small area (\*)
between Newry and South
Paris is one of the famous
gem collecting areas of the
United States. It is now
being redeveloped under
the impetus of Stanley Perham, mineral dealer at
Trap Corner, and of sev-
eral universities that have
mined the pegmatite dikes
for tourmaline, beryl, apatite, lepidolite, etc.

QUARTZ: The Perham Mine,
near West Paris, is reached
by taking High Street to
a sign reading "Perham
Mine," thence a half mile
up the mine road. In the
open pits in feldspar are
found smoky quartz crys-
tals, sometimes with pale
amethyst tints. (The mine
is owned by the Bell Min-
eral Company of West
Paris, from whom permis-
sion to collect should be
obtained.)

BERYL, STAR QUARTZ, ROSE AND
SMOKY QUARTZ: South and
east of nearby Greenwood
are three mines. The Heikkinen Mine, owned by
Stanley Perham, is reached
from Greenwood by going
S 500 feet, then to the

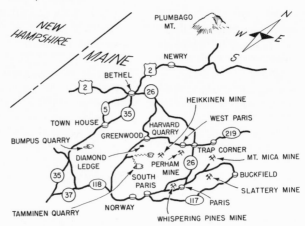

Rawleigh Hayes house on Hayes Hill, and walking ¾ mile on the mine road.

BERYL, STAR QUARTZ, ROSE AND SMOKY QUARTZ: Gems found in the feldspar workings.

TOURMALINE, BLUE BERYL, STAR QUARTZ: To reach the Harvard Mine, drive S 2½ miles from Greenwood to a crossroad below Mud Pond, turn left 1,000 ft. to a rise above Nestor Tamminen's house. Park and walk ½ mile to mine on SW brow of Noyes Mountain. (Permission to collect at the Heikkinen and Harvard Mines should be obtained from Perham.)

Nearby is the Tamminen Mine, where the same gem minerals are found. (Permission and directions can be obtained at the Tamminen house.)

QUARTZ CRYSTALS (SOME WITH PHANTOMS): Found at Diamond Ledge. Go 1½ miles S from Greenwood to a gravel pit road on the right between Hicks and Mud Pond. Park and go up Noyes Mountain, which lies to left of the road S from Greenwood. (Permission to collect should be obtained from property owners, Rawleigh and Elmer Hayes.)

ROSE QUARTZ, BERYL, SMOKY QUARTZ: The Bumpus

Quarry lies below Bethel about 10 miles on Route 5-35. The mine dumps are alongside the E edge of the highway.

STAR ROSE QUARTZ, SMOKY QUARTZ, CITRINE QUARTZ: Whispering Pines Mine is reached from Trap Corner by going 6 miles S on Route 26 to a tea room of the same name, then taking a mine road E from just below the tea room. The small open pit is about 300 yards from the road.

TOURMALINE, GEM BERYL, SMOKY QUARTZ, QUARTZ CRYSTALS: Still found at Mount Mica, which is $1\frac{1}{3}$ miles E of Paris and is reached by a mine road to left up a hill. There are two open pits and extensive dumps. This has been one of the celebrated tourmaline regions. (Permission to collect can be obtained from Mrs. Howard Irish of Buckfield.)

QUARTZ, SMOKY QUARTZ: Found in the three pits at the Slattery Mine. Take right turn in the village of Paris (instead of the one that leads to Mount Mica) and go a half mile to the mine

road. Walk in 1,000 ft. (Obtain permission from Stanley Perham.)

*Stoneham, Oxford County*
PHENACITE: At Lord's Hill.

*Stow, Oxford County*
AMETHYST, APATITE, SMOKY QUARTZ: At Deer Hill. Drive E, across Cold River Bridge, 3 miles to end of road; turn left 4 miles to fork; take left fork 5 miles to area of Lord Hill, Deer Hill and Harndon Hill.

*Topsham, Sagadahoc County*
RED GARNET, TOURMALINE, SMOKY QUARTZ, BLUE BERYL: At quarries. Take Hwy 24 for 3 miles N; turn on left fork at Topsham Quarry Company sign; cross Cathance River and go mile to top of hill. Turn left on dirt road to Fisher (the best), Consolidated, Staples, and Willes Quarries.

*West Minot, Androscoggin County*
GROSSULARITE GARNET: At Pitts and Tenney Mine.

*West Paris, Oxford County*
BERYL: At Scribner Mine 9 miles SW.

*Winslow, Kennebec County*
BLUE BERYL: In Winslow Mine.

## MARYLAND

The easternmost part of Maryland along the line of Baltimore and Washington is coastal plain, backed up by the Piedmont plateau of crystalline rocks containing a diversity of mineral wealth, and giving way in the west to mountains and valleys of the Appalachian system, made up of sedimentary and metamorphic rocks of lesser mineral interest.

*Baltimore, Baltimore County*
MOSS AGATE: In the Bare Hills.
SERPENTINE: In the Bare Hills quarries at Falls and Old Pimlico Roads.
QUARTZ CRYSTALS: At Silver Spring in Druid Hill Park.
AQUAMARINE: At Arundel Gneiss quarry on W bank of Gunpowder River and N of Harford Road.

*Beltsville, Prince Georges County*
PETRIFIED WOOD: In old iron mines.

*Cockeysville, Baltimore County*
BROWN TOURMALINE, SMOKY QUARTZ, QUARTZ CRYSTALS: At H. T. Campbell quarry near Texas.

*Conowingo, Cecil County*
QUARTZ CRYSTALS: N on U.S. 1 to Rising Sun and collect crystals loose in soil at Rawlings place.

*Hereford, Baltimore County*
SERPENTINE, QUARTZ CRYSTALS: In N wall of Blue Mount Trap Rock quarry, one mile SW and 2 miles E.

*Granite, Baltimore County*
AMETHYST, QUARTZ CRYSTALS: Nash farm.

*Jarrettsville, Harford County*
SERPENTINE: At Reed chrome mine.
At Wilkins chrome mine $1\frac{1}{2}$ miles SE along road to Cooperstown.

*Oakwood, Cecil County*
SERPENTINE: In Weiant quarry one mile W on W bank of Conowingo Creek.
JASPER, MOSS AGATE: Loose on surface of nearby serpentine barrens.

*Owings Mills, Baltimore County*
SERPENTINE: In dumps of Choate chrome mine.
At Weir mine 4 miles W.
MOSS AGATE, PINK JASPER: In creeks and on surface of Soldier's Delight barrens near Choate mine.

*Reistertown, Baltimore County*
SERPENTINE, JASPER, MOSS

AGATE: At Dyer quarry.

*Rockdale, Baltimore County*

QUARTZ CRYSTALS: N of Liberty Road ⁷⁄₁₀ mile in Milford quarry.

*Rock Springs, Cecil County\**

WILLIAMSITE (SERPENTINE, TRANSLUCENT), YELLOW AND PURPLE CHALCEDONY: The best known area to collect the translucent variety of serpentine known as williamsite is at the Line Pits chrome mine dumps on the Pennsylvania-Maryland line north of Conowingo Dam on the Susquehanna River. Route 222 leads north to a gravel road to the left that reaches the dumps in less than a mile. The williamsite is found enclosing the chromite ore. With it is associated yellow and purple chalcedony. (Obtain permission to collect.)

North and east of the Line

Pits are several other mines that contain similar deposits.

MOSS AGATE: NE 1¼ miles in Lancaster County, Pa.

*Rockville, Montgomery County*

GREEN IDOCRASE WITH DIOPSIDE AND SERPENTINE: NW in quarry.

*Silver Spring, Montgomery County*

GOLDEN BERYL: N 2 miles at Kensington Mica mine near Sligo Creek.

*Simpsonville, Howard County*

AMETHYST, QUARTZ CRYSTALS: In Maryland mica mine on Arrington farm.

*Union Bridge, Carroll County*

QUARTZ CRYSTALS: SW 3 miles in Mountain View lead mine at Beaver Dam Churches on Beaver Dam Run.

*Westminster, Carroll County*

QUARTZ CRYSTALS: N of New Windsor Road ¼ mile at Hyde limestone quarry.

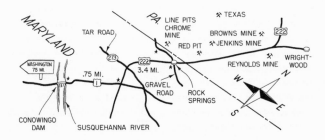

*Whiteford, Harford County*
SERPENTINE: In dumps of Car-

diff quarry to N at state line.

## MASSACHUSETTS

Massachusetts, like Connecticut, is divided into two geographical provinces by the Connecticut River. East of the river, the land falls with few elevations toward the ocean, although the underlying rocks are contorted metamorphic schists; to the west lies an Appalachian Mountain region. Most gem-producing areas lie in the Connecticut River valley or just east of it, except the Essex County area in the extreme northeast part of the state.

*Deerfield, Franklin County*
BANDED AGATE: In Deerfield River.

AMETHYST: At Cheapside quarry.

*East Deerfield, Franklin County*
PREHNITE: At Cheapside quarry.

*Fitchburg, Worcester County*
GOLDEN BERYL: In pegmatite in W side of Rollstone Hills.

*Gloucester, Essex County*
SMOKY QUARTZ: In Pomroy quarry.

*Marshfield, Plymouth County*
JASPER PEBBLES: At beach.

*Newburyport, Essex County*
SERPENTINE: On turnpike 2 miles to Newbury, then first road left for 2 miles. Park, walk to Devil's Den, and look in mine dumps.

*Pelham, Hampshire County*
GREEN APATITE: At asbestos mine.

*Royalston, Worcester County*
BLUE-GREEN BERYL: In Robinson mine 2½ miles NE at Beryl Hill.

*West Cummington, Hampshire County\**
RHODONITE: The West Cummington manganese mine is ½ mile N of Hwy 9 on a mine road that leaves Hwy 9 roughly 3 miles from the fork of Hwys 9

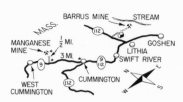

and 112 just NW of Cummington. Rhodonite is found in the mine ore and on the dumps.

TOURMALINE, LEPIDOLITE, CAT'S-EYE SPODUMENE: Farther E and just N of the hamlet of Lithia is the Barrus mine, the first farm N of Lithia on the right of Hwy 112. Take trail to the diggings alongside a small stream. (Obtain permission at the farmhouse to collect.)

*Westfield, Hampden County*
AMETHYST: At Lane's traprock quarry.

## MICHIGAN

Lower Michigan is quite level and not much elevated above the Great Lakes, and is underlain by sedimentary deposits of limestone, salt, and gypsum. Upper Michigan, however, is a rugged land of ancient igneous and metamorphic rocks, highly contorted and containing some of the world's richest iron and copper deposits, as well as a wealth of specimen minerals.

*Allouez, Keweenaw County\**
CHRYSOCOLLA: From dump at Allouez Mine.

AGATE: The Keweenaw beach agate is distinctive for its pastel shades. It is rarely large and is not easy to distinguish from the other pebbles on the beach. These agates are found along the NW shore from Tamarack waterworks to the tip of the peninsula. Also on Manitou Island.
The best beach pickings are at Pete's Beach, reached

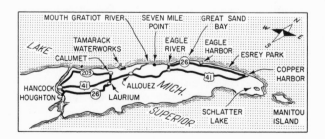

by taking the Five Mile Point Road from Allouez to turnoff marked with sign and through woods to lake shore. (Fee.)

At Gratiot River Beach, reached from Five Mile Point Road by turning S on very rough road.

LEDGE AGATES: Larger and of a more conventional type. Found in the ledges that cross the road from Allouez to the lake shore.

In the ledges back of Esrey Park on Agate Harbor.

Inland from Seven Mile Point and on the N side of Schlatter Lake.

PINK, GREEN THOMSONITES: Found on the Keweenaw, Pete's, and Gratiot River beaches.

*Alpena, Alpena County*

FOSSIL CORAL (PETOSKEY STONES): In Rockport Quarry, 11 miles NE.

*Copper Harbor, Keweenaw County*

DATOLITE, GREEN EPIDOTE (SHOT THROUGH WITH COPPER), THOMSONITE: Datolite on Clark mine dump. Massive green epidote is found in many of these mines and makes an attractive cut stone. Thomsonite occurs in nodules and seams in the basalt.

AGATE: At northern point of peninsula, reached by taking logging road at northern end of U.S. 41 5 miles to clump of three birches at fork, and taking left fork 3 miles to point. Traffic is permitted only on Sundays.

Long hike to right around point leads to less picked area on Keystone Bay.

*Grandville, Kent County*

ALABASTER: In gypsum quarry.

*Gull Point, Ontonogan County*

AGATE PEBBLES: On beach.

*Ishpeming, Marquette County*

JASPER, HEMATITE (JASPILITE): Jasper layered with specular hematite (jaspilite) at Jasper Hill.

In dumps of Republic mine E of Hwy 95 near Republic.

In dumps of mine to N.

KONA DOLOMITE: In Lindberg quarry (private claim).

*Isle Royale*

AMETHYSTINE AGATE: In Siskiwit Bay.

On Thomsonite Beach.

AGATE, CARNELIAN: At head of Siskiwit Bay.

NE of McGinty Cove.

N side of Amygdaloid Point.

THOMSONITE: At point N of Stockly Bay.

On main island S of Hawk Island.

Near end of Scoville Point thomsonite has been found.

CHLORASTROLITE: At Mott Island.

At Smithwick Island.

At Caribou Island.

At Rock Harbor.

On S shore of Siskiwit Lake.

At Scoville Point.

At Todd Harbor.

At Chippewa Harbor.

At Tobin Harbor.

(Isle Royale is a national park and collecting is forbidden there.)

*Michigamme, Marquette County*

STAUROLITE: In road cut S of Lake Michigamme.

*Newport, Monroe County*

AMETHYSTINE QUARTZ: At Point aux Peaux.

*Petoskey, Emmett County*

FOSSIL CORAL (PETOSKEY STONES): On shores of Little Traverse Bay.

At Burt and Torch Lakes.

At other beaches and quarries near Petoskey and Charlevoix.

## MINNESOTA

Southern Minnesota rises from the Midwestern prairies into a rolling upland which, in the northwest, is dominated by the flat bed of the ancient extinct Lake Agassiz. In the northeast lies the Mesabi iron range, and in central Minnesota the Cuyuna range. The whole state is covered with lakes left by glaciers, which also left a rich deposit of agates in the beach and river gravels.

Areas marked on state map* are locations where there are active gravel pits. Permission can usually be obtained to examine the stock piles of gravel for agates of the Lake Superior type. These are common over most of the upper central half of the state and especially along the Mississippi River and eastward into the Mille Lacs area. The agates, of fortification type and usually red and white striped, may run as large as 14 pounds but most of them are fist-size and smaller. (Map on next page.)

*Beaver Bay, Lake County*

AGATE: On beach.

*Buhl, St. Louis County*

AGATE: Go E on U.S. 169 to Top's Tavern on N side

of road, turn N on dirt road to Dormer dumps on left side of road.

*Crosby, Crow Wing County*\*

BINGHAMITE: Silicified iron mineral known as binghamite at Evergreen (Portsmouth) mine dump. The mineral, which resembles red and yellow tigereye, is found in the dump, especially on the E side, and on the W side of the dump S of the road and near the pit.

Farther along a side road W from Hwy 6 and slightly S is the tipple and dump of the Louis Mine, where another form of the same material is obtained. William Perpitch, of the Yankee and Portsmouth Mine, knows the locations of this material in the area.

*Duluth, St. Louis County*

AGATE: In shoreline gravels (especially at low water) of Island Lake Reservoir 18 miles N.

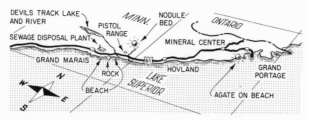

*Grand Marais, Cook County\**

THOMSONITE: 3 miles SW in ledges along road cut where power line crosses Hwy 61, above road in ledges. (Under private claim.)

In gravel of lake shore at point. (Permission to collect at shore difficult to obtain.)

HOVLANDITE: Just beyond Grand Marais is the town's sewage-disposal plant on the lake shore and just beyond it is a small beach and a rock. An attractive dark-spotted rock known as hovlandite is obtained on the NE side of this rock.

AGATE NODULES: Beyond this spot lies the Devil Track River, and 1½ miles NE of its mouth is a side road to a pistol range. A dim road or trail N from it leads to an area where agate nodules may be dug.

*Little Marais, Lake County\**

AGATE: In gravels at County Line Beach.

Five miles SW at the Baptism River's mouth. Park just east of the state's black-top depot and take trail down to the lake for blue agates. Stay S of the rock in the lake.

*Mineral Center, Cook County*

AGATE: Take side road to Grand Portage until it dips close to the lake. Here a faintly marked road leads through a shale ridge to the collecting spot on the beach.

*Osseo, Hennepin County*

AGATE: At Anderson Aggregate pit.

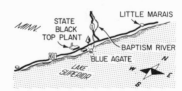

*Red Wing, Goodhue County*

QUARTZ CRYSTALS: In cavities in limestone bluffs along Mississippi River.

*Royalton, Morrison County*

STAUROLITE: In schist outcrops at Blanchard Dam; best under railroad bridge.

*Tofte, Cook County*

AGATE: In gravels at Two Islands Beach.

*Two Harbors, Lake County*

AGATE: NE 11 miles in gravels at Gooseberry Falls State Park Beach.

*Virginia, St. Louis County\**

AGATE: Up a side road from U.S. 169 about 10 miles W of Virginia are the Atkins and the Wade mines. About 3 miles up this side road is a large spoil bank. On its W face Lake Superior agates can be dug.

Beyond and to the left of this spoil bank is another which contains the same type of agates along its S face.

JASPER: Take Hwy 135 from Virginia toward Biwabik, stop a mile short of Biwabik, take mine road marked "M.E." to Mary Ellen mine; look for jasper with swirl patterns on dump at this mine location. Finds have been reported there.

## MISSISSIPPI

Most of the state is built up of sand, gravel, and mud brought down by the Mississippi River and which has filled a great bay in the Gulf Coast. The surface rises from the Gulf Coast and the river toward the oldest sedimentary rocks in the state that form a ridge in the northeast counties. Thus, petrified wood and agates in river gravels are the only gem resources.

*Flora, Madison County*
PETRIFIED WOOD: At petrified forest SW.

*Gulfport, Harrison County*
PETRIFIED WOOD, JASPER: In Bell Creek, 18 miles NW and generally in creeks to NW.

*Natchez, Adams County*
PETRIFIED WOOD: Generally to E in area including Brookhaven, Monticello. Georgetown, Gatesville, McComb and as far E as Hattiesburg.

*Wesson, Copiah County*
AGATE: E 6 miles, in Bahala Creek.

E 4 miles, in gravel pit agate is found.

## MISSOURI

Missouri north of the Missouri River is, like most of Illinois and Iowa, a fertile plain formed by glacial action and underlain by sedimentary rocks. Southern Missouri, however, contains not only an area of rolling plains to the west, as in Arkansas, but also the Ozark Highland which becomes gradually rougher as it sweeps from southern Illinois southwestward into Arkansas and Oklahoma. These peaks and valleys expose not only sedimentary rocks but also granites.

*Creighton, Cass County*
PETRIFIED WOOD: In quarry on Cornett farm 3 miles E.

*Kahoka, Clark County*
QUARTZ GEODES. (See Warsaw, Ill.)

*LaGrange, Lewis County*
AGATE, PETRIFIED WOOD: In gravel pits along Mississippi River.

QUARTZ CRYSTALS, ROSE QUARTZ: Take U.S. 61 S to gravel road, turn left to quarry.

*Lincoln, Benton County*
JASPER (MOZARKITE): To E.

*Stanton, Franklin County*
RUTILATED QUARTZ: At Cherry Valley iron mine.

## MONTANA

The Rocky Mountains dominate the western part of Montana, crossing the state from northwest to southeast, and exposing a great variety of rocks. From them have come the gold, silver, copper, corundum, and other minerals which have caused Montana to be called the Treasure State. Eastward lie the high plains, sloping eastward, formed of erosional deposits and broken by bluffs, gullies and isolated mountains. In these areas are found moss agate and like materials.

*Alder, Madison County*

BANDED RHYOLITE (WONDER-STONE): Take dirt road along Ruby River from Alder 12 miles to right-hand fork. Take road 8 miles; collect by road NW toward Dillon.

ALMANDINE GARNET: In gravels of Ruby River above storage dam to S.

*Anaconda, Deer Lodge County*

AMAZONITE: N 3 miles at falls of Lost Creek.

*Bozeman, Gallatin County*

PETRIFIED WOOD: Fossil forest at headwaters of Buffalo Horn, Black Butte, and Specimen Creeks on Yellowstone-Gallatin divide in Gallatin range.

REDDISH OPAL: To S near top of Mount Blackmore.

*Butte, Silver Bow County*

AMETHYST: To E in Little Pipestone Creek.

W fork of Rader Creek.

At old Pohndorf mine reached by taking Hwy 10 E to 19 Mile Inn, then dirt road $1\frac{1}{2}$ miles N.

SMOKY QUARTZ: In pegmatites of Whisky Gulch N of Pohndorf mine.

SAPPHIRE: In Brown's Gulch to NW.

RHODONITE: In Alice mine dumps and at Lexington mine.

*Canyon Ferry Dam, Lewis and Clark County*

GREEN SAPPHIRE: At Magpie Gulch, 1 mile above in Missouri River.

*Deer Lodge, Powell County*

SAPPHIRE: To SE in Dry Cottonwood Creek.

*Dillon, Beaverhead County*

PETRIFIED WOOD: To NW in Frying Pan Basin.

STAR CORUNDUM: 18 miles SW in Sweetwater Creek on the Rebish ranch. (Ask permission.)

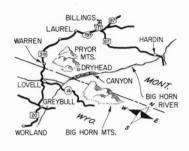

Three Mile Gulch.

*Lewistown, Fergus County*

SAPPHIRE: Near confluence of South and Middle forks of Judith River.

*Neihart, Cascade County*

GREEN SPHALERITE: In Hartley mine.

*Manhattan, Gallatin County*

ALABASTER (ONYX): 5 miles NW in quarry.

*Philipsburg, Granite County*

SAPPHIRE: Take U.S. Alt. 10 S to Porters Corners, W 17 miles on Hwy 38 to bridge over fork of Rock Creek, follow sign to collecting area.

Also at Bentz guest ranch 25 miles W.

QUARTZ CRYSTALS: In Granite Mountains.

RHODOCHROSITE: On dumps of Bimetallic mine.

*Sidney, Richland County\**

MOSS AGATES: Montana moss agates are found all the way from the Big Horn River upstream on the Yellowstone River to beyond Sidney near the North Dakota line. They are in old gravel beds, on bluffs, and in ravines below bluffs. West of Miles City, the best collecting seems to be S of the Yellowstone, but farther E

*Dryhead, Carbon County\**

AGATE: Take road N to ranch at foot of Pryor Gap. Agate is found on the rim rocks of the canyon where Dryhead Creek flows into the Big Horn River, and at the mouth of Big Horn Canyon. It is also scattered over much of the surrounding grazing area.

*Elkhorn Hot Springs, Beaverhead County*

QUARTZ CRYSTALS: N 4 miles at Crystal Park.

*Helena, Lewis and Clark County*

SAPPHIRE, GARNET: On the American, Eldorado, Emerald, French, Metropolitan, Ruby and Spokane bars in the Missouri River.

CHALCEDONY: E 3 miles.

PETRIFIED WOOD: NE 10 miles.

ROSE QUARTZ: SE 10 miles.

SMOKY QUARTZ: SE 3 miles at

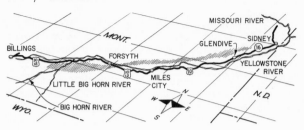

it ranges for 50 miles N of the river on ranches. Spring, when fresh supplies have been uncovered by winter snows and rain, is the best time to search, and the best agates are found far from the main roads in less heavily picked areas (agate areas are shown shaded on map).

*Sula, Ravalli County*
BERYL: In pegmatite 2 miles N.
*Twin Bridges, Madison County*
QUARTZ CRYSTALS: W at Crystal Butte.
*Utica, Judith Basin County*
SAPPHIRE: 11 miles SW by gravel road to Yogo Gulch at foot of Little Belt Mountains, sapphire-bearing dike runs 5 miles E from Yogo Gulch. (This location is a private claim.)

*Vaughn, Cascade County*
BLACK AGATE, PETRIFIED WOOD: Along U.S. 89 and 91 E and S look for black agate and petrified wood.
*Warren, Carbon County*
AGATE: N 5 miles, in the Pryor Mountains.
*Whitehall, Jefferson County*
SPHENE, SMOKY QUARTZ: 18 miles NW in Hay Canyon at the Gem Queen claim sphene and smoky quartz have been found.

## NEBRASKA

Nebraska is a plain sloping from northwest to southeast, including rich loess farm lands in the east backed by a region of sand hills to the west which lead into the more rugged bluffs, tablelands, and occasional mountains of the High Plains. In the extreme northwestern corner, Nebraska shares an area of badlands with South Dakota. Agates in stream gravels and petrified wood are the principal gem materials under such geological conditions.

*Bridgeport, Morrill County*
MOSS OPAL: Take Hwy 385 N to Angora Hill. Halfway up, turn E on dim road for 2 miles, then N up hill on another faintly marked road. Park here and walk to deposit on top of hill.

*Crawford, Dawes County*
RED JASPER: Take Hwy 2 for 20 miles NW toward Orella railroad station, turn W ½ mile S of station, cross tracks and drive into badlands 2 miles W. Collect in hills.

AGATE: Go ½ mile· beyond Orella and turn E for 2 miles to Bald Butte.

*Chappell, Deuel County*
PETRIFIED WOOD, JASPER: In nearby hills.

*Fremont, Dodge County*
AGATE: In gravels and pits along Platte River.

*Humboldt, Richardson County*
AGATE: Along Nemaha River agate has been found.

*Louisville, Cass County*
AGATE: In gravel pit to E. (Get permission from Lyman-Ritchie Gravel Co., Waterloo.)

*Valentine, Cherry County*
PETRIFIED WOOD: In streams.

*Waterloo, Douglas County*
AGATE: In Lyman-Ritchie gravel pit to SW. (Get permission.)

## NEVADA

Nevada is part of the Great Basin area of ancient sedimentary rocks that have been deformed and folded by granite intrusions, especially those associated with the Sierra Nevada uplift on the western edge of the state. Mineral occurrences are associated with the granite intrusions and the lavas. Much of the state is made up of arid plains and valleys broken by short mountain chains.

*Battle Mountain, Lander County*
CHALCEDONY, PETRIFIED WOOD:

Go N across Southern Pacific railroad tracks and continue 18 miles to windmill, then take E fork to bridge over Rock Creek and collect in and along creek.

CINNABAR: Continue 7 miles farther, take left fork N for cinnabar in chert (myrickite) in washes and at dumps of Silver Cloud mercury mine.

TURQUOISE: At No. 8 mine, 30 miles NE.

At Blue Gem mine and Pedro claim, 8 miles SW.

At Blue Matrix mine, 31 miles SE, near Tenabo.

CINNABAR IN OPAL: At mercury mine to S.

OBSIDIAN: NW 25 miles.

*Carlin, Elko County*

GREEN TURQUOISE (FAUSTITE): NW 10 miles at Copper King mine in Tuscarora Mountains.

*Coaldale, Esmeralda County*

TURQUOISE, VARISCITE: NE 4 miles at Bonnie Blue mine on W side of canyon.

JASPER: W 5 miles on Hwy 6, then N to collect on flats.

PETRIFIED WOOD, JASPER: E 6 miles to Hwy 47, turn N into Monte Cristo Mountains, collect in hills and ravines.

OBSIDIAN, CHALCEDONY: Take Hwy 6 for 6 miles W,

then S on Hwy 3A 8 miles, and take road E to Sump Hole.

PETRIFIED WOOD, AGATE: Take Hwy 6 $7\frac{1}{2}$ miles E, then N to Esmeralda Lake bed. From highway, take same side road but keep right 7 miles, watch for bluff; sagenitic agate is in debris from bluff face.

VARISCITE: In old diggings 5 miles NE on SW side of Monte Cristo Mountains.

To W in old silver workings.

*Cortez, Lander County*

TURQUOISE: At Fox and Smith mines.

At White Horse mine, $2\frac{1}{2}$ miles NW.

*Denio, Humboldt County*

FIRE OPAL: At Rainbow Ridge mine (private property) 30 miles on Hwy 8A, then S 7 miles to mine in Virgin Valley.

At Bonanza mine farther up Virgin Valley. (Fee.)

At Green Fire mine on E side of Virgin Valley.

COMMON YELLOW OPAL: At Virgin Valley ranch.

*Ely, White Pine County\**

GARNET: Take Hwy 50 NW from Ely for 5 miles, then right on a gravel road $\frac{7}{10}$ of a mile along the power

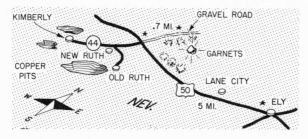

line into canyon. Go to summit on foot. The largest garnets are in rhyolite in area marked on map. They can be found by breaking the rhyolite or by searching in soil for those that have weathered out.

Canyons N from Lane City for a mile in either direction also contain garnet-bearing rhyolite.

BANDED RHYOLITE (WONDERSTONE): 40 miles W on U.S. 50 at Little Antelope summit.

*Fallon, Churchill County**

BANDED RHYOLITE (WONDERSTONE): Take U.S. 50 E and then SE for 11½ miles, turn off through dump and 2½ miles into saddle to gravel pit for banded rhyolite (wonderstone).

GREEN AGATE: Mile south of the above gravel pit.

RED AND YELLOW JASPER: Continue on to turnoff 32 miles S from Fallon on Hwy 50, 7 miles to road angling to E, take a branch road E 2½ miles

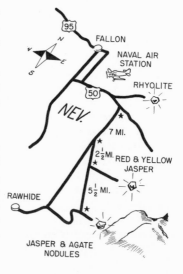

on and go to end for red and yellow jasper in weathered volcanic rock in canyon.

JASPER, AGATE NODULES: Come back to angling road and go 5½ miles to another branch road E. Take it into hills for jasper and agate nodules on hillsides.

*Fernley, Lyon County*

AGATE: On W side of Lake Lahontan and between lake and Fernley, 7½ miles S in hills E of U.S. 95A.

PETRIFIED WOOD, AGATE NODULES: NE on Hwy 95A for 15½ miles; collect on flats and low hills.

*Gabbs, Nye County*

PETRIFIED WOOD: N and S along Hwy 23 and to W of highway.

*Gerlach, Washoe County*

PETRIFIED WOOD: Hwy 34 N for 41 miles past Black Rock desert, turn left to site of Leadville.

13 miles N on Hwy 34, collect in ravine.

FIRE OPAL, OBSIDIAN NODULES: In volcanic ash 2½ miles farther N.

*Goldfield, Esmeralda County*

GREEN OPAL, AGATE: N on U.S. 95 2⅓ miles, then dirt

road W 3½ miles. (Fee.)

*Henderson, Clark County*

GREEN JASPER: E past manganese plant a scant quarter of a mile, then left a mile, park and walk to hill.

BANDED CHALCEDONY: S 2 miles, turn W across tracks and go 2 miles.

*Jarbidge, Elko County*

AGATE: Take road N along Jarbidge River to Jack Creek, then trail into canyon SE to seam agate deposit near fork in creek. (Get permission, Rene Sprague in Jarbidge.)

*Las Vegas, Clark County**

BLACK AGATE: Take U.S. 91 to turnoff road to Nellis Air Force Base, then 2½ miles to entry road to Lake Mead Base. Go SE to Base hobby shop, turn left on unpaved road 4½ miles, then right to a gypsum wash. Walk S through gypsum piles to black agate field.

RED JASPER, PINK OPAL NODULES: Go back to U.S. 91 and continue N to Crystal, turn E for 3⅓ miles, then take right fork toward Muddy Mountains and go 5 miles to entrance

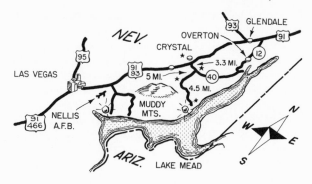

to a canyon. Continue 4½ miles more to area where red jasper and pink opal nodules are found.

AGATE, JASPER: Collect by boat in gravels of N shore of Lake Mead between Las Vegas and Callville Bays.

*Lovelock, Pershing County*
FIRE OPAL: W 10 miles in E flank of Trinity Range.

*Luning, Mineral County*
PINK THULITE, OPALIZED WOOD (HOWARDITE): Hwy 23 N almost to bridge, take left fork 34 miles to Rawhide, then 6 miles farther to ravine; collect in ash.

*Midas, Elko County*
CINNABAR IN OPAL: At Rand mine.

*Mill City, Pershing County*
AGATE GEODES: To S on Hwy 50 and then W to collect on E slope of Star Peak.

*Millers, Esmeralda County*
TURQUOISE: At Myers & Bona mine, 13 miles NW on W slope of Monte Cristo Mountains.

At Petry mine, 11 miles NW in foothills of Monte Cristo Mountains.

At Royal Blue mine, 12 miles NW on E edge of plateau.

*Mina, Mineral County*
SATIN SPAR: 3 miles S on Hwy 95, follow power line to mine.

TURQUOISE: At Nevada Turquoise Co. mine.

VARISCITE: Mile S of Candelaria and on E side of hill in Candelaria Mountains.

COPPER CUTTING MATERIALS: In dumps of Wilson mine near Candelaria.

*Oreana, Pershing County*
BLUE DUMORTIERITE: In quartz in Bullion Canyon.

*Paradise Valley, Humboldt County*

CHALCEDONY: At Coyote Springs.

FIRE OPAL: 22 miles N at Firestone opal mine.

*Reno, Washoe County*

CINNABAR IN OPAL: S on U.S. 395 to Steamboat, backtrack to macadam road, go W ½ mile and take dirt road left across bridge into canyon to road junction. Collect in hills above road.

*Rochester, Pershing County*

PINK DUMORTIERITE: At Lincoln Hill.

*Schurz, Mineral County*

PETRIFIED WOOD: W on dirt road 19 miles to cattle guard, S on faint road petrified wood has been found.

*Silver Peak, Esmeralda County*

OBSIDIAN: SE 10 miles.

*Sodaville, Mineral County*

VARISCITE: SW 8 miles at E end of Excelsior Mountains.

*Tonopah, Nye County*

TURQUOISE: At Smith Black Matrix mine, 3 miles NE.

GREEN MOSS AGATE: W 26 miles on Hwy 6, N on Gilbert Road into canyon. Park at right-hand wash off canyon. Collect there and in hills to right.

OBSIDIAN: W on Hwy 6 to Hwy 3A, 5⅕ miles and take E fork 2 miles straight ahead to collect in Fish Lake Valley.

*Wendover, Elko County*

CHALCEDONY: Hwy Alternate 50 S 38 miles, turn right at sign to Victoria, go N 12 miles to mine dumps.

*Yerington, Lyon County*

TURQUOISE: NW and W of Walker River 8 miles, and 2 miles NW in Walker River Valley.

## NEW HAMPSHIRE

The White Mountains of the Appalachians are the dominating geographical feature of New Hampshire. They occupy the north-central part of the state, an area of noteworthy mineral occurrences but of poor, thin soil. Above the mountains is a region of ridges and valleys and south of them is the plateau characteristic of the New England upland. Glaciers have stripped the rocky granite highlands and created many lakes.

*Acworth, Sullivan County*

BROWN BERYL: At mine dump on W side of Beryl Mountain.

*Alexandria, Grafton County*

BERYL: In mine dump at 2,000 ft. level on N side of Hutchins Hill.

*Berlin, Coos County*

JASPER: At cave W of trail and at 1,200 ft. level on S side of Jasper Mountain.

*Center Strafford, Strafford County*

BLUE BERYL, APATITE: At Foss mica mine mile NW.

At Parker Mountain mine on Blue Hill.

*Chatham, Carroll County*

BROWN AND BLUE TOPAZ, PHENACITE, AMAZONITE: At 2,900 ft. level on E side of South Baldface Mountain, in pockets where pegmatites meet talus slope.

*Concord, Merrimack County*

SMOKY QUARTZ: In Crowley granite quarry.

RUTILATED QUARTZ: In New England Granite Works.

*Conway, Carroll County*

AMETHYST: At Redstone granite quarry, E of Hwy 302 between Conway and North Conway.

At White Mountain granite quarry, at 700 ft. level on W side of Birch Hill.

TOPAZ, SMOKY QUARTZ, AMAZONITE: NW $2\frac{1}{2}$ miles at Lovejoy Pit.

AMETHYST, SMOKY QUARTZ, QUARTZ CRYSTALS: On ledges on Hurricane Mountain. Take trail from top $\frac{1}{4}$ mile W, then follow old road.

*Danbury, Merrimack County*

BERYL: At Wild Meadows mine.

*Eaton Center, Carroll County*

SMOKY QUARTZ: NE 2 miles at Randall lead mine.

*Enfield, Grafton County*

QUARTZ CRYSTALS WITH EPIDOTE INCLUSIONS: At Shaker Hill granite quarry.

*Fitzwilliam, Cheshire County*

RUTILATED QUARTZ: At Victoria White and Webb-Fitzwilliam granite quarries.

*Franconia, Grafton County*

JASPER: In Ammonoosuc River.

*Gilmanton, Belknap County*

QUARTZ CRYSTALS: In Shellcamp Road.

*Gilsum, Cheshire County*

GOLDEN AND BLUE BERYL: North of Gilsum along W side of road to Mill Hollow is a group of mines where golden and blue beryl has been found on dumps:

At the Blister mine.

At the Davis mine, ¾ mile N of Mica Mine School.

At the Island mine, W of school on knoll between swamp and pond.

At the Big mine, N of school.

At the Golding-Keene mine, NW of the Big mine.

S of Gilsum on E side of Hwy 10 at the J. White mine.

*Grafton, Grafton County*

BLUE BERYL: In dumps of mine 3 miles SW on E side of Melvin Hill.

BLUE AND GOLDEN BERYL: At Kilton mine, reached via Ruggles Mine Road, crossing Manfeltree Brook, keeping right and then ¾ mile NE.

At Ruggles mine on Isinglass Hill, reached by taking direct road W from Grafton Center 1½ miles to crossroads, then right across brook and up hill.

At Sargent mine, on N end of Horse Hill, reached by driving to top and taking ridge trail on foot.

BLUE BERYL, ROSE AND SMOKY QUARTZ: At Alger mine, reached by taking road S

where Ruggles Mine Road leaves Grafton Road and going mile.

*Hanover, Grafton County*

RUTILATED QUARTZ: At Moose Mountain.

*Haverhill, Grafton County*

QUARTZ CRYSTALS: In limonite at Black Mountain.

*Hebron, Grafton County*

BERYL, LEPIDOLITE: SW 2 miles at mine dump on E side of Hobart Hill.

*Hinsdale, Cheshire County*

PINK RHODONITE: Mile SE near Ashuelot River.

*Keene, Cheshire County*

BERYL: NE 5 miles ..i pegmatite of Bassett Hill.

4½ miles E at Horse Hill.

BERYL, SMOKY AND ROSE QUARTZ: At Keene granite quarry 3 miles SE.

*Lincoln, Grafton County*

AMETHYST: On upper slopes of Mount Nancy.

*Littleton, Grafton County*

STAUROLITE: On hill ¾ mile W of Garnet Hill.

*Marlboro, Cheshire County*

ALMANDINE GARNET: Mile S at Webb granite quarry.

*Marlow, Cheshire County*

GREEN TOURMALINE: At Turner mine.

ROSE AND SMOKY QUARTZ: In E cut of Windham mine.

*Milan, Coos County*

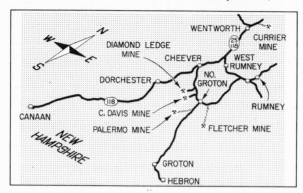

AMETHYST, TOPAZ: To W and 3 miles S at 1,700 foot level of Green's Ledge.

*Milford, Hillsboro County*

RUTILATED QUARTZ: In Bishop and Carlton granite quarries 2 miles NW.

In Connoli granite quarry 3½ miles SW.

In Kittridge granite quarry 1½ miles SW.

*Newport, Sullivan County*

BERYL: At G. F. Smith mine and 3 miles E at Young's Hill.

*North Groton, Grafton County\**

BERYL, QUARTZ CRYSTALS, ROSE QUARTZ: At the Palermo mine, reached via the first dirt road to the SW to the E of the town. Lazulite also found here.

At the Rice mine on the same road.

At the Charles Davis mine. About ¾ mile W of North Groton, the dirt road S from the Cheever Road leads to the mine. Lazulite here, too.

At the Diamond Ledge mine, reached by a road a mile W of North Groton leading from the Cheever Road.

At the Mica Products mine located on a hillside a quarter mile W of the Davis mine.

At the Fletcher mine. Take the Rumney Road but turn off on a side road up Fletcher Mountain and go 1¼ miles.

BERYL, APATITE: At the Valencia mine, located on the next hill NW of the

Fletcher mine.

*Orange, Grafton County*
BERYL: At Keyes Mine.
Mile NE at Pinnacle Mine.

*Orford, Grafton County*
STAUROLITE: On Strawberry and Blackberry Hills.

*Ossipee, Carroll County*
SMOKY QUARTZ: In ledge S of road at Passaconway quarry near Albany.

*Percy, Coos County*
AMETHYST: On W slope of Hutchins Mountain.
TOPAZ: NW $1\frac{3}{4}$ miles at Victors Head.

*Raymond, Rockingham County*
PINK BERYL, TOURMALINE, ROSE QUARTZ: W 2 miles at Chandler Mine.
QUARTZ CRYSTALS: In boulders on ridge just N of Raymond-Nottingham town line and W of road.

*Richmond, Cheshire County*
IOLITE: In Richmond soapstone quarry.

*Rumney, Grafton County*
BERYL: At Belden mine.

*Springfield, Sullivan County*
GOLDEN BERYL, AMETHYST, SMOKY QUARTZ: At Columbia gem mine on N end of Springfield Mountain.
AMETHYST, QUARTZ CRYSTALS: In soil at George Hill.
BERYL, SPESSARTITE GARNET:

At S end of Melvin Hill in ledge on Joe Hill farm.
GREEN BERYL: At Playter mine on S end of Pillsbury Ridge.
BLUE BERYL, GARNET, QUARTZ CRYSTALS: At Reynolds mine near top of NE slope of Robinson Hill.
At Davenport mine just below.
AMETHYST, SMOKY QUARTZ CRYSTALS: At Diamond Ledges on Long Mountain.

*Stratford, Coos County*
AMETHYST: Along road near Sugarloaf.

*Sugar Hill, Grafton County*
GREEN QUARTZ: S $1\frac{1}{2}$ miles at Franconia iron mine.
STAUROLITE: In slate near Franconia iron mine, S of summit of Ore Hill.

*Sunapee, Sullivan County*
RUTILATED QUARTZ: At Perry Sunapee quarry.
At Spectacle Pond quarry.

*Wakefield, Carroll County*
BLUE BERYL: At Weeks mine $\frac{1}{2}$ mile W of Province Lake.

*Walpole, Cheshire County*
ROSE QUARTZ: At Howe Lodge on W side of Derry Hill.

*Warner, Merrimack County*
ROSE QUARTZ: Near top of Mount Kearsarge.

*Warren, Grafton County*
GOLDEN BERYL, QUARTZ CRYS-
  TALS: SW 1½ miles on
  SW side of Beech Hill.
*Wentworth, Grafton County*
BERYL: At the Currier mine.
  Take Hwy 25 N past rail-
  road tracks, then first dirt
  road right ¾ mile. Park.
  (Ask permission to collect
  at houses nearby and take
  road through fields to
  mine.)
*West Lebanon, Grafton County*

RUTILATED QUARTZ PEBBLES:
  In Connecticut River.
*Westmoreland, Cheshire
  County*
AMETHYST, QUARTZ CRYSTALS:
  At Stoddard mine.
STAUROLITE: At Park Hill.
*Wilmot Flat, Merrimack
  County*
BERYL: In mine dumps at
  Stuart Hill.
*Winchester, Cheshire County*
RHODONITE: Near top of Stony
  Mountain.

## NEW JERSEY

The northwest corner of New Jersey contains the famous
Delaware Water Gap, where the river has cut through the
Kittatinny mountain range of the Appalachians. Southeast of
these mountains is a belt of ridgeland known as the Highlands,
and paralleling it is a lowland marked by traprock ridges,
such as the Watchung Mountains and the Palisades on the
Hudson. Southeast New Jersey is coastal plain, much of it
marsh. Glacial terminal moraines cross the central part of
the state.

*Bound Brook, Somerset County*
AGATE, AMETHYST, JASPER: At
  the New England quarry.
*Cape May, Cape May County*
QUARTZ CRYSTALS WITH HER-
  MATITE INCLUSIONS: In
  beach gravels.
*Dover, Morris County*
SUNSTONE: In Alan Wood iron
  mine dumps on Mine
  Hill.

*Franklin, Sussex County*
RHODONITE (FOWLERITE), IDO-
  CRASE (CYPRINE): In
  dumps of New Jersey Zinc
  Company mines. Best are
  Buckwheat dump outside
  Franklin and the nearby
  Parker dump.
BLUE APATITE: In Atlas quarry.
*Montville, Morris County**
YELLOW AND GREEN TRANS-

LUCENT SERPENTINE: A short distance W of Montville on U.S. 202 is a sign for Valhalla Lake. Turn up this side road and up a hill to a left turn between two stone gate posts marked Valhalla Lake. Continue on hardtop road N and around lake for a mile to a brook. Park here and walk up a wagon road parallel to brook to a fork. Take left-hand trail for 130 paces. Here, a faint trail leads to the left. Follow it $\frac{1}{4}$ mile to the top of the mountain and to a large white boulder. The dump is a few feet beyond. The area is known as Turkey Hill. The quarry was worked for limestone, and yellow to green translucent serpentine was discarded on the dump where it can now be found.

*Neptune City, Monmouth County*
AMBER: In marl along Shark River.

*Paterson, Passaic County*
AMETHYST, SMOKY QUARTZ: At Prospect Park quarry.

*Phillipsburg, Warren County*
GREEN SERPENTINE: At Royal Green marble quarry. Go NE to Harmony, take road to right marked Harmony Station, go 2 miles to quarry dumps. (Get permission for week-end collecting.)

*Trenton, Mercer County*
BLACK JASPER: N 9 miles on Hwy 29 in Delaware River at Washington Crossing State Park.
AMBER: To S in Crosswicks Creek.

*Watchung, Somerset County\**
CARNELIAN, QUARTZ CRYSTAL: Route 512 from Summit intersects the road S to

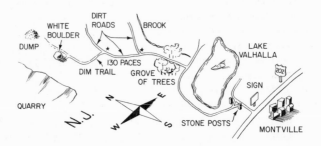

WHITE BOULDER · DUMP · DIRT ROADS · BROOK · 130 PACES · DIM TRAIL · GROVE OF TREES · QUARRY · N.J. · LAKE VALHALLA · 202 · SIGN · STONE POSTS · MONTVILLE

Watchung just E of the road N to Stirling. By turning S on the Watchung Road and crossing the Passaic River, it is possible to go almost 2 miles

toward Watchung to a power line over the road, then past a tavern beside a brook. Park here and follow the brook S ¼ mile. Dig in the green sand of the brook, and about 18 inches down pieces of carnelian and quartz crystal will be found. It is convenient to dam off a bit of the bank, dig, and wash the sand for the carnelian in a screen with a wooden frame.

## NEW MEXICO

New Mexico lies at the southern end of the Rocky Mountains, the Sangre de Cristo range extending down into the state from Colorado. Through the central part of the state, short chains of mountains run to the Mexican border, while another group parallels the Rio Grande River to the west. Plateaus cut by canyons form the borders with Texas and Arizona, and long plateaus lie between the central mountains. New Mexico owes its great variety of mineral and gem wealth to these exposures of many kinds of rock.

*Abiquiu, Rio Arriba County*
AGATE, PETRIFIED WOOD: Along Chama River and in hills ¼ mile N.

*Afton, Dona Ana County*
PERIDOT: Cross railroad to S and take road E along railroad almost 6 miles, turn S 2¼ miles to ranch house and continue 5 miles more S to Kilbourne Hole. Collect in basalt rim or in sand inside crater. (Get permission at ranch.)

*Albuquerque, Bernalillo County*
PETRIFIED WOOD: W on west mesa ½ mile.
W on U.S. 66 11 miles to

filling station and S ½ mile on ridges.

UNAKITE: Along U.S. 66 on S slopes of Sandia Mountains to Tijeras.

*Ancho, Lincoln County*

JASPER: N 2 miles.

*Artesia, Eddy County*\*

QUARTZ CRYSTALS (PECOS "DIAMONDS"): Take Hwy 83 ½ mile past bridge over Pecos River, turn S along river on ranch road and collect in low hills and washes near river.

*Buell Park, McKinley County*\*

PYROPE GARNET, PERIDOT: The garnet area extends into three states.

Garnet Ridge lies close to the Utah border, and a few miles W of Mexican Water, Apache County, Arizona.

Ten miles N of Mexican Water, in San Juan County, Utah, is the Moses Rock field.

Best known of the areas, however, is Buell Park, a

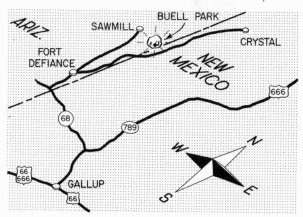

basin almost on the Arizona–New Mexico line and 10 miles N of Ft. Defiance. The garnets and peridot are found in the soil, and, to a lesser degree, W and N of Red Lake, and E to the edge of the Nacimiento desert. (Permission to collect in Indian reservation should be obtained at Chinle or Window Rock.)

*Caballo, Sierra County*

RHODONITE: Take Hwy 90 W to Hillsboro and collect at Comstock mine 10 miles W.

*Cebolla, Rio Arriba County*

AGATE NODULES: In canyon to E, take dirt road 2 miles S of Cebolla.

*Cerrillos, Santa Fe County*

PETRIFIED WOOD: At Sweet's ranch 3 miles E.

TURQUOISE: Take Hwy 10 S for 12 miles, turn on to dirt road to dumps W at Mt. Chalchihuitl and to N at Castilian and Tiffany mines. (May be off limits.)

*Cochiti Pueblo, Sandoval County*

OBSIDIAN NODULES: Take dirt road 8 miles NW at base of Tent Rocks. Collect in canyon.

*Columbus, Luna County*

HONEY ONYX: At mine 4 miles W.

PURPLE AGATE: W on Hwy 9 20 miles and collect just E of railroad station in Hermanas.

DUMORTIERITE: In quartz, 13 miles NW in Tres Hermanas Mountains.

*Coyote, Rio Arriba County*

AGATE: On both sides of Hwy 96, 2 miles E.

*Cuba, Sandoval County*

PETRIFIED WOOD: Along Hwy 44 to W and to S in Rio Puerco River.

JASPER: Just N of Chaco Canyon National Monument jasper is found.

*Deming, Luna County*

AGATE NODULES: Generally to S between Florida and Little Florida Mountains. Specific locations follow (most of these charge fees for collecting):

On Spanish Stirrup guest ranch to E.

On Spaulding property to SE.

At Baker ranch.

At the Lindberg claims.

CARNELIAN: Take U.S. 260 N to Hwy 26; go E for 5 miles and then N for 5 miles, hunt in hills E of road and S of Cook's Peak for carnelian.

*Elephant Butte Dam, Sierra County*

YELLOW AND BROWN PETRIFIED WOOD: In swamp at S end of reservoir.

*Engle, Sierra County*

TUBE AGATE: W 8 miles N on side of railroad tracks.

PETRIFIED WOOD: In hills ½ mile W near road.

CARNELIAN: Go 13 miles S to Aleman ranch, circle around buildings and go W across railroad tracks and into hills to collect.

*Fra Cristobal Range, Sierra County*

OPALIZED WOOD: In N end of range.

*Galisteo, Santa Fe County*

JASPER: Can be found along Galisteo River near Kennedy.

*Glorieta, Santa Fe County*

PETRIFIED WOOD: Along Glorieta River.

*Hachita, Grant County*

MOSS OPAL, AGATE: To SW at Playas Dry Lake.

TURQUOISE: At Turquoise Mountain 6 miles W.

*Hatch, Dona Ana County*

RED, GREEN JASPER: Take Hwy 26 E to dirt road, N across tracks and into canyon. Hunt on hills to E and beyond canyon.

MOSS OPAL: Drive S, then hike to diversion dam and dig opal from seams in side of arroyo.

OPALIZED WOOD: To W of

Hatch over wide area N and W.

GREEN ALABASTER (ONYX): S 1½ miles on Mammoth Creek.

*Laguna, Valencia County*

AGATE: Along Rio San Jose.

*Las Cruces, Dona Ana County*

PETRIFIED WOOD: Along Hwy 478 S.

To W of Mesilla.

*Lordsburg, Hidalgo County*

AGATE NODULES: NW on U.S. 70 10 miles, turn W at ranch sign, go 20 miles to ranch house for permission to collect N about 3 miles.

*Los Lunas, Valencia County*

RED AGATE, JASPER: W on Hwy 6 16 miles. Collect along E side of river and to N of road.

OBSIDIAN NODULES, JASPER: W 6 miles, on Hwy 6, then S and keeping to right 6 miles to collect in hills.

*Luna, Catron County*

BANDED AGATE, AMETHYST GEODES: To W along U.S. 260. Collect N of road and as far W as creek.

*Magdalena, Socorro County*

BLUE SMITHSONITE: On dumps of Kelly Mine 3 miles SE.

PETRIFIED PALM WOOD: Take road N for 16 miles, then left on ranch road through ranch yard and 6 miles farther to collect in Bear Mountains area.

MOSS AGATE: Go 20 miles W on U.S. 60, then S 9 miles and turn right and go 27 miles to Farr ranch.

*Petaca, Rio Arriba County*

BLUE BERYL: At Sunnyside Mine 3 miles S.

AMAZONITE: Take road to La Madera S for 3½ miles and then W for 1½ miles; collect in dump of old Cribbensville Mine to collect amazonite.

*Pilar, Taos County**

STAUROLITES, GARNETS: Just N of the hamlet of Pilar on the left side of Hwy 64 is a sign pointing out the Rio Grande River Gorge. Continue 2 miles past this sign, then turn right into a dirt road and go 3 miles to a big sawdust heap. Park and take right-hand trail into Hondo Canyon. In this canyon and those to the S (Piedras Lumbres, Tierra Amarila and Agua Caliente Canyons) staurolites are plentiful in the schist, along with small garnets. (Map follows.)

THULITE: In pegmatite, just S

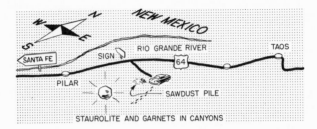

of Pilar on E bank of Rio Grande.

*Portales, Roosevelt County*

PETRIFIED WOOD: SW 68 miles on Hwy 70 to Bob Crosby Draw, go back 2½ miles and take dirt road S into Bitterlake wildlife refuge. Collect in hills.

*Quemado, Catron County*

CHALCEDONY ROSES, PETRIFIED WOOD: N 40 miles at Zuni Salt Lake.

*Radium Springs, Dona Ana County*

OPAL NODULES, SEAM OPAL: To N in Broad Canyon W of Hwy 85.

*Ramon, Lincoln County*

AGATE, JASPER: E 8 miles.

*Redrock, Grant County*

SERPENTINE (RICOLITE): Take road N across Gila River to first road E, follow it for 3 miles to canyon. A half mile W of main vein of green serpentine is one of yellow serpentine.

*Reserve, Catron County*\*

BANDED AGATE: Take Hwy 12 for 11 miles NE to Apache Creek; then take Hwy 12 N for 5 miles to national forest fence. Park above fence, take trail to left to Lee Russell Canyon until

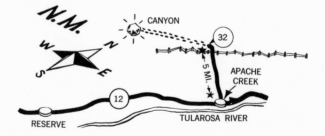

it widens out into a flat, which is the best collecting area.

MOONSTONE: In headwaters of San Francisco River, 18 miles E of Arizona line.

*Rincon, Dona Ana County*

BANDED JASPER: Go N on W side of railroad and into hills toward television tower. Collect at cattle guard.

*Roswell, Chaves County* (map, p. 190)

QUARTZ CRYSTALS (PECOS "DIAMONDS"): Pecos R. halfway N to Ft. Sumner; halfway south to Carlsbad.

*Socorro, Socorro County*

DENDRITIC AGATE: Take U.S. 85 N for 13 miles to San Acacia, then road W into hills.

MOONSTONE: 'To SW in San Mateo Mountains.

AMETHYST: Take U.S. 85 N across Rio Salado, follow ranch roads W, and collect on SW slopes of Ladrones Peak.

OPALIZED WOOD: Continue N past the Rio Salado, and turn W before crossing Rio Puerco. Bear left around Ladrones Peak after crossing cattle guard, passing broken windmill

and cow skull nailed to tree, and go 1½ miles farther. Collect on both sides of road.

*Truth and Consequences, Sierra County*

AGATE, CARNELIAN: To S on W side of Caballo Mountains.

JASPER, AGATE, OPALIZED WOOD: E 13 miles in Jornado Valley.

OPALIZED WOOD: Along Rio Grande River to N at Nogal Canyon.

AGATE: Take U.S. 85 S to Hwy 180, turn W through Hillsboro and just past Perchas Creek to collect N of road on side and top of mountain.

BANDED RHYOLITE (WONDERSTONE): Take road into arroyo past television tower on hill.

*Tyrone, Grant County*

TURQUOISE: In mine dumps all the way S to Leopold.

*Valle Grande, Sandoval County*

OBSIDIAN: In headwaters of Jemez River.

*Wagon Mound, Mora County*

AGATE, JASPER: Few miles E.

*Winston, Sierra County*

AMETHYSTINE QUARTZ: In Montezuma mine dumps at Chloride.

## NEW YORK

More than half of New York state is a plateau sweeping down from the Adirondacks in the northeast and underlain by very old sedimentary rocks. The Adirondacks, however, are formed of crystalline rocks like the Laurentians in Canada. The central plateau rises from Lake Erie and Lake Ontario, becoming mountainous in the south and east, where the Appalachians enter the state, and where the plateau has been carved into the Catskill Mountains. The topography of lower New York is like that of New Jersey, except that Long Island is a part of the coastal plain.

*Bedford, Westchester County*
ASTERIATED ROSE QUARTZ: Take Hwy 22 S, turn off on road to Greenwich, Conn., take first dirt road N and follow around old quarry to dump at mill ruins.

*Blooming Grove, Orange County*
BLOODSTONE: To S on Hwy 94 at Craigsville.

*Brant Lake, Warren County*
BROWN TOURMALINE: In road cut on S shore.

*Fowler, St. Lawrence County*
SERPENTINE: S to Balmat, collect at International Talc Co. quarry. (Ask permission.)

*Johnsburg, Warren County*
SERPENTINE: In asbestos mine to SW at Garnet Lake.

*Mineville, Essex County*
SUNSTONE: At Fisher Hill Mine.

*Newcomb, Essex County*
PERISTERITE, BROWN TOURMALINE: On S shore of Lake Harris.

*North Creek, Warren County*
ALMANDINE GARNET: Take Hwy 28 N for 4 miles, turn at Barton Mines sign, go 5 miles up Gore Mountain to shop.

*Port Henry, Essex County*
ROSE QUARTZ: NW 6 miles.

*Port Kent, Essex County*
LABRADORITE: Along shore to S.

*Richville, St. Lawrence County*
BROWN TOURMALINE: On Reese farm and to N and NE.

*Salisbury, Herkimer County**
QUARTZ CRYSTALS ("HERKIMER DIAMONDS"): Found in the Little Falls dolomite, which is exposed in Herkimer County around

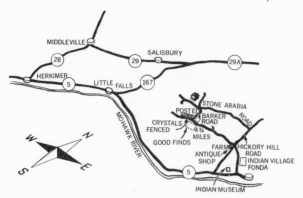

Middleville, around Little Falls, and at Salisbury particularly, but also at other places in the area. The crystals occur in pockets in the stone and loose in the soil where they have weathered out.

At Little Falls, there is a great cliff of the dolomite along the Mohawk River as it cuts through the city.

At Middleville, West Canada Creek and its tributaries have cut the dolomite to the S and along Hwy 28.

Salisbury's Diamond Hill is another well-known collecting spot.

A number of locations lie S and W of Fonda. Take Hwy 5 W for ½ mile, turn right on Hickory Hill Road for about 5 miles to Barker Road, a dirt road. Digging areas can be found near dolomite outcrops in the field S and W of the road intersection, and in field NE of it. Continue N on Barker Road 5 miles to Stone Arabia Road, a paved road, and left on it a half mile until an opening appears in bushes into field to S. Dig on tree covered slope and top (fee).

S of Fonda on Hwy 55 is Sprakers. Quartz crystals are found in fields in this area.

*Saratoga Springs, Saratoga County*

CHRYSOBERYL: In pegmatite dike, 12 miles W of road intersection on Hwy 9 N of Saratoga Springs.

QUARTZ CRYSTALS: In Maple Avenue Quarry.
*Wells, Hamilton County*
LABRADORITE: In anorthosite boulders to N along Hwy 8 in E branch of Sacandaga River labradorite has been found.

## NORTH CAROLINA

The eastern half of North Carolina is the low-lying coastal plain extending to the fall line, which divides it from the Piedmont plateau, a somewhat elevated level region containing the principal cities of the state. In the western part of the state the Blue Ridge escarpment rises abruptly to define the Appalachian Mountains, which in North Carolina form the greatest mountain mass in the eastern United States. In the varied rocks of these mountains are found most of the gem minerals in the state.

*Bakersville, Mitchell County*
GREEN FELDSPAR, THULITE, MOONSTONE: At Hawk Mine.
UNAKITE: N 10 miles at Roan Mountain.
SUNSTONE: A mile N at Meadlock Mountain.
CYANITE: SE 4 miles on Hwy 226 in quartz near top of Yellow Mountain.

*Bluff, Madison County*
UNAKITE: On Roaring Fork Creek, ½ mile W of its junction with Meadow Fork, 2 miles SW of Bluff; also ⅓ mile N of Bluff.
*Brasstown, Clay County\**
STAUROLITE: This well-known deposit of staurolite (fairy stones) is now easily accessible to collectors.

Good and perfect crystals are found in the bank of the gravel road and in the adjoining pasture land. Matrix specimens occur in great quantity over the mountainside woodland. The crystals are mostly single or oblique angle twins but occasionally good right angle twins are found. Staurolite also occurs at other places along the same belt in this area but is not so easily accessible and, being in the woodland, is not so easily found. (The property is owned by Robert Trout. Get permission to collect at places other than in the road bank.)

*Buck Creek Area, Clay County**

RUBY IN SMARAGDITE: A rock composed of anorthite feldspar and grass-green hornblende with ruby corundum, for which North Carolina is famous, comes from the Buck Creek area in Clay County. From Franklin, go SW on Hwy 64 to Rainbow Springs and then 9 miles to bridge where Buck Creek crosses hwy. Turn right at bridge

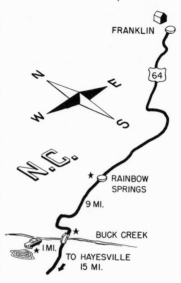

and go mile to where Buck Creek Road crosses another bridge. Park here and hike 1½ to 2 miles up mountain. Outcrops of ruby and smaragdite are found in many places on the mountain.

*Burnsville, Yancey County**

AQUAMARINE, GOLDEN AND GREEN BERYL, AMAZONITE: The best aquamarine in North Carolina comes from the Ray Mine. With it is golden and green beryl and good amazonite. From Burnsville go E on Hwy 19E to traffic

light opposite a funeral home. Turn S toward Pensacola for 1½ miles to a fork. Take left fork and go 1½ miles to a church on right-hand side of road. Opposite this church, a jeep road leads one mile to the mine.

THULITE: (*) Go 8 miles E on U.S. 19E to county line bridge over Crabtree Creek. Turn S on Crabtree Road 3 miles to sharp left turn; turn right here onto dirt road ¾ mile to Number 20 Mine for thulite.

BERYL, THULITE, AMAZONITE: Return to Crabtree Road and continue 3 miles E and S to bridge where pavement ends; turn left on dirt road 100 yards to McKinney Mine for amazonite, massive beryl and red thulite.

EMERALD: Continue on road to fork 2 miles, at church keep left a mile to end of

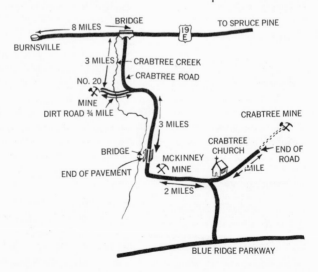

road, and hike 2 miles to Crabtree Emerald Mine to collect in dumps. (Fee.)

*Cashiers, Jackson County*

SAPPHIRE: SE 7 miles at White-water River to Whitewater Mine.

RUBY: E 7 miles near Sapphire Lake at Bad Creek Mine.

*Casar, Cleveland County*

RUTILATED QUARTZ: In soil 2 miles W.

*Charlotte, Mecklenburg County*

GRANITE (LEOPARDITE): E 1½ miles in dike in granite at Belmont Springs.

*Cowee Creek Area, Macon County**

RUBY, SAPPHIRE, GARNET: The Cowee Creek area NW of Franklin is the best for corundum gems in North Carolina. Rubies, lilac, pink and blue sapphire are found here, as well as rhodolite garnet. Go NW

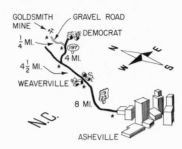

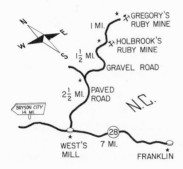

from Franklin 7 miles until the Cowee Creek Road is reached at West's Mill. Turn right and go 2½ miles to mine signs, which point to a gravel road. Go 1½ miles on this road to Holbrook's Mine and a mile farther to Gregory's Mine.

*Democrat, Buncombe County**

MOONSTONE: Moonstone with a good blue flash is found in the Goldsmith Mine. From traffic light in Weaverville, go N on Hwy 19-23 for 4½ miles to junction with Hwy 197. Go E on Hwy 197 exactly 4 miles and turn N on gravel road ¼ mile to mine.

*Franklin, Macon County**

RUBY, SAPPHIRE: Take Hwy 28 N 7 miles to West's Mill, follow "Gibson's Ruby Mine" signs (fee charged).

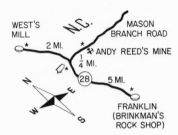

Also take Hwy 28 N 4 miles to Burningtown Road, turn W 8 miles to Roy Mason's Mine.

CORUNDUM, APATITE: SE 6 miles on Hwy 28 (1¼ miles NW of Gneiss) to the Culsagee Mine at Corundum Hill. (Difficult to get permission.)

PYROPE GARNET: In valley SW on Hwy 64 through Rainbow Springs, then 8 miles farther to Buck Creek.

MOONSTONE: N 5 miles on Hwy 28, right to head of valley to Mason Mountain.

AMETHYST, AQUAMARINE: S on Hwy 441 to Otto, E to Long and Connally Mines at Tessentee Creek.

Aquamarine also, 10 miles E at Sheep Knob Mountain.

GARNET, SAPPHIRE: The most reliable location for rhodolite garnet, one of the distinctive North Carolina minerals, is at the Reed or Mason Branch Mine.

Sapphire is also found in this area. Take Hwy 28 NW from Franklin 5 miles to Mason Branch sign pointing to Andy Reed's Mine. Take road ¼ mile to mine.

*Hiddenite, Alexander County*
GREEN SPODUMENE: Found N a mile on Warren farm.

Also, with emerald 1½ miles SE of Hiddenite, and ½ mile W and S of Hwy 90. Collect in dumps. (Fee.)

*Lexington, Davidson County*
GRANITE (LEOPARDITE): W 10 miles at Oaks Ferry on Yadkin River and at Hairston Farm.

*Marshall, Madison County*
ALMANDINE GARNET: N 6 miles on Redmon Dam Road. Cross dam, turn right, go to forks, take left fork to Lone Pine Mine.

*Morganton, Burke County*
ALMANDINE GARNET: In schist along Laurel Creek 8 miles SE.

*Shelby, Cleveland County*
EMERALD, RUTILATED QUARTZ: SW 5 miles near Broad River at Turner Mine.

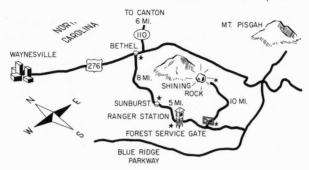

### Shining Rock, Haywood County*

QUARTZ: The only noteworthy rose quartz locality in North Carolina is on Shining Rock ledge in Haywood County, a place of scenic beauty as well as a good collecting area. The quartz boulders are in rhododendron thickets. Drive E from Waynesville 7 miles on Hwy 276 to Bethel. Go S 8 miles to Sunburst and then 5 miles farther S to U.S. Forest Ranger Station. Get permit and key to Forest Service Road here and drive 10 miles to Shining Rock, a knob of pure quartz.

### Spruce Pine, Mitchell County*

AQUAMARINE: The Grassy Creek Mine near Spruce Pine has been a producer of fine aquamarine. Go S from Spruce Pine on Hwy 226 for 3 miles, turn left at church on dirt road

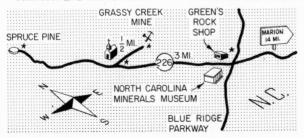

and go ½ mile to mine.
Also found at the Wiseman
Mine near Flatrock.
CYANITE: In soil of Young
farm.
*Statesville, Iredell County*
AMETHYST: S 11 miles on Hwy
21, on both sides of Hwy
in ditches and fields at
Shepherd's School House.
Also found on farms, 7 miles
S on Hwy 21, turn E at
Oswalt, go 6 miles, to
Amity Hill.

## NORTH DAKOTA

Eastern North Dakota lies in the level bed of the ancient
Lake Agassiz, an area of rich farm land. To the west is a
hilly plain, ridged with glacial moraines and dotted with lakes.
An abruptly rising ridge separates this area from western
North Dakota, which is part of the Missouri plateau, an almost unglaciated region of buttes and coulees culminating
in the picturesque badlands. Petrified wood is found in the
sandstones of the plateau, often associated with other quartz
minerals.

*Mandan, Morton County*
PETRIFIED WOOD, AGATE:
Worm-bored petrified
wood and agate in gravel
pits.
*Medora, Billings County*
PETRIFIED WOOD: In canyons S.
*Richardton, Stark County*
CHALCEDONY: S 25 miles.

*Watford City, McKenzie
County*
MOSS AGATE: In gravel pit ¾
mile E.
*Williston, Williams County*
MOSS AGATE, CHALCEDONY: On
river bank near Hwy 85
moss agate and chalced-
ony have been found.

## OHIO

Limestones and other sedimentary rocks underlie the
state. They arch upward toward the west so that progressively
younger rocks are exposed from west to east across the state.
Most of the upper part of the state shows the typical appear-

ance of Midwestern glaciation. Fossils are abundant but, with one exception, gem minerals are few and are difficult to find.

*Flint Ridge\**

FLINT: Flint Ridge is an area about 8 miles long and ¾ mile wide in Licking and Muskingum counties of central Ohio. It was the site of ancient Indian diggings for flint for artifacts and of the workshops where the artifacts were chipped out. Near the center of the area and on Ohio 668 is the Flint Ridge Memorial Park. The best collecting is on the corn fields S and E of this park, but it is also worthwhile to explore all along the E-W road E of Hwy 668. No gem flint of brilliant color—and it is always scarce—has ever been found by digging in the old Indian pits; all the good material has been found on the surface. The best hunting is in the bare fields after a rain or when the corn is young. A few pieces have been found in wooded areas. Most of the flint is pastel in color or mottled, but the best pieces are brilliantly colored in reds, greens and blues. (Permission is necessary to enter the fields.)

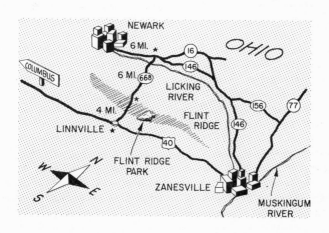

## OKLAHOMA

Much of Oklahoma is rough and even mountainous. The Ozarks cross into the east central part of the state and die out in hills in the south central region occupied by a plateau known as the Arbuckle Mountains. Northwest of this area rise the steep Wichita Mountains and the Chautauqua Mountains. Northwest Oklahoma is part of the High Plains, and northeastern Oklahoma is a region of buttes and valleys carved from shales and sandstones. Despite this diversity of geological features, Oklahoma affords only a limited variety of gem minerals, mostly agate and petrified wood.

*Ada, Pontotoc County*
BLACK PETRIFIED WOOD: To S in Jack Fork and Canyon Creek.

*Alva, Woods County*
PETRIFIED WOOD, MOSS AGATE: To S and W.

*Buffalo, Harper County*
PETRIFIED WOOD, AGATE: At Ed Price ranch.

*Camargo, Dewey County*
AGATE, JASPER: At Ames gravel pit.

*Dougherty, Murray County*
PETRIFIED WOOD, AGATE: At Makins gravel pit.

*Hobart, Kiowa County*
QUARTZ CRYSTALS: In quarries near Altus Reservoir.

*Hollis, Harmon County*
AGATE, JASPER: N 10 miles at Wilkerson pit.

*Idabel, McCurtain County*
PETRIFIED WOOD, JASPER: NE 9 miles at Mountain Fork River.

*Jet, Alfalfa County*
AGATE: S ½ mile at Cherokee Creek pit.

*Oakwood, Dewey County*
PETRIFIED WOOD: S 6 miles at Gooch gravel pit.

*Okemah, Okfuskee County*
AGATE, PETRIFIED WOOD: NE 13 miles at Coffman gravel pit.

*Seiling, Dewey County*
PETRIFIED WOOD: SE 7 miles at Carney gravel pit petrified wood can be found.

*Talihina, Le Flore County*
CHERT: To S.

*Taloga, Dewey County*
AGATE: S 4 miles at Lovett gravel pit.

*Tuttle, Grady County*
PETRIFIED WOOD, JASPER: S 4 miles at Dolese pit.

## OREGON

The Cascade Mountains, many of them extinct volcanoes, divide Oregon north and south into two diverse regions. West of the mountains, the land is well watered and contains the fertile Willamette Valley lying east of the Coast range, which merges in the south with California's Klamath Mountains. The eastern part of the state is a high plateau, generally arid, rugged, and made up of lava and rock debris, a region of salt lakes and even desert. Most of southeastern Oregon falls into the Great Basin. Oregon is celebrated for the agate formed in its lavas and the petrified wood and obsidian, also associated with volcanic rocks.

*Adrian, Malheur County\**

AGATE NODULES: Found in area S of Adrian along irrigation canal; also red petrified wood, to W at Alkali Springs. Canyon Road along Sucker Creek passes diggings to the left on canyon walls as the road begins to go deep into canyon S of Rockville. Here nodules containing moss agate are found.

Farther N in canyon, at a

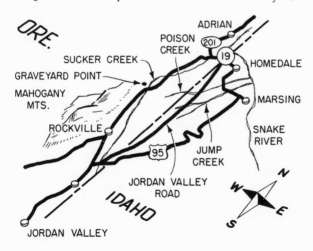

place known as Grave-
yard Point, is another
noted moss agate nodule
spot.

S from Homedale, Idaho, on
the old Jordan Valley, is
another collecting area at
Poison Creek. The area is
on a hillside 300 feet above
and W of the road for
agate nodules.

*Antelope,*
  *Wasco County*
MOSS AGATE: In creek E, on
ranches to E and S, and
in gravel pit 7 miles S on
Ashwood Road.

10½ miles E on Hwy 218
in quarry, with petrified
wood on ridge nearby.
AGATE NODULES: S 13⅓ miles
on Ashwood Road.
PETRIFIED WOOD: 4 miles E on
Hwy 218.
RED JASPER: One mile E on
Hwy 218 and ¼ mile S
to old quarry.

*Ashland, Jackson County*
GREEN AGATE NODULES: E 7½
miles from Klamath Falls
Junction on hills near road
cut in Hwy 66.

*Ashwood,*
  *Jefferson County*
PETRIFIED WOOD: W on Madras
Road on hill near inter-
section with road N to
Hwy 97.

*Austin, Grant County*
AGATE: NW 17 miles at Susanville.

*Baker, Baker County*
OPALIZED WOOD, ALMANDINE
GARNET: Near Pleasant
Valley.

*Bandon, Coos County*
SAGENITIC AGATE: Pebbles on
beach.

*Bend, Deschutes County*
OBSIDIAN: S 25 miles at Newberry Crater.

*Biggs, Sherman County*
AGATE: At Fields farm 5 miles
S on Hwy 97. (Fee.)

*Brothers, Deschutes County*
QUARTZ CRYSTAL: At Sugar-
loaf Mountain.

*Brownsboro, Jackson County*\*
PETRIFIED WOOD, AGATE:
Found W of the road NE
from Brownsboro to
Butte Falls and in the area
E of the road and S of
Butte Falls.

DENDRITIC AND CLEAR AGATE:
In the desert 5 miles N
of Medford and E of Hwy
62 in Antelope Creek and
Little Butte Creek area.

MOSS AGATE, JASPER, QUARTZ
CRYSTAL GEODES: In the
area S and W of Crow
Foot, both in the creeks
and washes and on the
hills.

PETRIFIED WOOD: At Table

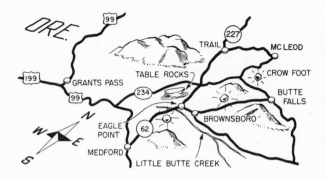

Rocks on the side of Table Rock Mountain.

*Burns, Harney County*

GREEN AGATE NODULES: 20 miles E on Hwy 20 and 3 miles S at Buchanan ranch. (Fee.)

BLACK AND WHITE AGATE: Hwy 20 E 40 miles and S 14 miles along W side of Warm Springs Reservoir. Collect along shore, and two gullies to W on hill.

OBSIDIAN: 35 miles SW on U.S. 20 at Juniper Ridge.

OPALIZED WOOD: 18 miles N on Hwy 395 and W 7 miles at Silvies Canyon.

*Canyon City, Grant County*

SERPENTINE (verd antique): to S along Canyon Creek.

*Coos Bay, Coos County*

AGATE, PETRIFIED WOOD: SW through Charleston to Seven Devils Beach.

*Durkee, Baker County*

CHALCEDONY: In Shirttail Creek.

FIRE OPAL: To E where stream cuts through volcanic rocks.

*Estacada, Clackamas County*

PETRIFIED WOOD, GREEN JASPER: In Clackamas River.

*Hampton, Deschutes County*

GREEN MOSS AGATE, JASPER, PETRIFIED WOOD: Take U.S. 20 NW, then N, 10 miles to Hampton Butte. Collect along next butte to W.

OBSIDIAN: Take U.S. 20 SE to Glass Butte just S of highway.

*Harper, Malheur County*

AGATE GEODES, OPALIZED WOOD: S 32 miles at Skull Springs.

*Holland, Josephine County*

JASPER, MASSIVE GROSSULARITE

GARNET: S 1½ miles in Althouse Creek.

*Lakeview, Lake County*

BLUE AGATE: Take Hwy 395 S 4 miles and hike mile into hills.

AGATE NODULES: S 5 miles in Crane Creek Canyon to E of Hwy 395.

AGATE, PETRIFIED WOOD: W 36 miles on Hwy 66 at Quartz Mountain Pass.

JASPER AND QUARTZ CRYSTALS: Take Hwy 395 S to New Pine Creek, then Fort Bidwell Road to summit. Collect in old mine tunnels.

*Lebanon,*
*Linn County*

CARNELIAN: Take Hwy 20 S to Central Ave., then W on Sodaville Road to Tyler ranch. (Fee.) Also at Moore diggings nearby.

*Madras, Jefferson County*

AGATE NODULES: NE 17 miles on Hwy 97 almost to Willowdale, take road E to Priday ranch.

*Maupin, Wasco County*

AGATE: Take Hwy 216 16 miles W and then S to Sunflower Flats.

BLACK AGATE: In Deschutes River to N.

*Newport, Lincoln County*

AGATE, JASPER, PETRIFIED WOOD PEBBLES: N and S on beaches.

*Oregon City, Clackamas County*

GREEN AND RED JASPER: In gravel bars of Clackamas River.

*Plush,*
*Lake County*

CHALCEDONY NODULES: Go 9 miles N, take the right fork 18 miles to refuge headquarters and S to Hart Mountain area. Hike to top and collect nodules in slopes of five canyons facing W.

FIRE OPAL: Collect in basalt on W rim of canyons.

SUNSTONE: N 9 miles, take left fork to just N of Rabbit Creek and to just W of Rabbit Creek Dam.

*Port Orford,*
*Curry County*

SAGENITIC AGATE PEBBLES: On beach.

*Prineville,*
*Crook County\**

Prineville has organized its numerous collecting spots into a tourist attraction with camping facilities and town-owned collecting areas.

DENDRITIC AND ANGEL WING AGATE: At Eagle Rock. Take Post (Combs Flat) Road 18 miles to Eagle Rock, turn right past rocks, and follow a sharp

incline left 1¼ miles.

PETRIFIED WOOD: At Bonney-view claim, 6 miles past Post. (Fee, get directions at Recreation Unlimited in Prineville.)

Likewise for Dick ranch claim 14 miles past Post.

AGATE, PETRIFIED WOOD: At Pine Creek ranch. E on Post Road mile past Post, right across bridge and left on Shotgun Road 4½ miles to Pine Creek ranch. (Fee.)

RED, GREEN AND MOSS AGATE: At Maury Mountain. E on Post Road 8 miles past Post to Milepost 33, turn right over wooden bridge, continue over 5 cattle guards to first road right past national forest sign, go a mile and then right a mile to diggings.

LIMB CASTS: At Milepost 51 on Crooked River Hwy, go 6 miles S to Congleton Hollow, which angles toward Crooked River. Dig on S side in mud slide. At Milepost 43, take Camp Creek Road S and then W to plateau. Dendritic and colored limb casts found in area between creeks both sides of S Fork of Crooked River.

AGATE NODULES: At White Fir Springs. Take U.S. 26 E 9 miles, turn right at store onto Mill Creek Road 10 miles, then right across bridge 4½ miles to road junction and collect a few hundred yards ahead.

BLUE AGATE AND NODULES: At White Rock Springs. Turn left at White Fir Springs junction 2 miles to campsite, then rough road mile to diggings.

At Whistler Springs. U.S. 26 E past Milepost 47 to Ranger Station, turn left on gravel road 5½ miles, go past View Point and turn left on gravel road to diggings.

GREEN JASPER: U.S. 26 E past Milepost 57, turn on Pisgah Lookout Road, 3½ miles to Old Mitchell Road, then right to fire road "E," turn right 2 miles and take trail to diggings.

WHITE AGATE: At Sheep Creek. U.S. 26 16½ miles E, angle right on gravel road 3 miles, turn right on Wolf Creek Road to Sheep Creek sign and take Cadle Road to Arvid Nelson Road and left to 21 mile sign.

MOSS AND WHITE PLUME AGATE: At Bear Creek. S down Main Street 20 miles over Prineville Dam and continue on new road until it joins old road. Turn left on old road several miles to Bear Creek and collect in diggings on W side of bank.

PETRIFIED WOOD: At Swartz Canyon petrified forest. W on Redmond Hwy to road sign indicating turnoff to left.

RED PLUME AGATE: At Carey ranch. Take Juniper Canyon Road to sign and turnoff. (Fee.)

JASPER: Found just above the dam at Ochoco Reservoir E of Prineville.

*Riddle, Douglas County*

CHRYSOPRASE: At Nickel Mountain.

*Rogue River, Jackson County*

RHODONITE: Take road along Evans Creek N for 15

miles to mine, collect in road cut and creek.

*Roseburg, Douglas County*

PETRIFIED WOOD, AGATE: In North Umpqua River to Glide.

*Rufus, Sherman County*

AGATE: In gullies mile S of Hwy 30.

*Scio,*
*Linn County*

PETRIFIED WOOD, AGATE: Go 9 miles SE to hunt at Prospect Mountain Mine, which is 2 miles NW of Roaring River hatchery. (Fee.)

*Sweet Home,*
*Linn County*

PETRIFIED WOOD, CARNELIAN: To SW in Ames Creek and at Chandler Mountain.

PETRIFIED WOOD: Take Hwy 228 SW to Rouell Hill Road. Go E on road to first house. (Fee.)

BLUE AGATE: Take Hwy 228 for 4 miles SW to Holley school, then right a bit more than 2 miles, and again right 2 miles to farmhouse. Hike logging road for 1 mile to site. Another location is at end of a gravel road from Holley to river. Walk across river and dig.

*Unity, Baker County*

AGATE: Take Hwy 26 NW to Hwy 7, then NE 6 miles to road N through Whitney toward Sumpter, collect in dredge dumps and river gravels.

*Vale, Malheur County*

PETRIFIED WOOD: Take road S 25 miles to sign reading "Owyhee Dam 8 Miles," go W 2 miles and S in creek bed to collecting area.

OPALIZED WOOD: NW 12 miles at Willow Creek opalized wood has been found.

*Vernonia,*
*Columbia County*

AGATE: Take road W along Clear Creek 2 miles, collect in stream and along bank.

CARNELIAN: In Nehalem River to N.

*Wedderburn,*
*Curry County*

MASSIVE GROSSULARITE GARNET, JASPER, PETRIFIED WOOD: In gravels at mouth of Rogue River, at Gold Beach, and on beaches and in coves for 6 miles N.

*Yachats, Lincoln County*

SAGENITIC AGATE, JASPER: On Cummings Creek Beach and at beach 10 miles S.

MOSS AGATE, MASSIVE GROSSULARITE GARNET, PETRIFIED WOOD: At Big Creek and Squaw Creek beaches.

## PENNSYLVANIA

Eastern Pennsylvania falls within the coastal plain made up of marine deposits, and lying west of it is the Piedmont plateau resting on crystalline metamorphic rocks and sedimentary rocks, the highlands formed of crystalline and volcanic rocks and, culminating in the Allegheny plateau, largely sedimentary rocks, which forms nearly half the state and is the most rugged region in the state. The belts or regions cross the state from northeast to southwest.

*Avondale, Delaware County*

GOLDEN AND GREEN BERYL, SPESSARTITE GARNET: In Leiper's Quarry Dump on E side of Crum Creek.

QUARTZ CRYSTALS: In quarry to SE on W side of Crum Creek.

AMETHYST: In quarry on George Sharpless farm mile W.

*Bart, Lancaster County*

SMOKY QUARTZ: E of ruins of smelter ¾ mile N of Gap Nickel Mines.

*Boothwyn, Delaware County*

AMETHYST: At J. B. Okie's farm 2 miles N.

At Armstrong farm ½ mile N.

RUTILATED QUARTZ: Loose in soil at McCay's farm.

QUARTZ CRYSTALS, GARNET: In pits on W side of E branch of Naaman's Creek.

*Bucktown, Chester County*

PETRIFIED WOOD: On George Clawser farm.

*Carlisle, Cumberland County*

BANDED AGATE: On S side of Hwy 11, a mile E of the Carlisle interchange on Pennsylvania Turnpike.

*Chester, Delaware County*

AMETHYST, BERYL, SMOKY QUARTZ: At Shaw & Esrey's Quarry ¼ mile S.

ALMANDINE GARNET: In soil above Peter's Mill Dam in Green Creek and in creek mile S of Chester Heights Station.

*Darby, Delaware County*

BERYL: Near White Horse 3 miles S.

*Easton, Northampton County*

TOPAZ, SERPENTINE: To N at Chestnut Hill in Verdolite and other quarries.

*Gettysburg, Adams County*

CUPRITE, AZURITE, MALACHITE IN QUARTZ: To W on Franklin County border in South Mountain area, especially at Bingham mine on Pine Mountain.

*Holland, Bucks County*

BLUE QUARTZ: At Finney's Quarry ¼ mile N.

*Kellyville, Delaware County*

SMOKY QUARTZ: In Maher's Quarry.

*Kennett Square, Chester County*

SUNSTONE: At Pierce's paper mill ½ mile SE.

At Cloud's farm 2 miles SE.

TOURMALINE: At Bailey's farm SW of Willowdale.

*Leiperville, Delaware County*

BLUE AND GOLDEN BERYL, THULITE, QUARTZ CRYSTALS: At Deshong's quarry ½ mile W on E side of Ridley Creek.

*Lenni, Delaware County*

SUNSTONE, AMAZONITE, MOONSTONE: In cut on railroad ⅜ mile E of station.

AMETHYST: W ½ mile of Crozierville on S side of Chester Creek.

*Ligonier, Westmoreland County*

QUARTZ CRYSTALS: W 3 miles at quarry on Hwy 30.

*Lionville, Chester County*

BLUE QUARTZ: N 2 miles.

*Media, Delaware County*

AMETHYST: NE 1½ miles on Crum Creek on James Worral, Morgan Hunter and Randolph farms.

AMAZONITE, MOONSTONE: A

mile W at Mineral Hill W of Ridley Creek, in quarry N of Crump's Quarry on grounds of School for the Feeble Minded.

SUNSTONE: S ¼ mile of Black Horse at old corundum pits, and ½ mile E of Black Horse on J. Smith farm.

NW 2½ miles at Blue Hill.

GREEN QUARTZ: At quarry ½ mile NE of Black Horse for gem material.

*Morton, Delaware County*

SPHENE: At Mullen's Quarry.

*Neshaminy Falls, Bucks County*

MOONSTONE: N 2 miles at Vanartsdalen's Quarry.

*Pocopson, Chester County*

AMETHYST: E of station ¼ mile in field NW of Minshall Painter's house.

At Darlington's farm ¼ mile W.

*Redington, Northampton County*

CAT'S-EYE QUARTZ: On South Mountain.

*Rock Springs Run, Lancaster County*

MOSS AGATE, CARNELIAN: In small branch of run 1¼ miles N of Rock Springs, Md.

*Stroudsburg, Northampton County\**

QUARTZ CRYSTALS: Steep,

CRYSTAL HILL
STROUDSBURG
PENNA.
ARMITAGE FARM
1.4 MI.
E. STROUDSBURG
191
3.1 MI.
DELAWARE WATER GAP
611
NEW JERSEY
EASTON
DELAWARE RIVER

wooded area located on the Christian Armitage farm S of Stroudsburg. Crystal Hill is reached by taking Rt 611 E from Stroudsburg to a blinker light and turning S on Hwy 191 for 3.1 miles, then keeping right 1.4 miles to Armitage house. Walk up steep hill to site where quartz crystals of great variety are loose in fine-grained quartz conglomerate. (Ask permission to collect and pay fee first.)

*Sycamore Mills (near Media), Delaware County*

SMOKY QUARTZ: W ½ mile on Walker Yarnell's farm for smoky quartz.

AMETHYST: S ½ mile on Marshall farm near Dismal Run.

GREEN QUARTZ: S ¾ mile at J. Tyler's farm green quartz has been found.

Crystals loose in soil NE ¾

mile at Blue Hills cross-roads.

*Trainer Station, Delaware County*

SMOKY QUARTZ, QUARTZ CRYSTALS, GREEN BERYL: At William Trainer's farm ½ mile N.

*Upper Darby, Delaware County*

SMOKY QUARTZ: Along West Chester Pike ½ mile W for smoky quartz.

*Unionville, Chester County*

TOURMALINE, SERPENTINE: NE 2 miles on Northbrook Road at Corundum Hill for tourmaline and serpentine finds.

*Valley Forge, Chester County*

AMETHYST: W 1½ miles at abandoned Jug Hollow Mine.

*Vera Cruz, Lehigh County*

CHERT: In pits along Pennsylvania Turnpike.

*West Chester, Chester County*

AMETHYST: S 3 miles on Birmingham Road at Brinton's Quarries.

SMOKY QUARTZ: S 2½ miles at Osborn Hill.

# RHODE ISLAND

Once a plain not much above sea level, Rhode Island has been uplifted and its surface carved by stream action into low hills and valleys; some of the latter have become ocean bays. Glaciation has completed the work of forming the surface.

*Bristol, Bristol County*
AGATE, JASPER: On shore of Mount Hope Bay.
*East Greenwich, Kent County*
AGATE: On shore.
*Foster, Providence County*
YELLOW QUARTZ CRYSTALS: In Moosup River.
*Ashton, Providence County*
SERPENTINE (BOWENITE): In Conklin and Harris Quarries at Lime Rock for serpentine or bowenite.
*Manville, Providence County*
JASPER: Across Blackstone River at Diamond Hill.
CAT'S-EYE QUARTZ: At Cumberland Hill cat's-eye quartz has been found and reported.
SAGENITIC QUARTZ: At Calumet Hill, ½ mile W of Diamond Hill.
*Warwick, Kent County*
CARNELIAN: On shore of Narragansett Bay.
*Providence, Providence County*
SERPENTINE: 5 miles N at Conklin and Harris Quarries.

# SOUTH CAROLINA

Near the ocean, South Carolina is a region of islands and marshes in the coastal plain. Behind this is the upcountry, the rolling Piedmont plateau, while the northwest corner of the state rises abruptly into the Blue Ridge Mountains of the Appalachian system, adjoining noted gem areas in Georgia and North Carolina. Most of the gem locations lie in the more mountainous northwestern part of the state.

*Abbeville, Abbeville County*
AMETHYST: At McCalla place on road to Iva.

*Anderson, Anderson County*
AMETHYST, SAPPHIRE, GARNET: 15 miles S on Hwy 28, near old Storeville where road cuts dike near lake.
AQUAMARINE: 3 miles NE at McConnell place and also ½ mile SW of McConnell place, in pegmatite dikes.

*Blacksburg, Cherokee County*
SAPPHIRE: In pegmatite 2½ miles NW at Andrew Moon place.

*Blenheim, Marlboro County*
PETRIFIED CYCAD: In sand pits 4 miles S.

*Columbia, Richland County*
AMETHYST: At Lake Murray.

*Due West, Abbeville County*
AMETHYST: Across road from old U.S. Weather Station.

*Edgefield, Edgefield County*
SERPENTINE: In Turkey Creek within sight of Hwy 25.

*Gaffney, Cherokee County*
SAPPHIRE: At Porter's Hill.

*Greenwood, Greenwood County*
AMETHYST: At Wrenn's place.
CHALCEDONY: At Harper's place at powerhouse.
GARNET: At Stockman's Quarry.
QUARTZ CRYSTALS, SMOKY QUARTZ: At Milford place.

*Iva, Anderson County*
BERYL: 8 miles SW at Sherard's place.

*Jefferson, Chesterfield County*
YELLOW AND BLUE TOPAZ: 3 miles W at Brewer Mine for topaz.

*Laurens, Laurens County*
CORUNDUM: At New Cemetery and inside city at Dead Man's Cut in railroad.
PYROPE GARNET: At Dead Man's Cut.

*Lowndesville, Abbeville County*
AMETHYST: One mile N at the Barnes place.

*Piedmont, Greenville County*
BERYL: At the D. D. McNeely place.

*Princeton, Laurens County*
AMETHYST: At spring 1½ miles SW.

*Saluca, Greenwood County*
UNAKITE: On W shore of Lake Greenwood.

*Shoals Junction, Greenwood County*
AMETHYST: 1½ miles SE and mile SW.

## SOUTH DAKOTA

East of the Missouri River, South Dakota is a fairly level, glaciated plain; to the west of the Missouri lies rolling prairie broken along the White River and north of it by the

Badlands, and in the far south and central west by granite mountains known as the Black Hills. One of them, Harney Peak, is the highest point in the United States east of the Rockies. The agates of the prairies and the pegmatite minerals of the Black Hills are the principal gem resources of the state.

*Ardmore, Fall River County*
AGATE: At Sugar Loaf Butte.

*Custer, Custer County*
AGATE: Take U.S. 16 E to State Park, turn off toward State Farm, go beyond cattle gate, search in hills to right.

BERYL: At Helen Beryl Mine. U.S. 16 W 4½ miles, then SW on gravel road to sign to mine to W. Collect in dumps.

ROSE QUARTZ: At White Elephant Mine. S on Hwy 385 7½ miles, E on dirt road to mine on ridge. Collect on dumps.

AGATE: For Tepee Canyon agate, go 14 miles W on U.S. 16 to campground on left. Continue 1 mile to road on right up canyon. Collect at top of hill left, or go up canyon to small gully and collect on hill left. Also go back to U.S. 16, drive W to logging road on right. Agates are in limestone.

GARNET, TOURMALINE: Go 7 miles W on U.S. 16, turn

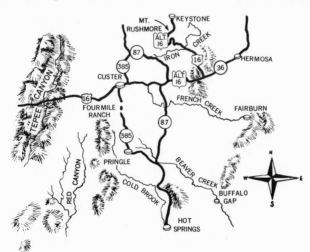

N at Deer Camp sign, go ¼ mile, and search in stream, or take trail up steep hill and look in mica schists.

### Fairburn, Custer County*

JASPER (CONGLOMERATE): Take road W and S to a windmill, search in Lame Jonny Creek.

AGATE: The brightly colored Fairburn agates were never plentiful and they are now difficult to find. Experts advise that the best place to look is where the agates have been found before, and that the fall of the year, after the grass has died back, is the best time. Fairburn-type agates have been found over a three-state area (shown by dotted line on map) extending down into Nebraska and Wyoming. Well-patterned jaspers and agatized fossils are also found in the agate beds. To reach the original collecting location, take road E along French Creek for 14 miles past McDermond ranch and turn N through picnic grounds. Collect in stony hills and fields to N.

Other well-known collecting grounds are E from Ardmore on dirt road 7 miles to a ranch S of the road. Turn S and E here until you come to badlands.

East of Oelrichs on Hwy 18, beds containing Fairburn agates lie S and E of the road in rugged buttes and gullies.

Another spot in the same area lies ½ mile E of town on the main street,

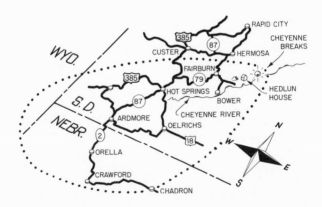

then one mile E on a dirt road and 2 miles S to a farmhouse, and 4 miles E and then left on a dim road a mile to rocky fields. (A good place to collect is in the Cheyenne breaks about 23 miles E of Fairburn. After passing a hill, you reach the Hedlun log cabin. Ask here for permission to collect north of the Hedlun property.)

*Hot Springs, Fall River County*
PETRIFIED WOOD: At Fall River Canyon.

*Interior,*
*Jackson County*
AGATE: Take Hwy 40 W, go ¾ mile farther after it becomes gravel. Along road pick up agates which look like wads of gum.

*Kadoka,*
*Jackson County*
AGATE: Collect off Hwy 40 7 miles W.

*Keystone, Pennington County*
ROSE QUARTZ: In pegmatite dikes along gravel road connecting Alt. 16 and Hwy 89 near Mount Rushmore National Monument.

BERYL: At Robert Ingersoll Mine.

LEPIDOLITE: At Etta Mine.

*Little Eagle, Corson County*
PETRIFIED WOOD: Along Grand River.

*Minnekahta, Fall River County*
PETRIFIED WOOD, CYCAD: S 2 miles on Parker Mountain and to E of mountain.

*Mission, Todd County*
BLACK PETRIFIED WOOD: W 12 miles along Little White River.

*Oelrichs, Fall River County*
JASPER, AGATE, PETRIFIED WOOD: In buttes 10 miles SE.

*Pringle, Custer County\**
AGATE: Along Hwy 89 between Pringle and Minnekahta, and to NW and W of Pringle and in Custer State Park to NE.

*Rapid City, Pennington County*
RUTILATED QUARTZ: To E in Box Elder Creek.

*Scenic, Pennington County\**
BLACK AGATE: West of Scenic 2 miles and N of the railroad is a formation known as Hart Table, where black agate is found in the gullies and eroded bluffs. (Map follows.)

AGATE, PETRIFIED WOOD, ROSE QUARTZ: Loose on ground 3 miles S, mile off road in either direction, are agate, petrified wood, rose quartz.

GEODES: On Hwy 40 E from Scenic, the road reaches a pass. Turn S from here

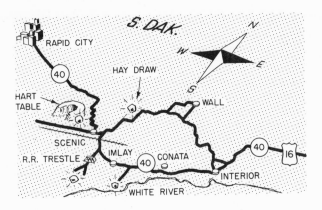

and past a railroad trestle for geodes.

BLACK, WHITE AGATE: Farther E past Imlay, a road turns S toward White River for black and white agate along banks.

NODULES: Northeast of Scenic on the road to Wall, the road passes a formation known as Hay Draw. Here nodules are found in a clay ironstone matrix, both in the stream and in its banks.

*Sioux Falls, Minnehaha County*

JASPER, AGATE: In gravels of Big Sioux River jasper and agate has been found.

*Spearfish, Lawrence County*

ALABASTER: On Crow Peak to W.

## TENNESSEE

East Tennessee rises in the mountains along the North Carolina border, an area of folded crystalline rocks, and extends across the valley of the Tennessee, cut in sedimentary rocks, to the Cumberland plateau. This plateau, bordered by steep escarpments, encloses a central basin running from northeast to southwest, in which Nashville lies. The basin rises to highlands on the west, cut by the lower Tennessee River, and then falls to a bluff along the Mississippi in a plateau which is part of the Gulf coastal plain. Except for the narrow belt of Appalachian Mountains in the east, Tennessee is formed mostly of sedimentary rocks.

*Beechgrove, Coffee County*
CHALCEDONY NODULES AND
    FRAGMENTS: S and W of
    U.S. 41.
*Cookeville, Putnam County*
JASPER, AGATE: In nodules in
    streams from Cumber-
    land plateau.

*Murfreesboro, Rutherford*
    *County*
AGATE NODULES: In chert in
    road cuts and ditches.
*Shelbyville, Bedford County*
JASPER: In streams draining
    Cumberland plateau jas-
    per has been found.

### TEXAS

Sandy sediments typical of the coastal plain make up southeastern Texas. Behind this lies the Llano uplift, a region of crystalline rocks. The Grand Prairie and Edwards plateau, primarily sedimentary rocks, link the Llano uplift to the north central plains and, toward the Panhandle, the High Plains themselves. In far western Texas is the Trans Pecos, formed of rugged mountains, both igneous and sedimentary in their structure. The great variety of sedimentary areas affords a wealth of agate and petrified wood, while in the Llano area occur topaz and garnet and other minerals characteristic of crystalline rocks.

*Alpine, Brewster County*
AGATE: At Woodward ranch
    16 miles S on Hwy 118
    and turn at sign.
  Also at Anderson ranch 20
    miles S and to left at sign.
  At Henderson ranch 32
    miles S and to left at sign.
    (All fees.)
POMPOM AGATE: At Needle
    Peak, 100 miles S of
    Woodward ranch between
    end of Hwy 118 and Rio

Grande River. This is just
    W of Big Bend National
    Park. (By arrangement
    with Woodwards.)
YELLOW LABRADORITE: S 20
    miles and loose in soil.
OPAL: In seams in rhyolite 16
    miles S.
*Amarillo, Potter County*
AGATIZED WOOD: SE 50 miles
    in Palo Duro Canyon.
*Balmorhea, Reeves County*
BLUE AGATE: On hills and in

washes on N shore of Lake Balmorhea.

*Brackettville, Kinney County*
JASPER: To N.

*Caldwell, Burleson County*
PETRIFIED WOOD: To S between Hwys 21 and 36.

*Calliham, McMullen County*
PETRIFIED WOOD: W along Hwy 72 as far as Tilden.

*Carmine, Fayette County*
PETRIFIED WOOD: Take road N ½ mile, then left ¼ mile and right ¼ mile to dirt road, follow it ½ mile to gate on left; go to creek and hunt in creek and along banks.

*Columbus, Colorado County*
PETRIFIED WOOD: In gravels 10 miles W.

*Cross, Grimes County*
PETRIFIED WOOD: To N along Hwy 39 all the way to Normangee and to NE along Hwy 90 to Madison-ville.

*Eagle Pass, Maverick County*
BROWN AMBER: In Cretaceous coal deposits.

*El Sauz, Starr County*
PETRIFIED PALM WOOD, AGATE: To S along Hwy 649.

*Falcon Dam, Starr County*
AGATE, JASPER: In gravels around Zapata Reservoir.

*Fort Stockton, Pecos County*
AGATE, PETRIFIED WOOD: W 10 miles on Hwy 290; then S on Hwy 67, 30 miles to sign pointing to Hovey. Collect near sign or take Hovey Road across Pai-sano Creek and collect along road.

*Fredericksburg, Gillespie County*
AMETHYST, CITRINE: To NE at Amethyst Hill.

ALMANDINE GARNET: In stream gravels.

*Katemcy, Mason County*
BLUE TOPAZ, AMAZONITE, SMOKY QUARTZ CRYSTALS: SW 4 miles on Awalt, Hays and Armine ranches.

*LaGrange, Fayette County*
PETRIFIED PALM WOOD: La-Grange is near the center of a belt of gravels 100 or more miles inland from the Gulf of Mexico and extending from Huntsville, 50 miles N of Houston, through LaGrange, Gon-zales, Whitsett and Co-tulla, 75 miles S of San Antonio, where petrified palm wood is plentiful on the surface and in creeks. Near LaGrange it is found to N along Rabs Creek and to SW toward Mul-doon.

*Laredo, Jeff Davis County*
MOSS AGATE, JASPER: On

ranches along Hwy 83 and in Rio Grande River gravels, especially to S to below Falcon Dam.

*Llano, Llano County*

SMOKY, SAGENITIC QUARTZ CRYSTALS: In pegmatites near Buchanan Lake.

GRANITE (LLANITE): Take Hwy 16 to where it crosses dike 10 miles N, collect in dike or go to quarry ¼ mile W.

Also found in other dikes parallel road to E.

*Marfa, Presidio County*

PLUME AGATE: At Bishop ranch; take Hwy 67 S for 7 miles, then take Hwy 169 18 miles to ranch gate, and follow ranch road. (Go to ranch house for permission to hunt.)

AGATE: Is also found along Hwy 67 S of intersection with Hwy 169.

*Mason, Mason County*

BLUE TOPAZ, SMOKY QUARTZ CRYSTALS: Take Hwy 377 to Hwy 29, then N to Grit and 2 miles farther to ranch road to Rocky Davenport ranch. Collect in stream beds. (Get permission to hunt at Rocky's drug store in Mason.)

Collect for fee at Garner Seaquist ranch near Grit, in Honey Creek Branch, or in same creek at Walter Eppler place (fee).

*McAllen, Hidalgo County*

AGATE: In Crow's gravel pit.

*Moulton, Lavaca County*

AGATIZED WOOD: On nearby ranches.

*Oxford, Llano County*

AMETHYST: In quartz veins near old town site.

*Pecos, Reeves County*

PLUME AGATE: Along roads N and S of Toyah, 19 miles W of Pecos.

*Pumpville, Val Verde County*

AGATE, JASPER, PETRIFIED WOOD: On Sidney Smith ranch.

*Sierra Blanca, Hudspeth County*

TURQUOISE: NW 8 miles in Sierra Blanca Mountains for gem material.

*Streeter, Mason County*

BLUE TOPAZ, SMOKY QUARTZ: W 8 miles in stream gravels and prospects.

*Sullivan City, Hidalgo County*

JASPER: W 3 miles to dirt road to Garcia ranch.

*Terlingua, Brewster County*

YELLOW AMBER: In Terlingua Creek.

*Tilden, McMullen County*

PETRIFIED PALM WOOD: To E along course of Frio and Nueces Rivers.

*Trinity, Trinity County*
PETRIFIED PALM WOOD: Along
    Hwy 405 toward Hunts-
    ville, and to N in road
    cuts toward Groveton and
    Lovelady.

*Van Horn, Culberson County*
TURQUOISE: To SW.

*Voca, Mason County*
QUARTZ CRYSTALS: In pegma-
    tites and streams.

*Whitsett, Live Oak County*
PETRIFIED PALM WOOD: To N
    and along Hwy 99.
    To E in creeks and gullies
    for petrified palm wood.

## UTAH

Utah falls into two grand divisions, the plateau, east of
a line from the middle of the northern border running to the
southwestern corner and for a long way following the Wasatch
Mountains, and the Great Basin region to the west of this
line. The Great Basin, formerly the bed of a lake of which
Great Salt Lake is a remnant, is level except for isolated
mountains. To the north the plateau is bounded by the wild
Uinta Mountains, which descend into the sandstone buttes
and cliffs that in southern Utah form the fantastic regions
of erosion seen in Zion and Bryce Canyon National Parks
and in the Grand Canyon of the Colorado. These sandstone
areas are rich in fossils and petrified wood.

*Beaver, Beaver County*
AGATE: Take left-hand road
    past city dump and then
    next right-hand road for
    2 miles.

*Black Rock, Millard County*
FLOWERING OBSIDIAN: Take
    Hwy 257 N 4½ miles,
    turn E across railroad
    tracks to area.

*Cedar City, Iron County*
AGATE: Take rim road in Cedar
    Breaks National Monu-

ment to gate and cattle
crossing. Turn outside
monument into field and
take first turn right to-
ward Brian Head. Collect
in washes below peak.
Also found on W side of
road leading from S gate
of monument.

*Central, Washington County*
AGATE, NODULES: Take Hwy
    18 to Dixie National
    Forest sign, turn left and

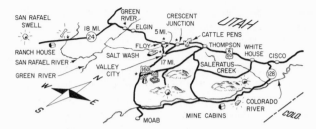

again left at fork into canyon.

*Cisco, Grand County\**

AGATE, OPALIZED WOOD: About 10½ miles SW of Cisco, across from a bridge on the Colorado River, is a hill where agate and opalized wood occur.

RED AGATE PSEUDOMORPHS: Farther west in the hills are red agate pseudomorphs after barite concretions. Some 17 miles S of Thompson is a windmill and former CCC camp.

AGATE, PETRIFIED WOOD, AND DINOSAUR BONE: In the hills E and SE of the windmill, agate, petrified wood, and petrified dinosaur bone are weathering out of the hills of the Morrison formation.

LACE AND GRAPE AGATE: Farther W and about five miles S of a deep wash across the road S from Floy, park and go into the wash and hills to S for agate.

PETRIFIED WOOD: South of Crescent Junction, petrified wood is found in the hills E of Hwy 160. A dirt road cuts S of the hills and then N to cattle pens, and near the pens the pseudomorphs after barite occur.

AGATE: Farther S, a dim road cuts S from the road that swings from Thompson to Hwy 160 N of Moab. After crossing a wet wash on this dim road, look in the hills to S for agate.

Below Green River, take Hwy 24 S until it crosses the San Rafael River (about 18 miles). In the hills just N of the reef is agate; to the W, dinosaur bone.

JASPAGATE: Farther S on Hwy 24 the road passes several ranches and then plunges into the San Rafael Swell. In this area jaspagate is loose on the desert floor.

*Deseret, Millard County*

YELLOW TRANSPARENT LABRA-DORITE: S on Hwy 257 to cinder mounds one mile N of Clear Lake Station, cross tracks and search ground.

*Fairfield, Utah County*

VARISCITE: W 5 miles in Clay Canyon. (Private claim.)

*Grantsville, Tooele County*

VARISCITE: S 9 miles at Ama-trice Hill in Stansbury Mountains.

*Hanksville, Wayne County*

AGATE, JASPER, PETRIFIED WOOD: About 18 miles W on Hwy 24 just W of small canyon; also just W of Hanksville in butte area N of road.

JET: 10 miles S in Coaly Basin.

*Heber, Wasatch County*

PETRIFIED WOOD: In Lake Creek.

*Kanab, Kane County*

PETRIFIED WOOD: E 20 miles in Vermilion Cliffs.

*Levan, Juab County*

BLACK AGATE: Take Hwy 28 S 13 miles, then mile E on dirt road and collect to the right beyond buildings.

*Lucin, Box Elder County*

VARISCITE: NW 5 miles at Utahlite Hill. (Private claim.)

*Milford, Beaver County*

QUARTZ CRYSTALS: E 12 miles in Mineral Mountains.

*Moab, Grand County*

PETRIFIED WOOD: At Dead Horse Point.

*Panguitch, Garfield County*

JASPER, AGATE: Take road to Panguitch Lake to end of pavement; then go $\frac{1}{2}$ mile to camp grounds and collect S of camp.

*Parowan, Iron County*

AGATE: Take road E up can-yon to second fork, then left to top of ridge.

Also to S along Hwy 143.

*Pelican Point, Utah County*

BLACK CALCITE ONYX: Along Utah Lake.

*Silver City, Juab County**

TOPAZ: The road to the topaz areas in the Thomas Mountains leaves Hwy 6 just below Jericho, 13 miles S of Silver City. After 11 miles, take the left fork, go $40\frac{1}{2}$ miles to another left fork, then $2\frac{3}{4}$ miles on the Joy Road to a right fork. After a mile, take side road right, then the first left-hand road, and take trail directly into the camping area for a distance of 2

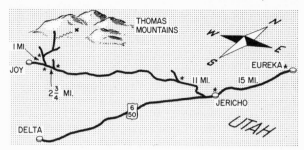

miles. The topaz crystals occur in rhyolite. Those crystals fresh from the rhyolite are wine-colored, those that have been exposed to the desert sun are colorless. They are found in the sand as well as the rock. The best place to dig is reported to be high up in a cove near the camp grounds half a mile E and W of a white knoll. It has also been found in the NE part of the Thomas range in rhyolite 3 miles S of the Dugway Road. Some of the crystals are pink.

*St. George, Washington County*
AGATE: Go E on Hwy 17 for 17½ miles to dirt road S, continue 4 miles to red dunes.
BANDED RHYOLITE (WONDER-STONE): At quarries.
MALACHITE: In Dixie Apex Mine.

*Snowville, Box Elder County*
AVENTURINE QUARTZ: In quarries.

*Vernon, Tooele County*
AGATE NODULES: From Hwy 36, go W over Lookout Pass and Dugway Pass to Callas; 4 miles W of Dugway Pass take faint road N across big wash to diggings.

*Woodside, Emery County*
JASPER, PETRIFIED BONE AND WOOD: S 5 miles on Hwy 50, then NW 5 miles on dirt road; hunt on slopes.

# VERMONT

Much of the area of Vermont is broken up by the Green Mountains and, parallel with them in the west, the Taconic

Mountains. As a result of its rugged topography and glaciation, Vermont has a number of lakes, of which Lake Champlain is the largest. Its soil is thin, so that underlying rock is often exposed.

*Burlington, Chittenden County*
JASPER: N 9 miles at Eugene Parrot farm.

*Chester, Windsor County*
CYANITE, STAUROLITE: In quarries.

*Eden, Lamoille County*
IDOCRASE: At Belvidere Mine of Vermont Asbestos Company, on Belvidere Mountain.

*Grafton, Windham County*
SERPENTINE, CYANITE: In quarries.

*Malletts Bay, Chittenden County*
DOLOMITIC MARBLE.

*Roxbury, Washington County*
SERPENTINE: Has been found in quarries.

*Swanton, Franklin County*
DOLOMITIC MARBLE.

## VIRGINIA

Drowned valleys along the coastal plain of Virginia form long bays and, in the southeast, swamps such as the Great Dismal Swamp. Behind the coastal, sandy plain lies the Piedmont plateau, its rolling surface broken by ridges of crystalline rocks. This passes into the Blue Ridge Mountains, running from northeast to southwest, and the Allegheny Mountains, with a great valley between them. Gem minerals in the crystalline rocks and caves in the sedimentary regions are notable occurrences.

*Altavista, Campbell County*
STAUROLITE: In schist toward Rustberg.

*Amelia, Amelia County**
AMAZONITE, MOONSTONE, SPESSARTITE GARNET: The Rutherford mine NE of Amelia is famous for its brilliant green amazonite, moonstone and gem quality spessartite garnet. To the SE is the Morefield mine where excellent amazonite can be found. (Both are open to collectors by permission ob-

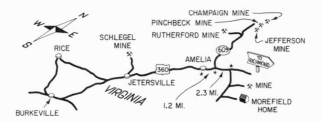

tained at the Keener farm-house at the Rutherford mine and the Silas More-field house S of the More-field mine.)

NE of the Rutherford mine are several old mines, the Champaign, Pinchbeck, Jefferson and, W of these, the Winston mine; and $\frac{3}{4}$ mile NW of Jetersville is the old Schlegel mine.

*Bland, Bland County*

AGATE: Near Point Pleasant N side of Walker Mountain.

*Brookneal, Campbell County*

AMETHYST: On Lacey Rush farm $\frac{1}{3}$ mile NE and Clay farm 10 miles NE.

*Farmville, Prince Edward County*

AMETHYST, SMOKY QUARTZ: SE on Hwy 460 to Rice, collect in soil 3 miles N at George Smith farm.

*Grant, Grayson County*

UNAKITE: NW $1\frac{1}{2}$ mile along Hwy 16.

*Independence, Grayson County*

RHODONITE: SE 7 miles.

*Louisa, Louisa County*

AMETHYST: W on Hwy 33 to Trevilians and SW 4 miles in field at Rudinger farm.

*Luray, Page County*

UNAKITE: Go E on U.S. 211, then S on Hwy 689, cross stream just N of Ida; turn W several miles on dirt road; collect in stream bed and on hillside.

*Martinsville, Henry County*

BERYL: Half mile S of. Hwy 58 crossing of Grassy Creek.

STAUROLITE: SE 9 miles in road cut near S bank of Smith River.

*Massies Mill, Nelson County*

AMETHYST: Mile SE at Stratton farm.

SW at John Saunders farm.

*Newport, Giles County*

SMOKY QUARTZ CRYSTALS: SW $3\frac{1}{2}$ miles on Spruce Run.

*Stuart, Patrick County*

STAUROLITE: In belt of schist-
ose rocks extending from
SW of Stuart for 20 miles
NE.

Another similar belt runs
from about 9 miles NE of
Stuart across Henry
County. Many of the
stones are loose in the soil.

*Vesuvius, Rockbridge County\**
UNAKITE (a mixture of green
epidote with pink feld-
spar, quartz and other
minerals): There are two
noted areas in the Shen-
andoah Mountains of Vir-
ginia. The best colored
material is found in creeks
and an old quarry and
road cut near Vesuvius
below the Blue Ridge
Parkway.

At Fisher's Gap just NW of
Syria is another extensive
deposit, where the ma-
terial is in the Rose River
and broken loose below
the mountain ridge.

*Willis, Floyd County*
QUARTZ CRYSTALS: ESE 2 miles,
loose in soil.

## WASHINGTON

The Cascade Mountains, containing a number of extinct
volcanoes and ranging north from the Columbia River to
Canada, divide the state into two regions. To the east of
the mountains is a plain rising from the Columbia River,
formed of lava beds and extending to the Okanogan highland
to the north. West of the mountains is the great basin in which
lies Puget Sound, cut off from the ocean by the rugged coast
range and Olympic Mountains. Washington's lavas are the
matrix of rich petrified wood and agate materials.

*Aberdeen, Grays Harbor*
*County*

FLOWER JASPER: On beaches
and in stream banks all

the way to Raymond.

*Adna, Lewis County*

CARNELIAN: Take road NW for 3½ miles to Ceres Road. Take Ceres Road S for 2 miles, dig E of road and in creek.

*Anacortes, Skagit County*

JASPER PEBBLES: On beach.

*Beverly, Grant County*

OPALIZED LOGS: In volcanic ash on slopes of Saddle Mountains S of hwy from Beverly to Corfu. Access to summit and N slopes via road S from Corfu.

PETRIFIED WOOD: Take Hwy 243 S 14 miles to Vernita ferry. Drive up bluffs on W side of river to cafe, ask way to Bennett claim. (Fee.) Or go 6 miles upstream to wooden bridge over Crab Creek and collect on N bank of creek or in hills.

*Bucoda, Thurston County*

AGATE, JASPER: Take road S to Tono, then over hill to coal mine spoil piles. Dig by creek bed, or go to right to dig from under clay stratum.

*Chehalis, Lewis County*

CARNELIAN: E and S in gravels of Lucas and Cedar Creeks.

Also go 5 miles S on Hwy 99 and E 4 miles to bridge, and collect in gravels of N fork of Newaukum River.

*Clearwater, Jefferson County*

AGATE, PETRIFIED WOOD: As pebbles on Kalaloch Beach.

*Cle Elum, Kittitas County*

BLUE AGATE: Widely distributed from Leavenworth along Hwy 97 S to Yakima. Some specific locations: Take Hwy 97 3 miles NE to steel bridge, cross, take road left 15 miles to Jack Creek sign. Turn right on this road and continue for 5 miles up mountain to a fork. Take left road almost 1 mile. Dig nodules in cliff up the bank or through woods on right. Also take Hwy 97 NE through Virden, then follow Blue Creek Road left at Mineral Springs gas station for 9 miles. Park, take upper trail to ridge, and dig. Also take Hwy 97 N through Virden, then right beyond second bridge that crosses creek. Walk ¼ mile up road and to left up hill. Dig in basalt cliffs.

*Concrete, Skagit County*

JADE, SERPENTINE: Take Dallas Bridge Road S 10 miles toward Darrington, keeping left at fork. Take Finney Creek Road right and follow creek on left 13 miles, using Gee Point Road to parking area. Collect in first creek.

*Duvall, King County*

BLACK PETRIFIED WOOD: Take Hwy 203 N, stay N at fork for 3 miles, cross Cherry Creek, and go 2½ miles more to road E up hill. Take it 1 mile to fork, then right to second fork, and stay right to locked gate. Hike 1 mile through woods to creek to collect.

*Forks, Clallam County*

ORBICULAR JASPER: Go N on Hwy 101 to Calawah and Soleduck rivers, collect in gravel and along banks. Also just SW of Lake Crescent.

PETRIFIED WOOD: Take Hwy 97 S for 13 miles to parking area on right where footbridge crosses river. Dig on hillsides across river.

*Gilmore Corners, Cowlitz County*

BLOODSTONE, CARNELIAN: Take Sightly Road S until it turns E, continue E to first road S, take it to Walter Swift farmhouse. Collect in area to E. (Fee.)

*Issaquah, Kings County*

AMBER: Go S on Hobart road 3 miles, turn E on Tiger Mountain Road for 1½ miles and then N on dirt road. Go ½ mile to E side of Fifteen-mile Creek, collect in place and on E side of road. (Get permission at caretaker's house.)

*Kalaloch, Jefferson County*

BEACH AGATE, PETRIFIED WOOD: N and S to Queets along beach.

*Liberty, Kittitas County*

QUARTZ CRYSTALS, PETRIFIED WOOD, JASPER: Take road SE along Boulder Creek to fork. Park and take trail up Robinson Gulch 2½ miles to Crystal Mountain.

*Lyle, Klickitat County*

AGATE, JASPER, PETRIFIED WOOD: To N 10 to 15 miles in gullies and on hillsides.

*Mount Vernon, Skagit County*

JADELIKE MATERIAL: In talc on SW side of Cultus Mountain. Take road from Clear Lake E 3½ miles to mine.

*Newport, Pend Oreille County*

AMETHYSTINE QUARTZ: On W bank of Pend Oreille

River 2 miles NW.

*Olympia, Thurston County*
AGATE, PETRIFIED WOOD: In sand to S at Tono.

*Palisades, Douglas County*
OPALIZED WOOD: To W of road at Moses coulee and S to Appledale.

*Pasco, Franklin County*
AGATE: In bluffs on E bank of Columbia River to NW.

*Port Angeles, Clallam County*
JASPER PEBBLES: At Agate and Crescent Beaches.

*Prosser, Benton County*
OPALIZED WOOD: In volcanic ash in canyons of Horse Heaven Hills.

*Riverside, Okanogan County*
PINK THULITE: To NE at Tunk Creek.

*Roosevelt, Klickitat County*
PETRIFIED WOOD: Take Hwy 12 7 miles E to Pine Creek, turn N up road on left bank to canyon and 2 miles to Ford Creek. Dig in E bank of creek.

*Sunnyside, Yakima County*
PETRIFIED WOOD: In road cuts on road to White bluffs.

*Tenino, Thurston County*
CARNELIAN, JASPER: Go to Johnson Creek Road, then 5½ miles E to Rocking B ranch. Collect above creek. Also take Hwy 507 S to Skookumchuck Road, go E for 7 miles to John-son Creek Road, then N ⅓ mile to Anderson house. (Fee.)

*Toledo, Lewis County*
CARNELIAN: Take any road E or N to Salmon Creek, collect in river bars.

*Valley, Stevens County*
RED MARBLE: Take Waits Lake Road W to Carr's Corner, go left 6 miles to quarry.

*Warwick, Klickitat County*
CARNELIAN, GREEN JASPER: W 2 miles at bridge over wash in Hwy 8. Collect in fields and wash.

*Westport, Grays Harbor County*
JASPER, AGATE, PETRIFIED WOOD: Look among the pebbles on beach for gem material.

*Wiley, Yakima County*
PETRIFIED WOOD: To S at Ahtanum ridge petrified palm wood has been found.

*Woodland, Cowlitz County*
CARNELIAN: Go N on U.S. 99 5 miles to Cloverdale, then E on Todd Road to Cloverdale Road and N and E to Green Mountain Road. Collect in Cloverdale Creek.

*Yakima, Yakima County*
OPALIZED WOOD: In wash 33 miles E and mile N of Hwy 24 at Yakima Ridge.

## WEST VIRGINIA

The western two-thirds of West Virginia is a rough area of hills and valleys cut in sedimentary rocks and forming a part of the Allegheny plateau that extends from New York to Alabama. The eastern half lies in the Great Valley, in which mountain ridges and valleys have been the result of intense folding and erosion of the sedimentary rocks.

*Berkeley Springs, Morgan County*

QUARTZ CRYSTALS: In Pennsylvania Glass Sand Corporation pit quartz crystals have been found.

## WISCONSIN

Wisconsin is a rolling plain laid down on sedimentary rocks and broken in places by upthrust igneous and metamorphic rocks, such as the Baraboo Hills in the south central region, the granite exposures in Waushara and Marathon counties, and the gneisses of the northeastern part of the state. Wisconsin's extensive glaciation is shown by its many lakes and the famous moraine district west of Milwaukee.

LAKE SUPERIOR TYPE AGATES (DERIVED FROM GLACIAL GRAVELS): Are found in a number of places in Wisconsin. Among them are:

Along Hwy 64 E of New Richmond and generally from Hudson to New Richmond.

Just W of Hudson at gravel plant in Minnesota.

On gravel bars of the Hay River.

H. Turner and Son Plant at Cassville.

At Rush River Plant where Rush River crosses Hwy 10.

At the River Falls Sand and

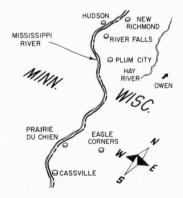

Gravel Plant.

At Owen in gravels of Black River.

At Dillman Plant on Villa Louis Road in Prairie du Chien.

Bock Bros. Plant at Eagle Corners.

*Dickeyville, Grant County*
ONYX: Take Hwy 151 for 4 miles, then dirt road right to pine tree on hill at quarry.

*Pepin, Pepin County*
AGATE: On beaches on Lake Pepin and at Deer Island to N.

*Pittsville, Wood County*
RED AND GREEN AVENTURINE QUARTZ: To S.

*Redgranite, Waushara County*
PINK GRANITE: In quarries to NW.

*Waupaca, Waupaca County*
RED AND GREEN GRANITE: N 5 miles in quarry.

*Wausau, Marathon County**
LABRADORITE: At Anderson Bros. and Johnson quarry.

## WYOMING

Much of Wyoming consists of rolling prairie more than a mile above sea level, broken by occasional buttes and erosion ridges. The northeastern part is a continuation of the Black Hills, while through the central part from east to west runs a long pass or valley below the Big Horn Mountains in north central Wyoming. Northwestern Wyoming is a complex region of igneous intrusions and upturned sedimentary rocks which holds the marvels of Yellowstone Park, the majesty of the Tetons, and the beautiful Wind River range to the south. Agate and petrified wood of many types exist in the gravels of all the regions, and jade in the eroded mountain ridges of the south central part.

*Buffalo, Johnson County*
PETRIFIED WOOD: SE 12 miles along Crazy Woman Creek.

*Casper, Natrona County*
PETRIFIED WOOD: Along N bank of North Platte River E to Glenrock.

CARNELIAN: To W in area between Poison Spider Creek and S fork of Casper Creek.

*Cheyenne, Laramie County*
CHALCEDONY: In gravels to W.
QUARTZ CRYSTALS: In Cheyenne Pass.

*Chugwater, Platte County*

MOSS AGATE: In Reshaw Creek.

BLOODSTONE: In Chugwater Creek.

*Douglas, Converse County**

BLUE MOSS AGATE: Two collecting localities near graded road S to U.S. 30: first, Moss Agate Hill, about 30 miles SW of Douglas, a prominent hill W of road.

Second, S of this locale about halfway to a place known as Coldspring lying in the Laramie Mountains— Specimen Hill, for dark blue moss agate in masses. E of road black agate is found on the ground.

*Dubois, Fremont County*

PETRIFIED FOREST: Drive 30 miles N to Wiggins Fork Creek, then 15 miles to edge of wilderness area; hike or ride horseback up canyon to Emerald Creek to Emerald Lake. Canyon is lined with logs. (Some restrictions on collecting.)

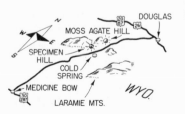

*Farson, Sweetwater County*

PETRIFIED (EDEN VALLEY) WOOD: Take Hwy 28 15 miles to sign, "Hay Ranch 4 Miles," turn on ranch road right through ranch and turn E at north gate and go 5 miles to collect on top of hills.

*Glendo, Platte County*

CHALCEDONY: NE in hills along North Platte River.

*Granger, Sweetwater County*

SILICIFIED SHELLS (TURRITELLA AGATE): In ledge capping buttes to E along Hwy 30N and 30 as far as Blacks Fork.

AGATE: In badlands along Hams Fork.

*Guernsey, Platte County*

RED AND MOSS AGATE: NW 2 miles at Wilde and Deercorn mine.

*Kemmerer, Lincoln County*

AGATE, PETRIFIED WOOD (TEMPSKYA): In hills to S and SW.

*Kortes Dam, Carbon County*

BLACK JADE: On Kortes Ranch.

*Lander, Fremont County*

NEPHRITE JADE: Over wide area in Fremont County in place or as boulders. Dark colored float jade is found along the course of the Sweetwater River between Crook's Creek on the E and the Wind River Mountains on the W.

BLACK JADE: Is found generally in the Granite Mountains and N of Split Rock.

LIGHT GREEN JADE: Has come from the Crook's Mountain area 65 miles SE of Lander and from the E side of Cottonwood Creek wherever black diorite boulders appear. To reach this area, take Hwy 287 12 miles past the Sweetwater River crossing and turn S for 8 miles.

NEPHRITE JADE: Abernathy claims, Fremont County, 40 miles SE of Lander, in diorite dike in granite, the material contains quartz crystals.

Curtis and Marion claims, Sec. 13, 18, T. 30, R. 92, 93 W; black, olive green outcrop ½ mile SW of this one. ,

Lucky Strike Claim, Secs. 19, 20, T. 30 N., R. 92 W., 61 miles from Lander, olive green pieces containing quartz crystals, at apex of a fold.

As float near Marston Lake, 40 miles from Lander, and at Moneta, Fremont County.

Copper Chief Gold Mine: 3 miles NE of Atlantic City, Fremont County.

Olive green, outcrop of East fork NE of Dubois and NE of Circle Ranch, Fremont County.

As float along Beaver Creek, 25 miles SE of Lander along Hwy 287, Fremont County.

In Green Mountains, 20 miles W of Bairoil, Fremont County.

Pathfinder Dam, Natrona County.

Along Dry Creek in Rattlesnake Mountains, Natrona County.

JADE, NEPHRITE, BLACK: As float over large area S of upper drainage of Sulfur Creek, 30 miles W of Bairoil, Fremont County.

*Medicine Bow, Carbon County*

PETRIFIED WOOD, AGATE: N 18 miles and take right fork 13 miles to petrified forest to·W of road.

PETRIFIED WOOD, BONE: To E at Como Bluff.

*Riverton, Fremont County*

MOSS AGATE NODULES: Take dirt road that runs W to Hwy 287; park where wires cross above road and collect in washes to NE.

PETRIFIED WOOD, AGATE: In

gravels and streams in area between Hwy 287 N from Lander and Hwy 26 W from Riverton.

*Sage Hen Creek Area, Fremont County\**

SWEETWATER TYPE MOSS AGATES: Are found in southeastern Fremont County to the SE of the Wind River and N of the Sweetwater River. The best are found along Sage Hen Creek. They are loose on the ground or dug from the beds. Those dug are covered with a white coating. The collecting area is reached by going 20 miles W on U.S. 287 from the intersection with Hwy 220 and turning N through ranch gate, continuing through ranch yard and to flats beyond.

AGATE, JADE: Ten miles farther W on U.S. 287, a road turns S to Crooks Gap, where agate and some jade have been found.

*Saratoga, Carbon County\**

PETRIFIED WOOD: On flats along Hwy 130 N to Walcott. The flats from Saratoga N to Walcott are strewn with petrified wood and chalcedony, especially on the E side just N of a road cut.

*Shell, Big Horn County*

PETRIFIED WOOD AND BONE: N 4 miles at Elkhorn ranch.

*Shoshoni, Fremont County*

AQUAMARINE: In dikes 15 miles

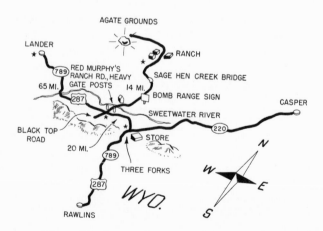

AGATE GROUNDS

LANDER

RED MURPHY'S RANCH RD., HEAVY GATE POSTS

65 MI.

789

287

14 MI.

RANCH

SAGE HEN CREEK BRIDGE

BOMB RANGE SIGN

SWEETWATER RIVER

CASPER

220

BLACK TOP ROAD

20 MI.

789

STORE

THREE FORKS

287

*WYO.*

RAWLINS

N
W E
S

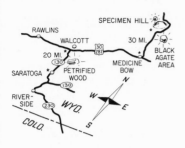

NE in Bridger Mountains.
*South Pass City, Fremont
County*
PETRIFIED WOOD: To N on
divide between Hall and
Twin creeks.
*Split Rock, Fremont County*
RUBY: In schist on Sweetwater
divide.
JADE: In place at American
Jade Company claim N
of junction of Longs Creek
and Sweetwater River.
*Tipton, Sweetwater County\**
BROWN ALGAE AGATE, OÖLITE,

FOSSIL FISH, SILICIFIED
SHELLS, "TURRITELLA"
AGATE: South of the ham-
let of Tipton on Hwy 30
lies a mesalike area known
locally as Delaney's Rim.
Along the southwest edge
is found the beautiful
brown algae agate, and
above, in huge blocks,
silicified oölite, and blocks
of layered sandstone con-
taining fossil fish. Loose
in the debris of the top
of the area are silicified
shells, the so-called "turritella" agate.

*Wamsutter, Sweetwater County*
SILICIFIED (TURRITELLA) AGATE,
PETRIFIED WOOD: Go S 8
miles toward Baggs, then
W on Ranch Road 15
miles to barn, continue
past barn and corrals,
then take trail right over

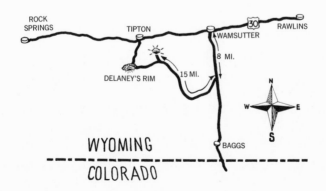

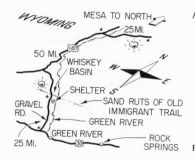

AGATE: A gravel road that takes off N from Hwy 30 a few miles W of Green River leads in 25 miles to the ruts of the old immigrant trail and to an area known as Whiskey Basin. To the W are hills where agate is found.

PETRIFIED WOOD: Another 50 miles up the road is a road to the right and a crossing of the river. It winds within 25 miles between two mesas to N and S that carry petrified wood limbs of the Eden Valley type.

*Worland, Washakie County*

CHALCEDONY: To W of town chalcedony has been found.

ridge a mile to escarpment. Algae agate is found on ridge W of barn, and black petrified wood in gullies. Wood is also found along the road S from Wamsutter to Baggs.

*Whiskey Basin Area, Sweetwater and Sublette Counties\**

# Canada

## ALBERTA

Most of the province is a part of the vast continental plain of Canada, but on the west its boundary is set by the Rocky Mountains, which rise in places to 10,000 feet. The southern part of the plain is prairie, while the northern part is rolling and wooded.

*Calgary*

PETRIFIED WOOD: E 90 miles in Red Deer River Valley. The wood is limb sections like Eden Valley wood.

## BRITISH COLUMBIA

Mountains cover almost all of British Columbia, from the Rockies to the Coast ranges. These were formed by giant granite masses forcing up the Coast and Selkirk ranges, and the overthrust toward the east that created the Rockies. Later, lavas poured into the lower part of the province, as they did in the United States farther south, and the exposed rocks were carved into valleys by glaciers of the ice ages. Most of the mineralization has been in the western ranges, while vast quantities of quartz, jade and petrified wood are contained in the enormous deposits of gravel along the rivers.

*Canim Lake*

PERIDOT: At Timothy Mountain in Cariboo Mountains.

*Clinton*

AGATE NODULES: Take Hwy 97 N to road to Dog Creek, take it across Fraser River, then S through Empire Valley ranch to collecting area 3 miles S of Black Dome.

*Fort St. James*

AGATE: At beach at Sowchea Bay on Stuart Lake.

*Francois Lake*

RED AGATE: On N shore of lake beyond end of road.

*Kamloops*

GREEN JASPER: On Sunday Summit.

MOSS AGATE: E 27 miles on Vernon Road at Monte Lake.

W 3 miles at Mission Flats.

AGATE NODULES: At Bernhardt's

vale and 20 miles S at Douglas Lake.

FIRE OPAL: In Deadman's Creek Valley.

AGATE, JASPER: In Tranquille Creek area and to W to Dew Drop Road.

AGATE, AMETHYST GEODES: Between highway and Kamloops Lake, E of Cherry Creek.

*Keremeos*

RHODONITE, RED JASPER: In slide area at gravel pits beyond road fork.

*Lytton**

JADE, JASPER, PETRIFIED WOOD, RHODONITE: In the vast river terraces and gravel bars of the Fraser River from Chilliwack N to the Bridge River and NW in the Yalakom, Coquihalla and Lillooet Rivers.

JADE, JASPER: To E in the Thompson River as far as

Spences Bridge, especially
at rock slide 4 miles down
river from Spences Bridge.

*Penticton*

AMETHYST, GEODES: W 8 miles
on Green Mountain Road.

*Prince George*

JASPER, AGATE: In gravels of
Delta of Necheko River
within city limits, and 8
miles W at Miworth gravel
pit on S side of river, and
7 miles W on N side of
river.

*Princeton*

AGATE, PETRIFIED WOOD: At
Vermillion Bluffs along
Tulameen River and
Agate Bluffs and in nearby
stream gravels.

*Queen Charlotte Islands*

AGATE PEBBLES: On N shore
of Graham Island.

*Savona*

MOSS AGATE, JASPER: To S at
Savona Mountain.

*Squilax*

AMETHYST NODULES, BLUE
AGATE: Above road at
Little River Camp on
Little Shuswap Lake.

CARNELIAN: At Little River.

*Trail*

PREHNITE: In Le Roi mine 7
miles W at Rossland.

*Vanderhoof*

AGATE: In streams along road
to Kenney Dam.

*Victoria, Vancouver Island*

JASPER: At beach at foot of
Dallas Road.

RED JASPER: 8 miles N Mill Bay.

RHODONITE: On Hill 60 near
Lake Cowichan.

## MANITOBA

Northeastern Manitoba is covered by rocks of the great shield that forms much of central Canada, but below Lake Winnipeg these dip below the limestones, forming a more fertile region. The southwest corner of the province is a plateau of younger sedimentary rocks.

*Cedar Lake*
AMBER: On beach on SW edge near mouth of Saskatchewan River.

## NEW BRUNSWICK

Most of the province is a lowland of sedimentary rocks, but granite rocks are exposed in the western areas and the more rugged northern part.

*Dalhousie, Restigouche County*
CHALCEDONY GEODES: On W side of Little Dipper Harbor.
AGATE: On beaches of Chaleur Bay.
*Grand Manan Island, Charlotte County*
AMETHYST: In geodes.

*Hillsborough, Albert County*
ALABASTER: In gypsum quarry.
*Upsalquitch, Restigouche County*
AMETHYST: Above forks of Upsalquitch River 7 miles.
*St. Martins, St. John County*
JASPER: At Cave View Beach.

## NEWFOUNDLAND

Newfoundland is the northernmost extension of the Appalachian Mountain system that skirts the Atlantic Ocean in the United States. The province is a low plateau of ancient rocks rounded and scraped by extensive glacial action which has filled the valleys with drift. Labrador, which is administered as a part of Newfoundland, is the eastern tip of the great shield of ancient Laurentian crystalline rocks which are the source of most of Canada's mineral wealth.

## 246 / Canada

*Lawn, Placentia West County*
AMETHYST: In dumps of La-
   Manche mine.
*Nain, Labrador*
LABRADORITE: On Paul Island.

On Tabor's Island labradorite has been reported.
On Black Island labradorite
   has been reported.
At Ford's Harbor.

## NORTHWEST TERRITORIES

The northeastern part of this large region is an arctic prairie of thin soil and almost entirely devoid of trees. Most of the rest of the territories is covered with forests, except the desolate Arctic Islands of which Baffin Island is the principal example.

*Fox Islands, Great Slave Lake*
SAPPHIRE: At Philmore Mine.

## NOVA SCOTIA

Like southeastern Quebec and New Brunswick, Nova Scotia shows the Appalachian topography which dominates the eastern landscape of the United States. It is an ancient mountain land, much folded and intruded by granite, especially south of Halifax. Erosion has created the valleys that are the routes of communication, and sinking of the land has further left its mark in the harbors and offshore islands.

*Bay of Fundy\**
AGATE, AMETHYST: The best
   collecting spot on the Bay
   of Fundy is near Sandy

Cove on Digby Neck. It is possible to drive to the shore. Agate seams in the boulders and in the rock

—red, black, and gray, including some cameo material, as well as amethyst—can be collected with hammer and chisel.

*Chester, Lunenberg County*

QUARTZ CRYSTALS: In Joe Bell Brook.

*Granville Center, Annapolis County*

CARNELIAN.

*Minas Basin**

AGATE: Two locations for collecting agate in Nova Scotia that are accessible by car are in the Minas Basin. The first is the Two Islands area reached by taking the shore road from Parrsboro and continuing past the golf course until the road approaches the edge of the cliff. This is 2 or 3 miles. A trail leads down the cliff to the collecting area, which extends several miles each way. Look for brown, yellow, and red jasp-agate veins among the boulders that contain chalcedony of a lacy pattern. The beach is covered at high tide, so get the tide timing for the day at Parrsboro.

The second location is on Moose Island across the inlet from Bruce Patterson's Island View Motor Court at Lower Five Islands. Agate and amethyst are collected on the island. (Bruce Patterson will take collectors over in his boat.)

AGATE, AMETHYST: Nearby in Kings County are amethyst and seam agate at Cape Blomidon and Scotts Bay.

Partridge Island and Cape Sharp, in Cumberland County, also have amethyst in geodes and seams.

*Lake Ramsay, Lunenburg County*

SMOKY QUARTZ.

*Pictou, Pictou County*

JET: In coal mines.

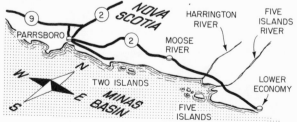

## ONTARIO

Southeastern Ontario is a fertile area of glacial soils bordering the lakes. To the northeast lies more rolling country set off by a great ridge known as the Niagara escarpment. North and west of Lake Superior, however, Ontario is part of the vast Laurentian or Pre-Cambrian shield of granite and other crystalline rocks containing gold and other minerals. (Sites are arranged by location and not necessarily alphabetically.)

*Bancroft, Hastings County*

SODALITE: Take road E toward Hermon 2 miles to two gravel pits left of road and go over hill above second pit.

At Lots 25 and 29 of Concession 12 in Dungannon Township.

At Lot 12, Concession 11.

At the Golding-Keene quarry on the W side of the York River, and N of the Bancroft-Hermon Road.

*Bird Creek, Hastings County*

PERISTERITE: Near road N of Bird Creek.

At the Burnham mine, Lot 3, Concession 10, in Portland Township, Frontenac County.

At Lot 9, Concession 9, in Bathhurst Township, Lanark County.

AMAZONITE: Reported at the Woodcox mine in Monteagle Township, Hastings County.

SUNSTONE: In pegmatite at Lot 3, Concession 6, in North Burgess Township, Lanark County.

*Drag Lake, Haliburton County*

PERISTERITE: In Dudley Township.

*Hybla, Hastings County*

AMAZONITE, PINK PERISTERITE: At McDonald mine across

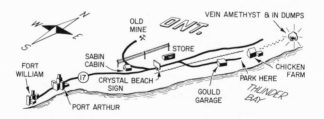

VEIN AMETHYST & IN DUMPS
OLD MINE
ONT.
STORE
SABIN CABIN
FORT WILLIAM
17 CRYSTAL BEACH SIGN
CHICKEN FARM
PARK HERE
GOULD GARAGE
THUNDER BAY
PORT ARTHUR

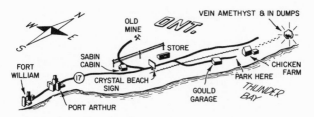

from Hunsol home. (Fee.)

*Kingston, Frontenac County\**

(Map on next page.)

QUARTZ: The Steele quartz crystal mine E of Kingston, Ontario, produces optical quartz and has many small crystals in the dump and larger crystals that are not of suitable quality for optical use for sale at the mine. The mine is reached by crossing the Thousand Island Bridge from New York, taking the road along the St. Lawrence River left to Gananoque, then north 11.9 miles on Hwy 32, turning right on a dirt road at cemetery. Take dirt road 2.3 miles to small store and keep on right fork here for 3.2 miles to a road intersection where there is a school on the left. Go right 1.6 miles across Black Rapids Bridge, and then take a left fork to a farmhouse. (At farmhouse permission can be obtained to collect at mine.)

*Kearney, Parry Sound County*

AQUAMARINE: In pegmatite in Butt Township.

*Nolalu, Thunder Bay County \**

AMETHYST, FLUORITE, STEPHENITE (rare silver mineral): Not far above the border in Ontario is an old silver mine S of Nolalu. Take the road E of that village to the Aleck Teukula house near the mine. (Permission can be obtained there to collect.)

*Michipicoton Island, Lake Superior*

CARNELIAN, AGATE: At Schaefers Bay in boulders.

At Agate Islet in Quebec Harbor on south shore.

At headland E of Cozens Harbor.

SE shore where there are seams of agate in rock.

THOMSONITE: Found in basalt on some of the beaches.

*Port Arthur, Thunder Bay County\**

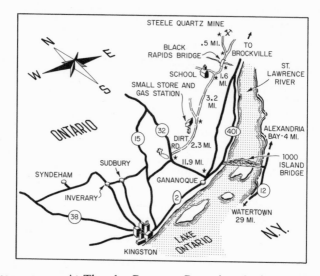

MOSS AGATE: At Thunder Bay.

JASPER: At Kakabeka Falls.

AMETHYST: Not many miles north of Port Arthur is the hamlet of Crystal Beach along Hwy 17. By taking a road left at the sign for Crystal Beach it is possible to reach a good amethyst collecting area on a back ridge where silver was once mined. (The property belongs to a St. Paul man named Sabin and his written permission is needed to enter. The guard is a man named Carron who lives just north of the Sabin house.)

By going farther north on Hwy 17, then turning across railroad tracks just before reaching a store, you will wind up at a garage. Take a side road to a chicken ranch, and from this spot a trail leads up to a ridge where there is amethyst in place and in the dumps.

*Quadville, Renfrew County*

AQUAMARINE: In pegmatite in Lot 23, Concession 15.

*Rossport, Thunder Bay County\**

AGATE: On islands along N shore of Lake Superior.

On beach of Salter Island W of Old Man's Pocket Harbor.

GREEN AND WHITE AGATE: On S shore of Copper Island green and white agate is found.

PREHNITE, GREEN AGATE: On W shore of Wilson Island and at E end of S shore.

AGATE, PREHNITE: On S shore of Simpson Island. (Guides and boats can be engaged in Rossport for the trip.)

*Sault Ste. Marie, Algoma County*

AGATE: On shore at Goulais Bay 15 miles N, agate can be found.

THOMSONITE: In lava 40 miles N on beach at Mamainse Point.

RED AND GREEN JASPER: E 39 miles along Hwy 17 at Bruce Mines is found red and green jasper.

*Stony Lake, Peterborough County*

BROWN SAPPHIRE: On ridge at lake.

BLUE SAPPHIRE: In Burleigh Township on Lot 7, Concession 12 blue sapphire has been found and reported.

SAPPHIRE: At Lot 2, Concession 9, Burgess Township (Hastings County) sapphire has been reported to have been found.

E of York River on Lot 12, Concession 14, Dungannon Township sapphire has also been reported to have been found.

PERISTERITE: On N shore of Stony Lake near mouth of Eel Creek, in Burleigh Township.

*Wilberforce, Haliburton County*

APATITE: At Fission Mine in Monmouth Township, apatite has been reported to have been found.

At Liscombe Mine ¾ mile to SW.

PINK PERISTERITE: E 4 miles at Richardson Mine pink peristerite has been discovered and reported.

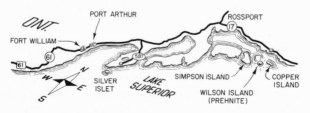

## QUEBEC

Most of Quebec lies within the Canadian or Laurentian shield, a vast area of ancient granites and gneisses, covered with thin glacial deposits and dotted with typical glacial lakes. A part of this region near Lake Abitibi on the Ontario border is rich in minerals. Most of the population of the province lives in the sedimentary St. Lawrence area which lies in the bed of the former Champlain Sea. Eastern Quebec is Appalachian, like much of eastern Canada, formed of sedimentary rocks broken by granite hills.

*Black Lake, Megantic County*
PURPLE IDOCRASE: At Montreal Chrome pit in Coleraine Township.
SERPENTINE: In Megantic mine.

*Buckingham, Papineau County*
PERISTERITE: At Lot 2, Range 5 of West Portland Township.
At Villeneuve mine, Lot 31, Range 1 of Villeneuve Township.

*Calumet Falls, Pontiac County*
BROWN TOURMALINE: In Litchfield Township brown tourmaline has been found.

*Château Richer, Montmorency County*
LABRADORITE.

*Hull, Gatineau County*
MASSIVE, CRYSTALLINE GROSSULARITE GARNET: N 21 miles on right bank of Gatineau River.

*Labelle Station, Labelle County*
GARNET: In quarry 2 miles S on Canadian Pacific Railroad right-of-way.

*St. Jerome, Terrebonne County*
LABRADORITE: Nearby and at St. Morin.

*Sherbrooke, Sherbrooke County*
RED JASPER.

*Wakefield, Gatineau County*
SERPENTINE: 2 miles SE at Canadian Aluminium Company quarry.

## *Mexico*

Most of Mexico is a high plateau, underlain by folded sedimentary rocks and extensively altered by thick layers of volcanic rocks. Mountains linked with American ranges border both coasts. Baja California, for instance, is a continuation of the California Coast range. Between the mountains and the sea on both coasts are narrow lowlands. Southeastern Mexico belongs to the mountainous Central American plateau. Yucatán is a low limestone plain. In many respects Mexico resembles the Great Basin area of the United States.

## BAJA CALIFORNIA

*Ensenada*
PREHNITE: S 50 miles at Punta China.

*Mexicali*
BANDED RHYOLITE: W 26½ miles on Tijuana Highway, turn N 4½ miles on jeep road to collect at N end of Pinto Mountains.

*Rancho Viejo*
TOURMALINE: In pegmatite 2 miles S at Socorro mine.

SPHENE, TOURMALINATED QUARTZ, EPIDOTE: At Pino Solo near Rancho Viejo in pegmatite pits 100 yards N of landmark tree and 300 yards W.

ALABASTER: Take Hwy 1 SE to San Agustin, then 10 miles E to quarry for alabaster (onyx).

TURQUOISE: S 23 miles in dumps of La Turquesa mine.

## CHIHUAHUA

*Chihuahua*
AGATE: There are enormous deposits of banded agate nodules on ranches from 45 miles S of El Paso, Texas, all the way to Chihuahua. (Private claims.)

## DURANGO

*Durango*
APATITE CRYSTALS: In dumps at Cerro de Mercado iron mine.

AGATE NODULES: Take Mazatlán Highway 17 miles to first bridge, then 1¾ miles more, collect in road cut to right.

## GUERRERO

*Balsas*
AMETHYST.

*Huitzuco*
FIRE OPAL.

*Real del Monte*
CAT'S-EYE OBSIDIAN: At Aztec obsidian mine.

*Zimapan*
FIRE OPAL.

## HIDALGO

*Hidalgo*
FIRE OPAL: In rhyolite, at Bar-

ranca de Tepezala in Atotonilco district.

*Pachuca*
GOLDEN SHEEN OBSIDIAN: 10 miles E near Atotonilco at the Serro de la Navajas.

*Rosarito*
AGATE: On beach one mile N of hotel.

*Tecate*
ROSE QUARTZ: S 32 miles.

## JALISCO

*Guadalajara*
OBSIDIAN: Take Tepic-Mazatlán Highway 16 miles, collect before reaching Tequila.

Continue through Tequila to La Magdalena, get guide to tour opal mine.

## MICHOACAN

*Tulancingo*
OBSIDIAN.

## MORELOS

*Xalostoc*
GROSSULARITE GARNET.

## PUEBLA

*Puebla*
ALABASTER: At La Pedrara quarry in Tecali district, 21 miles SE.

## QUERETARO

*Cardereita Mendez*
OBSIDIAN.

*Queretaro*
FIRE AND CHERRY OPAL: At Santa Maria Esperanza mine, take Toliman Road NE 20 miles to mine on right-hand side of road.

FIRE OPAL: Also mined at La Jurada nearby.

At the La Purisma mine in Amelaco district.

At Trinidad, 11 miles NE of San Juan del Rio.

OBSIDIAN: Along highway from Queretero to San Juan del Rio.

## SAN LUIS POTOSI

*Cerro della Enramada*
FIRE OPAL.

*Guadalcazar*
BLUE AND WHITE DUMORTIERITE.

*San Luis Potosí*
AGATE NODULES: Take Hwy 80 SW 12 miles to dam, then backtrack $\frac{1}{2}$ mile and collect on N side of road.

FIRE AGATE: S 45 miles on Tula Hill just N of El Tule Road.

# SONORA

*Navojoa*
BLACK CHALCEDONY.

# ZACATECAS

*Bonanza*
TURQUOISE: On mine dumps in Sierra de Santa Rosa.

*Pinos*
WHITE TOPAZ: In rhyolite at Hacienda del Tepetate white topaz has been discovered and the finds reported in recent years.

*Zacatecas*
AMETHYST: N 6 miles in dumps of El Bote mine gem material is found.

# 13

# *Glossary*

ABALONE: a shellfish of the genus *Haliotis,* noted for the variegated color of its pearly shell.

ACICULAR (a-sick'-u-ler): needle shaped, referring to mineral.

ACTIVATOR: foreign substance that causes mineral to fluoresce.

ADAMANTINE (ad-a-man'-tin): having luster like diamond.

ALLUVIAL (a-lew'-vi-al): sand or silt deposited by running water.

AMORPHOUS (a-mor'-fus): without crystal structure.

AMPHIBOLE (am'-fi-bole): a group of silicates that are common rock-forming minerals, usually dark.

AMYGDALOIDAL (a-mig'-dah-loyd-al): volcanic rock containing small round gas cavities, which are often filled with other minerals.

ANDALUSITE: an aluminum silicate, of which chiastolite is a variety.

ANGSTROM UNIT: unit used to measure wave lengths of light; equals $\frac{1}{250,000,000}$ inch.

ARAGONITE (a-rag'-o-nite): a mineral composed, like calcite, of calcium carbonate, but differing in crystallization and physical properties.

ARROYO (a-roi'-oh): creek, or its dry channel.

ASPARAGUS STONE: yellowish green apatite.

ASTERIATED (as-ter'-i-a-ted): showing starlike pattern.

AXIS: imaginary line fixing structural direction in crystal.

BAR: sand or gravel bank in stream.

BASAL: cleavage parallel to the base of the crystal.

BASALT (bah-sawlt'): dark, fine-grained igneous rock formed principally of feldspar, iron, and magnesium minerals.

BATHOLITH (bath'-o-lith): igneous rock formation of vast extent that was formed deep underground.

BIRTHSTONES: January—garnet, February—amethyst, March—bloodstone, April—diamond, May—emerald, June—pearl, July—ruby, August—sardonyx, September—sapphire, October—opal, November—topaz, December—turquoise.

BLADED: elongated, flat, thin.

BLANK: a slice or slab of gem material cut to the basic shape of the stone.

BOTRYOIDAL (bot-ri-oi'-dahl): shaped in rounded, grapelike masses.

BUFF: a wheel of felt, wood, or leather for polishing gem stones.

BUTTE (beaut): isolated hill or small mountain with very steep sides.

CABOCHON (ka'-beau-shon): gem cut with convex, rounded, unfaceted surface.

CANCRINITE: silicate and carbonate of sodium, calcium, and aluminum, found as masses of various colors in igneous rocks.

CARAT: unit of weight, usually 200 milligrams (about $\frac{1}{150}$ ounce).

CARBONATE: a salt of carbonic acid; that is, a compound of a metal with carbon and oxygen.

CAST: mineral taking shape of cavity left in rock by decay of plant or animal.

CAT'S-EYE: a gem showing a sharp streak of light across it caused by reflections from fibers within the stone.

CATTLE GUARD: loose pipes laid parallel on the ground at gate or opening to stop cattle, which are frightened by uncertain footing.

CHALK: a soft limestone of earthy character.

CHATOYANT (sha-toi'-aunt): reflecting light in form of moving or undulating streak—like a cat's eye in the dark.

CHLORITE: group of hydrous silicates, usually green.

CLEAVAGE: splitting of a mineral along a smooth plane surface.

COLOR ZONE: striping or segregation of color within a crystal.

COLUMNAR: like a column, referring to crystal.

COMPOUND: distinct substance formed by union of two or more elements in definite proportions.

CONCHOIDAL (kong-koi'-dahl): concave, like inside of bivalve shell; referring to shape of fracture of a crystal.

CONCRETION: lump of unlike material in sedimentary rock.

CONTACT METAMORPHISM: change in rock in contact with intruding igneous rock.

COULEE (coo'-lee): steep-walled valley.

CRAZE: tendency of a gem material to develop fine cracks on the surface.

CRUST: outer rocky layer of the earth.

CRYPTOCRYSTALLINE (kript'-oh-kris'-tal-in): composed of crystals so minute that they are not visible.

CRYSTAL: solid bounded by planes that meet at characteristic and definite angles, expressing an orderly arrangement of atoms.

CRYSTALLINE: having definite visible crystal structure.

CUBIC: having the form of a cube, as many of the isometric system crystals.

DELTA: Deposit of sand and gravel at mouth of a river, often a large tract of land.

DENDRITIC (den-drit'-ik): branching, treelike; referring to patterns produced in a mineral by a foreign mineral, or a branching form of a mineral.

DIAPHANEITY (die-ah-fa-nee'-i-tee): ability of a substance to pass light, expressed as transparent, translucent, or opaque.

DICHROSCOPE (die'-crow-skope): optical device for splitting light refracted by gem into its constituent colors.

DIGGINGS: place where excavation has been made, as by a prospector.

DIKE: vertical, tabular body of rock cutting through major rock mass.

DOP: a metal or wooden rod to which the gem blank is cemented for holding in the cutting and polishing process.

DRUSY (droo'-zi): rock surface covered with minute crystals.

DUMP: pile of waste rock at mine or other excavation.

EFFERVESCENCE: bubbling gas in a liquid, such as that generated by reaction of acid with a carbonate.

ELECTRON: very small, lightweight particle of negative electricity that is a part of all matter.

ELEMENT: simplest natural unit of ordinary matter, such as iron or hydrogen.

EROSION (e-ro'-zhun): wearing away of rocks at earth's surface by action of natural agents.

ESCARPMENT: a long cliff, especially one formed by faulting.

EUCLASE: a beryllium and aluminum silicate.

EXTRUSIVE: form of igneous rock that solidifies on the earth's surface.

FACET: a flat face cut on a gem; a style of cutting with facets.

FAULT: displacement up or down of rocks in earth's crust along a fracture zone.

FELSITE: igneous rock composed of quartz and feldspar.

FIBROUS: mineral formed of thread or needlelike crystals.

FIRE: brilliance of a gem, caused by its ability to split up light.

FLAT: a level area, especially in a desert.

FLAW: an imperfection in a gem material, such as a crack or inclusion.

FLOAT: rock fragments found on surface some distance from outcrop or vein from which they came.

FLOWER: a form of agate showing a pattern variegated in color and design resembling a bouquet.

FLUORESCENCE: light of one color emitted by a substance when it is illuminated by light of another color (usually ultraviolet).

FOLIATED: capable of being separated into thin sheets, like mica.

FORTIFICATION: a form of agate with a pattern of angular stripes resembling battlements on a castle.

FOSSIL: evidence of past life preserved usually in rocks.

FRACTURE: texture of a freshly broken surface of rock or mineral.

GEODE (gee'-owed): mineral shell lined with crystals or filled with mineral.

GEOLOGY: science of the origin, history, and structure of the earth and life as they are recorded in the rocks.

GLACIAL DRIFT: earth, sand, and stones transported and deposited by a glacier.

GLACIATED: subjected to glacial action.

GLACIER: ice field moving down a slope or covering a continental area.

GLASSY: vitreous, resembling the luster of glass.

GNEISS (nice): crystalline metamorphic rock having banded appearance because of segregation of its minerals.

GRAM: metric measure of weight; there are 28.35 grams in an avoirdupois ounce.

GRANITE: light-colored crystalline rock composed mainly of quartz and feldspar, with mica and hornblende.

GROUND MASS: the fine-grained mass of a rock in which crystals, such as those of a porphyry, have formed.

GULCH: sharply cut bed of a torrent, a ravine.

HABIT: characteristic manner of occurrence of a mineral.

HACKLY: a jagged fracture like that of cast iron.

HARDNESS: degree of resistance of surface to being scratched.

HERKIMER DIAMOND: quartz crystal from the Herkimer County (N.Y.) region.

HEXAGONAL: belonging to a crystal system in which a vertical axis is intersected at right angles by three axes intersecting one another at 60 degrees.

HIGH GRADE: to pick out the high value, choice ore or gem material.

HORNBLENDE: commonest of the amphiboles, a black or dark green constituent of many granites.

HYDROUS: containing chemically combined water.

IGNEOUS (ig'-nee-us): formed by solidification of molten material from deep within the earth.

INCLUSION: enclosure of foreign material in a mineral.

INORGANIC: derived from or pertaining to the inanimate world.

INTARSIA: pattern or picture made by fitting precisely cut pieces of stone together, like mosaic.

INTRUSIVE: form of igneous rock that has hardened before reaching surface.

IRIDESCENCE: rainbow play of colors, like that of a soap film.

IRIS: a form of agate that shows rainbow colors when light passes through it.

ISOMETRIC (eye-so-met'-rik): crystal system in which all three axes are equal in length and meet at right angles.

LAP: a plate of metal or plastic revolving horizontally for cutting and polishing gem stones, usually used in faceting.

LAPIDARY: pertaining to the process of fashioning a gem stone, and the person who does it.

LAVA: igneous rock extruded to the surface, as by a volcano.

LIMESTONE: sedimentary rock formed mainly of calcium carbonate.

LODE: an ore deposit occurring within definite boundaries, a vein or ledge or reef.

LOESS (low'-ess): soil composed of silt deposited by wind.

LUMINESCENCE (lew'-mi-nes-ens): light emitted by a substance because of any stimulation except heating; a more general term than fluorescence.

LUSTER: appearance by reflected light of a fresh surface of a mineral.

MAGMA: molten rock deep inside the earth from which igneous rock comes.

MASSIVE: lacking definite structure or form.

MATRIX (may'-trix): rock in which a mineral is imbedded or to which it is attached.

MELT: molten rock material, known as magma, deep within the earth, from which igneous rocks are derived.

MESA: flat-topped hill with steep sides.

METAMORPHIC: rock altered from its original state by the action of heat, pressure, solutions, or gases.

MICROSCOPIC: visible only under a microscope.

MINERAL: a natural, inorganic substance, with a definite chemical composition, which expresses itself by orderly internal structure and definite external shape.

MINERALOGY: the study of minerals.

MONOCLINIC: crystal system in which the axes are unequal in length, and two meet at right angles while the third meets them at an oblique angle.

MORAINE: accumulation of stones and earth deposited by a glacier.

NODULE: small roundish lump of mineral, often formed in a rock cavity.

OCTAHEDRON: a solid enclosed by eight triangular faces.

OPALESCENT: having a milky iridescence, like an opal.

OPAQUE: unable to pass light.

ORBICULAR: marked with circular patterns.

ORE: mineral or rock deposit that can be mined at a profit.

ORGANIC: derived from or pertaining to living organisms.

ORTHORHOMBIC: a crystal system in which the axes are all of unequal length but they all meet at right angles, as in an oblong.

OUTCROP: exposure of rock.

OVERBURDEN: rock or soil which must be removed to mine by open-pit method.

OXIDE: compound of oxygen with another element.

PAN: to wash earth and gravel in a pan in search of gold and other heavy materials.

PEARLY: having luster like that of a pearl.

PEGMATITE (peg'-ma-tight): igneous rock of coarse granite composition and texture, usually found as a dike.

PERFECT: cleavage that is readily started and leaves a smooth surface.

PETRIFACTION (pet'-ri-fak-shun): process of fossilization in which original cell structure of tissue remains but cells are filled with mineral; also called permineralization.

PHOSPHATE: compound of phosphorus and oxygen with one or more other elements, which are usually metallic.

PHOSPHORESCENCE: luminescence that persists after exciting cause is removed.

PITCH: dip or inclination of a mineral vein or bed at right angles to its strike.

PLACER: stream segregation of heavy minerals.

PLATEAU: high tract of level land of considerable extent, a tableland.

PLAYA: undrained desert basin that may occasionally contain water, a dry lake.

POCKET: cavity in rock.

PORPHYRY (por'-fi-ree): igneous rock containing well-developed crystals imbedded in a fine-grained ground mass.

PRECIOUS: of great value; the precious stones are diamond, ruby, sapphire, emerald, and opal.

PRISM: solid in which faces are parallel to one axis, usually longer than broad, and usually four- or six-sided and terminated by flat surfaces.

PROSPECT: unproved mineral property, or partly developed mine.

PSEUDOMORPH (sue'-do-morf): mineral that has replaced another mineral but has kept other mineral's crystal form.

PYRITE (pie′-right): iron sulphide, commonly called fool's gold.

PYROXENE (pie-rocks′-ene): a group of silicates that are common rock-forming minerals.

QUADRANGLE: the four-sided tract of land represented by an atlas sheet map of the U.S. Geological Survey.

QUARRY: open excavation to remove rock, usually for industrial uses.

RADIATING: fanning out from a center, like rays from a light.

RAVINE: steep-sided valley, larger than a gully and smaller than a canyon.

REFRACTION: the bending of light as it passes from one medium, such as air, into another, such as a gem material.

REFRACTOMETER: instrument for measuring bending of light passing through gem mineral.

RENIFORM (wren′-i-form): rounded, kidney-shaped mineral surface.

REPLACEMENT: fossil in which hard parts of organism have been removed and replaced simultaneously by mineral substance.

RESINOUS: having luster like that of resin.

RHYOLITE (rye′-oh-light): fine-grained volcanic rock composed of quartz and feldspar, the equivalent of a granite.

ROCK: a natural inorganic solid from the earth's crust.

ROUGH: uncut gem material.

RUTILATED (rue′-ti-late-ed): crystal shot through with needles of rutile (titanium oxide).

RUTILE: titanium oxide.

SAGENITIC (saj-eh-nit′-ik): crystal containing needlelike crystals of a foreign mineral.

SANDSTONE: a sedimentary rock formed of grains of sand compacted.

SCARP: see escarpment.

SCHIST (shist): metamorphic rock containing mica flakes arranged in layers so that rock readily splits along micaceous surface.

SEAM: thin layer, stratum, or vein of mineral.

SECTILE: capable of being cut into shavings.

SEDIMENTARY: formed of sediments or the debris of other rocks.

SEGREGATION: a grouping of like minerals by natural processes.

SEMIPRECIOUS: cut and worn as gems, other than those ranked as precious.

SHAFT: vertical or inclined entrance to a mine.

SHALE: laminated sedimentary rock formed from silt or clay.

SILICA: silicon oxide.

SILICATE (sil'-i-kate): mineral composed usually of one or more metals combined with silicon and oxygen.

SILICIFY: to replace organic substance by chalcedony or opal.

SILKY: having luster like that of silk.

SLATE: cleavable metamorphic rock formed by compression of clays and shale.

SLURRY: a thin, watery mixture.

SOIL: decomposed rock, sand, and decayed vegetable matter.

SPAR: a lustrous, cleavable, nonmetallic mineral, such as fluorspar (fluorite) or satin spar (gypsum).

SPECIFIC GRAVITY: comparison of the weight of a substance with the weight of an equal volume of water.

SPECTROSCOPE: instrument for analyzing chemical composition by measuring wave length of radiant energy (usually light) that is emitted or absorbed by the specimen.

STAR: an asteriated gem, or one that reflects a four- or six-rayed star from fibers embedded in the stone.

STRATIFICATION: bedding of sedimentary rock.

STRATUM (straight'-um): a distinct layer or bed of sedimentary rock (plural is strata).

STREAK: color of powder left on unglazed porcelain when mineral specimen is rubbed across it.

STRIATION (stri-a'-shun): one of parallel lines or ridges formed in development of a crystal face.

STRIKE: direction of a line formed by intersection of a geological structure with a horizontal plane.

SULPHIDE: compound of sulphur and a metal.

SYMMETRY (sim'-eh-tri): orderly arrangement of parts of a crystal or fossil.

SYNTHETIC: man-made, referring to a gem material that has the same physical and chemical qualities as a natural gem.

SYSTEM: one of six groups into which crystals are classified.

TABLELAND: broad, level, elevated region, for example, a plateau.

TABULAR: tablet shaped.

TALUS (tay'-lus): rock debris at base of cliff or slope.

TARNISH: surface change, usually of color, of a mineral.

TEMPLATE: a plate pierced with holes of various shapes for marking dimensions of a gem before cutting it.

TENACITY: ability of a substance to hold together under stress, such as pulling or pounding.

TERMINATION: face or faces at end of a crystal.

TETRAGONAL (te-trag'-oh-nawl): belonging to a system in which only two axes are equal in length, and all three axes intersect at right angles.

TEXTURE: size, shape, and pattern of a rock's components.

TOPOGRAPHIC MAP: map that shows surface features of an area, especially elevations and depressions, by means of contour lines connecting points of equal elevation from sea level.

TRANSLUCENT: able to pass light but not the image of an object.

TRANSPARENT: able to pass light so that objects can be seen through it.

TRAPROCK: any of several dark, fine-grained igneous rocks, such as basalt.

TRICLINIC: belonging to a crystal system in which all three axes are unequal in length and in which they meet one another at oblique angles.

TRISOCTAHEDRON: crystal formed of 24 faces arranged so that three take the place of each face of a regular octahedron.

TRUCK COLLECTOR: one who removes more gem material than he needs or can use.

TUMBLE: process of polishing gem material in a revolving barrel.

TWIN: compound crystal composed of two or more crystals or parts of crystals in reversed positions with respect to each other.

ULTRAVIOLET: having wave lengths shorter than those of visible light.

VEIN: mineral deposit in the form of a thin sheet or stringer.

VITREOUS (vit'-re-us): luster like that of glass.

WASH: gravel or sand spread out like a fan, often at the mouth of a canyon.

WASTY: gem material that yields only a small proportion of its bulk as finished stones.

WATER: the clarity of a diamond; a diamond that is perfectly transparent is described as of the first water.

WEATHERING: action of water, wind, and temperature in altering form, color, or texture of exposed material, such as rock.

ZEOLITE: a group of fairly soft hydrous silicates usually found in cavities in lavas.

# 14

## *Sources of information*

State geological publications, maps, and public displays of minerals are among the best means the gem hunter has to prepare himself for a field trip. Many displays are in colleges, where an appointment may be necessary to see the collection (which is primarily for teaching purposes). Following is a list giving (1) the state geological agency to which application should be made for printed and map material on state mineral resources, and (2) museums having mineral displays, and the cities in which they are located.

## *United States*

ALABAMA: (1) Geological Survey of Alabama, University. (2) Alabama Museum of Natural History, University.

ALASKA: (1) Division of Mines and Minerals of Alaska, Box 1391, Juneau. (2) State Museum in the State Capitol, Juneau.

ARIZONA: (1) Bureau of Mines, Tucson. (2) Museum of Northern Arizona, Flagstaff; Petrified Forest National Monument, Holbrook; Fairgrounds Museum, Mineral Building, Fairgrounds, Phoenix; Public Museum, Tombstone; Meteorite Museum, Sedona; University of Arizona, Tucson.

ARKANSAS: (1) Resources and Development Commission, State Capitol, Little Rock. (2) University of Arkansas Museum, Fayetteville.

CALIFORNIA: (1) Division of Mines and Geology, Ferry Building, San Francisco. (2) University of California, Berkeley; County Museum, and Museum of Science and Industry, both in Exposition Park, and University of California and University of Southern California, all in Los Angeles; Public Museum, Oakland; California Institute of Technology, Pasadena; Municipal Museum, Riverside; Natural History Museum, Balboa Park, San Diego; Division of Mines, Academy of Science Museum in Golden Gate Park, Junior Museum at 16th and Roosevelt Way, Recreational Museum, Wells-Fargo Bank, all in San Francisco; Natural History Museum, Santa Barbara.

COLORADO: (1) Bureau of Mines, State Services Building, Denver. (2) University of Colorado Museum, Boulder; Colorado College, Colorado Springs; Museum of Natural History, State Museum, and Bureau of Mines in State Capitol, all in Denver; Colorado School of Mines, Golden.

CONNECTICUT: (1) Geological and Natural History Survey, Box 128, Wesleyan Station, Middletown. (2) Bruce Museum, Greenwich; Trinity College, Wadsworth Athenaeum, both of Hartford; Wesleyan University, Middletown; Peabody Museum of Yale University, New Haven; and the Choate School, Wallingford.

DELAWARE: (1) Geological Survey, University of Delaware, Newark. (2) Robinson Hall of University of Delaware, Newark.

DISTRICT OF COLUMBIA: (1) Geological Survey and Bureau of Mines, both in the Department of the Interior, Washington 25. (2) National Museum of the Smithsonian Institution; Interior Department museum.

FLORIDA: (1) State Board of Conservation, Division of Geology, Tallahassee. (2) John B. Stetson University, De Land; University of Florida, Gainesville; Geological Survey Museum and Geology Department of Florida State University, Tallahassee.

GEORGIA: (1) Department of Mines, Mining and Geology, Agricultural Building, Atlanta. (2) State Museum, Atlanta.

HAWAII: (2) Bernice P. Bishop Museum, Honolulu, Oahu Island.

IDAHO: (1) Idaho Bureau of Mines and Geology, Moscow. (2) State Capitol, Boise; University of Idaho, Moscow.

ILLINOIS: (1) State Geological Survey, Urbana. (2) Southern Illinois University, Carbondale; Academy of Sciences, Natural History Museum, both in Chicago; Lizzadro Museum of Lapidary Arts, Elmhurst; Augustana College, Rock Island; State Museum, Springfield; Natural History Museum in Natural Resources Building at University of Illinois, Urbana (on the campus).

INDIANA: (1) Geological Survey, Indiana University, Bloomington. (2) Indiana University, Bloomington; Hanover College, Hanover; State Museum in the State Capitol, Children's Museum, both in Indianapolis; Purdue University, Lafayette; Earlham College, Richmond.

IOWA: (1) Geological Survey, Geological Survey Building, Iowa City. (2) Iowa State Teachers College, Cedar Falls; Public Museum, Davenport; Museum of State Historical Building, Des Moines.

KANSAS: (1) State Geological Survey, Lawrence. (2) St. Benedict's College, Atchison; Baker University, Baldwin; Kansas State Teachers College, Emporia; Fort Hays Kansas State College, Hays; Natural History Museum and Geology Departmental Museum at University of Kansas, Lawrence; Ottawa University, Ottawa; Kansas State Teachers College, Pittsburg; Smoky Hills Historical Museum, Oakdale Park, Salina; State Historical Society, Memorial Building, Topeka; Historical Museum Association, Wichita.

KENTUCKY: (1) Geological Survey, 120 Graham Avenue, Lexington. (2) Geology Department, University of Kentucky, Lexington; Public Library Museum, Louisville.

LOUISIANA: (1) Geological Survey, Baton Rouge. (2) Louisiana State University Geology Museum, Baton Rouge; Louisiana State Museum in Jackson Square, Tulane University, both in New Orleans.

MAINE: (1) Department of Economic Development, State House, Augusta. (2) State Museum, Augusta; Bates College, Lewiston; University of Maine, Orono; Hamlin Memorial Hall, Paris; Portland Natural History Society Museum, Portland.

MARYLAND: (1) Department of Geology, Mines and Water Resources, Johns Hopkins University, Baltimore. (2) Johns Hopkins University Geology Department, Natural History Society, and Academy of Sciences, all in Baltimore.

MASSACHUSETTS: (1) Geology Department, University of Massachusetts, Amherst. (2) Pratt Museum of Amherst College, Amherst; Society of Natural History, Children's Museum in Jamaica Plain, both in Boston; Mineralogical Museum of Harvard University, Cambridge; Smith College, Northampton; Peabody Museum, Salem; Mount Holyoke College, South Hadley; Museum of Natural History, Springfield; Williams College, Williamstown; Natural History Museum, and Clark University, Worcester.

MICHIGAN: (1) Department of Conservation, Lansing. (2) Mineralogical Museum of the University of Michigan, Ann Arbor; Alma College, Alma; Kingman Museum, Battle Creek; Cranbrook Institute of Science, Bloomfield Hills; Fort Wilkins State Park Museum, Copper Harbor; City Museum, Wayne State University, both in Detroit; City Museum, Grand Rapids; College of Mining and Technology, Houghton; Michigan State University Museum, State Historical Museum, both in East Lansing; Public Museum, Kalamazoo; Northern Michigan College, Marquette.

MINNESOTA: (1) Department of Conservation, Division of Lands and Minerals, Centennial Office Building, St. Paul. (2) Museum of Natural History at University of Minnesota, Science Museum at Public Library, and Walker Art Center, all in Minneapolis; Science Museum, St. Paul.

MISSISSIPPI: (1) Geological Survey, University. (2) Mississippi State College, State College; University of Mississippi, University.

MISSOURI: (1) Division of Geological Survey and Water Resources, Rolla. (2) University of Missouri, Columbia; Missouri Resources Museum, Jefferson City; City Museum, Kansas City; School of Mines, Rolla; Educational Museum of the Public Schools, Washington University, Museum of Science and Natural History, all in St. Louis; Palmer Little Museum, Webb City.

MONTANA: (1) Bureau of Mines and Geology, Butte. (2) School of Mines, Anaconda Employes' Club, both of Butte; Historical Society, Helena; State University, Missoula.

NEBRASKA: (1) Division of Conservation and Survey, University of Nebraska. (2) State Museum, Lincoln.

NEVADA: (1) Bureau of Mines, University of Nevada, Reno. (2) Lake Mead Natural History Association, Boulder City; State Museum, Carson City; Mackay School of Mines Museum, Reno.

NEW HAMPSHIRE: (1) Planning and Development Commission, Concord. (2) University of New Hampshire Geology Department, Durham; Wilson Museum of Dartmouth College, Hanover; Natural History Society, Keene.

NEW JERSEY: (1) Department of Conservation and Economic Development, Trenton. (2) Museum of the Newark Mineralogical Society, Newark; Rutgers University, Geology Department Museum, New Brunswick; New Jersey Mineralogical Society, Paterson; Princeton University Geology Department Museum, Princeton; State Museum in State House Annex, Trenton.

NEW MEXICO: (1) Bureau of Mines and Mineral Resources, Campus Station, Socorro. (2) University of New Mexico, Albuquerque; Museum of New Mexico in Palace of the Governors, Santa Fe; New Mexico Institute of Mining and Technology, Socorro.

NEW YORK: (1) State Museum and Science Service, Albany. (2) State Museum, Albany; Museum of Science, University of Buffalo, both of Buffalo; Knox Museum of Hamilton College, Clinton; Museum of Natural History of Colgate University, Hamilton; Cornell University, Ithaca; American Museum of Natural History, Columbia University Geology and Mineralogy Museum, both of New York; Vassar College, Poughkeepsie; University of Rochester Museum of Geology, Museum of Arts and Sciences, both of Rochester; Union College, Schenectady; Museum of Natural Science, Syracuse; Rensselaer Polytechnic Institute, Troy.

NORTH CAROLINA: (1) Department of Conservation and Development, Raleigh. (2) University of North Carolina, Chapel

Hill; Duke University, Durham; Museum of North Carolina Minerals of National Park Service at Gillespie Gap, Spruce Pine; North Carolina State College, State Museum, both of Raleigh.

NORTH DAKOTA: (1) Geological Survey, Grand Forks. (2) University of North Dakota, Grand Forks.

OHIO: (1) Department of Natural Resources, Division of Geological Survey, Ohio State University, Columbus. (2) Ohio University Museum of Natural History, Athens; Bowling Green State University, Bowling Green; Museum of Natural History, Cincinnati; Department of Geology of Case Institute of Technology, Museum of Natural History, Western Reserve University, all of Cleveland; State Museum, Orton and Lord Halls of Ohio State University, both of Columbus; Johnson-Humrickhouse Memorial Museum, Coshocton; Firelands Historical Museum, Norwalk; Oberlin College, Oberlin; Miami University, Oxford; Clark County Historical Society, Springfield; Heidelberg College Science Hall, Tiffin; Museum of Science, Toledo.

OKLAHOMA: (1) Geological Survey, Norman. (2) Woolaroc Museum, Bartlesville; Gould Hall and Stovall Museum of the University of Oklahoma, both in Norman; Science Building at Fair Grounds, and University of Tulsa, both in Tulsa.

OREGON: (1) Department of Geology and Mineral Resources, State Office Building, Portland. (2) Oregon State College, Corvallis; University of Oregon, Eugene; Museum of Science and Industry, State Department of Geology and Mineral Resources, Lewis and Clark College, all in Portland.

PENNSYLVANIA: (1) Department of Internal Affairs, Bureau of Topographic and Geologic Survey, Harrisburg. (2) Lehigh University, Bethlehem; Bryn Mawr College, Bryn Mawr; Dickinson College, Carlisle; Lafayette College, Easton; Geologic Survey, Harrisburg; Allegheny College, Meadville; Delaware County Institute of Science, Media; Academy of Natural Sciences, University of Pennsylvania, Wagner Free Institute of Science, all in Philadelphia; Carnegie Museum, Pittsburgh; Mineral Industries Building, Pennsylvania State University, University Park.

RHODE ISLAND: (1) Development Council, Roger Williams Building, Providence. (2) University of Rhode Island, Kingston; Roger Williams Park Museum, Rhode Island Hall of Brown University, both of Providence; Public Library, Westerly.

SOUTH CAROLINA: (1) Division of Geology, State Development Board, Wade Hampton State Office Building, Columbia. (2) University of South Carolina, Columbia.

SOUTH DAKOTA: (1) Geological Survey, Science Center, University, Vermillion. (2) School of Mines and Technology, Rapid City; Geology Department of State University of South Dakota, Vermillion; Zeitner Museum, Mission.

TENNESSEE: (1) Department of Conservation, Division of Geology, State Office Building, Nashville. (2) University of Tennessee Geology Department, Knoxville; Vanderbilt University Geology Department, State Division of Geology, State Museum in War Memorial Building, all in Nashville.

TEXAS: (1) Bureau of Economic Geology of University of Texas, Austin. (2) Texas Memorial Museum, Austin; Centennial Museum, El Paso; Natural History Museum, Houston; Witte Museum, San Antonio.

UTAH: (1) Geological and Mineralogical Survey, Mines Building, University of Utah, Salt Lake City. (2) Geology Museum of the University of Utah, Westminster College, both in Salt Lake City; Fieldhouse of Natural History in Vernal State Park, Vernal.

VERMONT: (1) Geological Survey, East Hall, University of Vermont, Burlington. (2) Fleming Museum of University of Vermont, Burlington; State Cabinet Building, Montpelier; Fairbanks Museum, St. Johnsbury.

VIRGINIA: (1) Division of Mineral Resources, Box 3667, Charlottesville. (2) Holden Hall of Virginia Polytechnic Institute, Blacksburg; Brooks Museum of the University of Virginia, Charlottesville; Washington and Lee University, Lexington; State Museum, Richmond.

WASHINGTON: (1) Division of Mines and Geology, General Administration Building, Olympia. (2) State Capitol Museum, Olympia; Grace Campbell Memorial Public Museum, Spokane; Washington State Historical Society, Tacoma; North Central Washington Museum, Wenatchee.

WEST VIRGINIA: (1) Geological and Economic Survey, Morgantown. (2) Geology Museum of Marshall College, Huntington; West Virginia University, Morgantown.

WISCONSIN: (1) Geological and Natural History Survey, Science Hall, University of Wisconsin, Madison. (2) Beloit College, Beloit; University of Wisconsin, Madison; Public Museum, Downer College, both of Milwaukee.

WYOMING: (1) Geological Survey, University of Wyoming, Laramie. (2) State Museum, Cheyenne; Geology Building of University of Wyoming, Laramie; Norris Museum, Yellowstone Park.

In addition to these museums listed above, most national parks and monuments in the United States have nature exhibits and museums which often include excellent displays of native rocks and minerals.

## Canada

(1) Geological Survey of Canada, Ottawa, Ontario. (2) Alberta—University of Alberta, Edmonton; British Columbia—University of British Columbia, City Museum, and British Columbia and Yukon Chamber of Mines, all Vancouver; Mineral Museum, Victoria. Manitoba—Museum in Civic Auditorium, Winnipeg. New Brunswick—New Brunswick Museum, St. John; University of New Brunswick, Fredericton; Mount Allison University, Sackville. Newfoundland—Memorial University, St. John's. Nova Scotia—Museum of Science, Dalhousie University Museum, Halifax. Ontario—National Museum of Canada and Victoria Museum, Ottawa; Miller Hall of Queen's University, Kingston; Royal Ontario Museum, Toronto. Quebec—Redpath Museum of McGill University, and College de Montréal, both Montréal; Musée de Minéralogie of Laval University, Quebec.

# 15

## *For further reading*

Every gem hunter and collector needs reference material on geology, minerals, gems, and related subjects. The following material forms a well-rounded working library.

*The Agates of North America,* edited by Hugh Leiper. Lapidary Journal, San Diego, Cal., 1962. (Paper)

*Compass and Map.* Girl Scouts of America, Catalog No. 19, 1953. (Pamphlet)

*A Field Guide to Rocks and Minerals* (3d edition), Frederick H. Pough. Houghton Mifflin Co., Boston, 1960. 349 pages.

*Gem Materials Data Book,* C. J. Parsons and E. J. Soukup. Gems and Minerals, Mentone, Cal., 1957.

*Gems and Gem Materials* (5th edition), Edward H. Kraus and Chester B. Slawson. McGraw-Hill Book Co., Inc., New York, 1947. 332 pages.

*Gemstones* (13th edition), George Frederick Herbert Smith, revised by F. C. Phillips. Pitman Publishing Corp., New York, 1958. 448 pages.

*Gemstones of North America,* John Sinkankas. D. Van Nostrand Co., Inc., Princeton, N.J., 1959. 675 pages.

*The Geologic Map,* Quintin A. Aune. Mineral Information Service, California Division of Mines, Ferry Building, San Francisco, August 1960. (Pamphlet)

*Handbook for Prospectors* (4th edition), Max W. von Bernewitz. McGraw-Hill Book Co., Inc., New York, 1943. 547 pages.

*Handbook of Gemstone Identification* (6th edition), Richard T. Liddecoat. Gemological Institute of America, Los Angeles, 1962.

*The Mineral Kingdom,* Paul E. Desautels. Grosset & Dunlap, Inc., 1968. 251 pages.

*Mineral Recognition,* Iris Vanders and Paul F. Kerr. John Wiley & Sons, Inc., 1967. 315 pages.

*Physical Geology* (3d edition), L. Don Leet and Sheldon Judson. Prentice-Hall, Englewood Cliffs, N.J., 1966. 502 pages.

*Rocks and Minerals,* Herbert S. Zim and Paul R. Shaffer. Golden Press, Inc., New York, 1957. 160 pages.

*A Textbook of Mineralogy* (4th edition), Edward S. Dana, revised by William E. Ford. John Wiley & Sons, Inc., 1932. 851 pages.

*Ultraviolet Guide to Minerals,* Sterling Gleason. D. Van Nostrand Co., Inc., Princeton, N.J., 1960. 244 pages.

## REGIONAL AND STATE GUIDES

Since the *Gem Hunter's Guide* first appeared in 1946, its example has been followed by issuance of a number of regional and local guides to gem locations. Because no national guide can hope to be as detailed as a specialized local guidebook, the reader is advised to consult such of these publications as will be useful wherever he plans to hunt for gem materials. Most of them are pamphlets or paperbacks.

### Regional Guides

*Desert Gem Trails,* Mary Frances Strong, a guide to the gems and minerals of the Mojave and Colorado deserts. Gembooks, Mentone, Cal., 1966.

*A Field Guide to the Gems and Minerals of Mexico,* Paul Willard Johnson. Gembooks, Mentone, Cal., 1965.

*Gem Hunters Atlas,* H. Cyril Johnson. Scenic Guides, Susanville, Cal. Three guides issued: Northwest (4th edition), 1960; Southwest (revised edition), 1960; and California-Nevada (revised edition), 1961.

*Geology and Scenery along the North Shore of Lake Superior,* E. G. Pye. Geological Circular 10, Ontario Department of Mines, Toronto, Canada, 1962.

*Northwest Gem Trails,* Henry C. Dake. J. D. Simpson & Co., West 19–27th Ave., Spokane 41, Wash., 1956.

*The Rock Collector's Nevada and Idaho,* Darold J. Henry. J. D. Simpson & Co., West 19–27th Ave., Spokane 41, Wash., 1953.

### State Guides

*Index to the Minerals and Rocks of Alabama.* Bulletin 65, Alabama Geological Survey, University, 1955.

*Arizona Gem Fields* (2d edition), Alton Duke. P.O. Box 1402, Yuma, Ariz., 1959.

*Minerals of Arizona,* F. W. Galbraith and D. J. Brennan. Physical Science Bulletin No. 4, University of Arizona, Tucson, 1959.

*Mineral Resources of Arkansas.* Bulletin 6, Arkansas Geological and Conservation Committee, Little Rock, 1942.

*California Gem Trails* (3d edition), Darold J. Henry. J. D. Simpson & Co., West 19–27th Ave., Spokane 41, Wash., 1957.

*Gem and Lithium Bearing Pegmatites of the Pala District,* R. H. Jahns and L. A. Wright. Special Report 7-A, California Division of Mines, Ferry Building, San Francisco, 1951.

*Minerals of California,* Joseph Murdoch and R. W. Webb. Bulletin 173, Division of Mines, Ferry Building, San Francisco, 1956.

*Colorado Gem Trails and Mineral Guide,* Richard M. Pearl. Sage Books, 2679 South York St., Denver 10, 1958.

*Minerals of Colorado,* Edwin B. Echel. Bulletin 1114, U.S. Geological Survey, Washington 25, D.C., 1961.

*Connecticut Minerals,* Julian A. Sohon. Bulletin 77, State Geological and Natural History Survey, Box 128, Wesleyan Station, Middletown, 1951.

*Minerals of Indiana,* R. C. Erd and S. S. Greenberg. Bulletin 18, Indiana Geological Survey, Bloomington, 1960.

*Maine Mineral Collecting.* Geological Survey, Augusta, Maine.

*Maine Minerals and Mineral Locations,* Phillip Morrill. Dillingham Natural History Museum, Naples, Maine.

*Minerals of Maryland,* Natural History Society of Maryland, Baltimore, 1940.

*Rocks and Minerals of Michigan.* Publication 42, Department of Conservation, Lansing, Mich., 1953.

*Guide to Mineral Collecting in Minnesota,* G. R. Rapp, Jr., and D. T. Wallace. Minnesota Geological Survey, 220 Pillsbury Hall, University of Minnesota, Minneapolis.

*Geology of New Hampshire,* T. R. Myers and G. W. Stewart. Part 3, "Minerals and Mines." State Planning and Development Commission, Concord, 1956.

*New Hampshire Mines and Mineral Locations,* Phillip Morrill. Dillingham Natural History Museum, Naples, Maine.

*The Minerals of New Mexico,* S. A. Northrup. Bulletin, Geological Series, Vol. 6, No. 1, University of New Mexico, Albuquerque, 1942.

*New Mexico Gem Trails,* Bessie W. Simpson. Gem Trails Publishing Co., Box 537, Granbury, Texas, 1961.

*Let's Hunt for Herkimer Diamonds,* C. H. Smith. Box 291, Geneva, N.Y.

*100 Minerals, Rocks and Fossils from Oklahoma,* W. E. Ham. Geological Survey, Norman, Okla., 1942.

*Mineral Collecting in Pennsylvania* (2d edition), David M. Lapham and Alan R. Geyer. Bureau of Topographic and Geologic Survey, Harrisburg, Pa., 1965.

*Gem Trails of Texas* (revised edition), Bessie W. Simpson. Gem Trails Publishing Co., Box 537, Granbury, Texas, 1962.

*Virginia Minerals and Rocks,* Richard V. Dietrich. Bulletin No. 90, Virginia Polytechnic Institute, Blacksburg, 1954. With supplement, 1955.

*Wyoming Mineral Resources,* F. W. and Doris Osterwold. Bulletin No. 45, Geological Survey, Laramie, Wyoming, 1952.

MAGAZINES

*Earth Science.* Box 550, Downers Grove, Ill. 60515.
*Gems and Gemology.* Gemological Institute of America, 11940 San Vicente Boulevard, Los Angeles 90049. Quarterly.
*Gems and Minerals.* Box 687, Mentone, Cal. 92359.
*Lapidary Journal.* Box 2369, San Diego, Cal. 92112. Also publishes *Rockhound Buyers Guide* annually in April.
*Rocks and Minerals.* Box 29, Peekskill, N.Y.

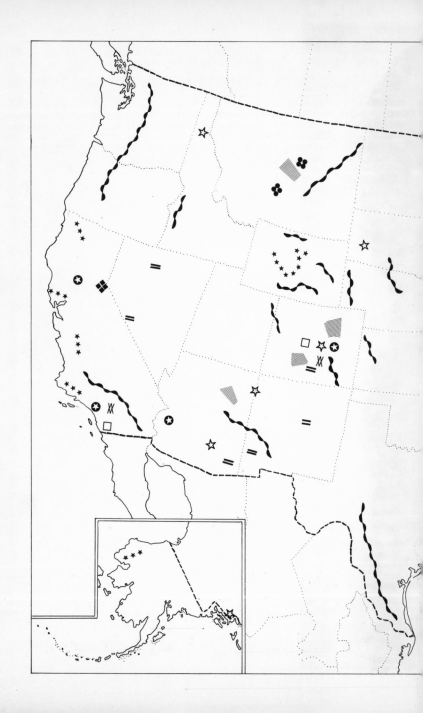